Contents

PREFACE

Although the foundations of electronics were laid in the late nineteenth century, the technology that we know as electronics is very much a product of the twentieth century, and the most rapid development of electronics has occurred in the years following the 1950s. Prior to that time, the word electronics had not been coined and the topics that we now consider as being part of electronics were then classed as part of radio engineering. Electronics has changed from being a development of radio engineering into an all-pervading subject in its own right, spawning various subdivisions and tangential topics as its growth exceeded that of any other engineering science. The rapid rise in the use of electronic devices has been brought about by the ubiquitous silicon crystal and the integrated circuit, products of the years since the Second World War. The integrated circuit itself was a by-product of the space race, one whose effect has been much further-reaching than the landing of a man on the moon.

As happens with any science that has been the subject of a rapid expansion, explanations and definitions have lagged behind the development of the technology. Each new development has brought with it a huge quantity of new terms, some of them slang words which have vanished almost as soon as they appeared, others of lasting value, and a few that, like *feedback*, have been assimilated into everyday English, though usually in an incorrect sense. Although the rate of growth of electronics has not really abated, the flow of new terms has been reduced to a level at which it becomes easier to take stock and select which terms are of lasting use and which were transient. There are still dictionaries which present slang words of the Second World War period as if they were a part of modern-day electronics; in contrast, the present volume is an attempt to define and explain the terms which I believe to be relevant to modern electronics.

The book is intended to cater for anyone who needs to know the definitions of electronics terms. This of course includes the student, whether at school or in the early years of a university, polytechnic, or technical college course, but it is important to remember the needs of the non-specialist. To an ever-increasing extent, electronic devices and methods are impinging on studies that at one time would have appeared to be unlikely users of such devices. From archaeology to music, from medicine to navigation, electronic measurements and methods now need to be understood by students and practitioners of subjects that appear to have very little in common. The need for, and use of, electronics now transcends all the artificial divisions of subject matter, and makes a dictionary of electronics that is expressed in plain language a necessity rather than a luxury.

This book has therefore been designed with more than the needs of the traditional electronics student in mind. Each explanation is couched in accessible terms, avoiding the use of mathematics except where a note on the mathematical aspect of a topic is necessary as a reminder to the prospective designer as distinct from the user of electronics. The form of the dictionary has been set out so as to make it easier to find an explanation of a device or principle under one heading rather than requiring the user to flit from one heading to another, picking up pollen-fragments of learning from each. Additionally, cross references (indicated by SMALL CAPITAL LETTERS) guide the user to related entries. I am most grateful to Ian Crofton and Edwin Moore, of Collins Publishers, for their unstinting efforts in working this book into its final form from the material on floppy disks, for it is their efforts that have made this a readable and usable dictionary. I am particularly grateful to Dr John Turner of Southampton University for reviewing the manuscript, and for his many helpful suggestions, elucidations and revisions.

Ian Sinclair

SUGGESTED REFERENCES

The numbers to the left of each entry are referred to at points in the text. The ten books listed constitute a good technical library for the electronic engineer of graduate level.

1. H. Ahmed and P.J. Spreadbury, *Analogue and Digital Electronics for Engineers*. Cambridge University Press, 1984 (2nd ed.). Good on how solid-state devices work, and on operational amplifiers.

2. P. Horowitz and W. Hill, *The Art of Electronics*. Cambridge University Press, 1985. A good general electronics text.

3. A. Colin, *Programming for Microprocessors*. Newnes–Butterworth, 1979. Despite the title, this book gives a clear explanation of microprocessor hardware functions.

4. Z.H. Meiksin and P.C. Thackray, *Electronic Design with Integrated Circuits*. Reward Books, 1981. A good general electronics text.

5. S.C. Lennox and M. Chadwick, *Mathematics for Engineers and Applied Scientists*. Heinemann, 1977 (2nd ed.). Gives essential mathematics background.

6. R.D. Stuart, *An Introduction to Fourier Analysis*. Science Paperbacks (Methuen), 1974 (2nd ed.). This and the next book between them cover practical and theoretical aspects of digital signal analysis.

7. Brüel and Kjær, *Frequency Analysis*. Available free from Brüel and Kjær Ltd., Harrow Weald Lodge, 92 Uxbridge Road, Harrow, Middlesex. See previous book.

8. E. Hughes, *Electrical Technology*. Longman, 1977 (5th ed.). The classic work on all aspects of electric motors/machines.

9. R.J. Smith, *Circuits, Devices and Systems*. Wiley, 1980 (4th ed.). A good general electronics text.

10. I.S. Grant and W.R. Phillips, *Electromagnetism*. Wiley, 1979. Excellent on the theory of electromagnetism. Very rigorous.

A

aberration, *n.* any distortion of an image by a lens system. In electronics the term denotes distortions in the electron lenses of TV CAMERA TUBES, CATHODE–RAY TUBES, ELECTRON MICROSCOPES, etc. See also BARREL DISTORTION, PINCUSHION DISTORTION, ELECTROSTATIC LENS, ELECTROMAGNETIC LENS.

abrupt junction, *n.* a JUNCTION (2) with a sudden change of MAJORITY CARRIER, in which one material is lightly doped (either as DONOR or ACCEPTOR) with the other material heavily doped in the opposite polarity.

absolute scale or **kelvin scale,** *n.* the scale of temperature that uses ABSOLUTE ZERO as its zero point.

absolute temperature, *n.* a temperature measured in the ABSOLUTE SCALE, with ABSOLUTE ZERO at around $-273°C$. All fundamental equations in electronics that make use of temperature will require the units of temperature to be in the absolute scale.

absolute value circuit, *n.* a circuit that gives a positive output equal to the magnitude of the input signal. See also BRIDGE RECTIFIER.

absolute zero, *n.* the zero of the ABSOLUTE SCALE, equivalent to around $-273°C$. The temperature is calculated theoretically from the behaviour of gases and is the point at which THERMAL NOISE ceases. In practice, the value is confirmed from the fact that the absolute zero temperature can never be exactly attained, though it is possible to reduce temperatures to within a fraction of a degree of absolute zero.

absorption, *n.* the extraction of energy, usually from a WAVE. A radio CARRIER WAVE is absorbed by many materials, resulting in the conversion of the absorbed energy into heat or some other form of energy. The alternatives to absorption are TRANSMISSION, reflection and refraction.

absorption loss, *n.* a measure of the amount of power loss

1

caused by ABSORPTION. The absorption loss is usually quoted in DECIBELS, and is equal to 20log (power lost/power input).

AC, see ALTERNATING CURRENT.

AC bias, *n.* an analogue audio tape-recording system used in the RECORDING OF SOUND. A graph of the retained magnetism (REMANANCE) of a magnetic material plotted against the AMPERE-TURNS of the magnetizing coils is never a straight line. When a high-frequency sine-wave AC signal is applied to the recording head, the lower frequency signal that is to be recorded can be mixed with this signal. The result is that the signal to be recorded causes values of remanent magnetism to be generated which lie on a comparatively straight part of the graph. On playback, the high-frequency signals can be filtered out. The use of digital recording methods is a better solution, and is now available for domestic tape recorders.

AC generator, *n.* any device or circuit that generates ALTERNATING CURRENT. The term usually denotes a rotating machine, such as an ALTERNATOR. Purely electronic circuits that generate AC are more commonly described as waveform or SIGNAL GENERATORS.

accelerated life test, *n.* a LIFE TEST that is conducted under unusually harsh conditions. This normally involves the use of a supply voltage higher than normal, greater than normal power dissipation, or repeated operation of switching devices. The aim is to check that samples have consistent lifetimes, rather than to predict actual life under normal conditions. If sufficient statistical evidence is available, however, it may be possible to correlate expected life with the results of accelerated life tests.

accelerating anode, *n.* a metal cylinder that is maintained at a positive voltage relative to the CATHODE of a CATHODE-RAY TUBE. The resulting electric field accelerates the electrons to high speeds, but because of the shape of this anode, few electrons strike it. The current that flows to the electrode is therefore negligible compared to the current to the FINAL ANODE, which is normally the screen.

acceleration voltage, *n.* the steady voltage, measured with respect to the CATHODE, that is applied to the accelerating anode.

acceptance angle, *n.* the maximum angle, measured relative to the optical axis of a PHOTOCELL, at which light can strike the cell and still cause an output.

acceptor, *n.* a P-TYPE material for DOPING a pure semiconductor that accepts electrons into its structure, thus releasing positive charges (HOLES) in the semiconductor. Compare DONOR.

access time, *n.* a delay in MEMORY response. When a memory is addressed by placing address bits onto the ADDRESS BUS, a short time will elapse before the memory makes connection with the data bus for reading or writing. This time is the 'access time'. For modern memory chips in microcomputers, access times of the order of 200ns or less are usual. Much shorter access times are required for larger machines using magnetic CORE STORES.

accumulator, *n.* **1.** the main REGISTER of a microprocessor. Each of the operations of addition, subtraction, AND, OR and XOR will affect a byte in the accumulator and a byte taken from memory or a secondary register. The result of the action is then stored in the accumulator. For further details see Ref. 3. **2.** a form of secondary storage cell (see LEAD–ACID CELL, SECONDARY CELL).

AC/DC, 1. *abbrev. for* alternating current/direct current. **2.** *adj.* (of electric motors and electronic equipment) being able to operate on either alternating current or direct current supply. The term was originally applied to radios and TV receivers that could be connected direct to the supply mains and which used no transformers. Nowadays the term is usually applied to equipment that can be operated either from mains AC, using a transformer, or from low-voltage DC, such as a car battery.

AC motor, *n.* any form of motor that requires an AC supply, i.e. all types of INDUCTION MOTORS, SYNCHRONOUS MOTORS and SHADED–POLE MOTORS. Compare UNIVERSAL MOTOR.

acoustic delay line, *n.* a method of delaying electrical signals by converting them into ULTRASONIC signals. A TRANSDUCER converts the electrical signals into acoustic (vibration) signals. These travel through a material at the speed of sound, which is much slower than the speed of electromagnetic waves, and are reconverted into electrical signals by another transducer. The original acoustic delay lines used mercury as the wave medium,

3

and were known as *mumble-tubs*. Modern acoustic delay lines are manufactured from glass for use in COLOUR TV receivers to equalize the time taken by colour signals which have different bandwidths. Acoustic waves are also used in wave FILTERS. See DELAY LINE, SURFACE ACOUSTIC WAVE.

acoustic feedback, *n.* the unwanted feedback of sound waves. The most common form is the squealing (known as *howl-round*, see HOWL) which is caused when a public address system is used with a loudspeaker placed too close to a microphone. This is a form of POSITIVE FEEDBACK in which the soundwave from the loudspeaker reaches the microphone to be amplified over again, resulting in oscillation. The cure is to use very strongly directional microphones, or circuits which ensure that the phase of acoustically fedback signals is always incorrect for oscillation. Acoustic feedback can also affect gramophone PICK-UPS which are placed too close to loudspeakers.

acoustic wave, *n.* any compression wave in a material in the form of a sound wave, whether the result can be detected by ear or not.

acoustic wave device, *n.* any electronic device that makes use of acoustic waves. See SURFACE ACOUSTIC WAVE, ACOUSTIC DELAY LINE.

AC power analyser, *n.* a measuring instrument that detects and records deviations from the normal sine wave mains supply.

AC resistance, *n.* the complex resistance (see COMPLEX NUMBER) of an AC circuit.

In an AC circuit there may be a phase shift between voltage and current. For this reason the resistance of an AC circuit cannot be specified since both the magnitude and PHASE of voltage and current are required. A COMPLEX NUMBER form of OHM's LAW can be defined as $\mathbf{V} = \mathbf{IZ}$, where $\mathbf{V}$, $\mathbf{I}$ are complex voltage and current and $\mathbf{Z}$ is complex IMPEDANCE. AC resistance R is then the real part of impedance, which can be expressed

$$\mathbf{Z} = R + jX,$$

where X is REACTANCE. See Ref. 2 for further details.

activated cathode, *n.* a hot CATHODE which is of the oxide-coated type. See THERMIONIC CATHODE.

active aerial, *n.* a transmitting aerial which is supplied with radio-frequency power. See also AERIAL, PASSIVE AERIAL, DIRECTOR.

active area, *n.* the area in a rectifier JUNCTION that actually passes current.

active component, *n.* a circuit component that is capable of increasing the power of a signal. Also called *active device*. An active component requires a power supply in order to operate, and can have a measurable POWER GAIN, as distinct from voltage gain or current gain. Compare PASSIVE COMPONENT.

active current, see IN-PHASE COMPONENT.

active device, see ACTIVE COMPONENT.

active filter, *n.* a form of FILTER that uses ACTIVE COMPONENTS (usually OPERATIONAL AMPLIFIERS). The PASSIVE COMPONENTS that determine the filter's performance are part of a FEEDBACK CONTROL LOOP around the active device. See Fig. 1. See Ref. 4 for details of filter design.

Fig. 1. **Active filter**. A typical active filter circuit, in this example a high-pass filter. The power-supply connections to the operational amplifier have not been shown.

active load, *n.* an active device used as a power-dissipating load. Since a TRANSISTOR, bipolar or FET, is a form of variable resistor, it can be used as a load whose resistance value is variable.

active network, *n.* a set of components that includes an ACTIVE COMPONENT. The term usually denotes any FILTER network that includes a transistor, operational amplifier, or other device with power gain.

active transducer, *n.* a form of transducer with power gain. Most transducers are PASSIVE COMPONENTS, but a transducer that is based on a transistor (such as a PHOTOTRANSISTOR) can supply power gain in addition to energy conversion.

active voltage, see IN-PHASE COMPONENT.

activity, *n.* a measure of the efficiency of a QUARTZ CRYSTAL. A crystal oscillator provides a driving voltage which sets the crystal into natural oscillation or resonance. The peak signal voltage across the crystal is many times greater than the driving voltage, and the ratio of peak crystal voltage to peak driving voltage is the activity figure of the crystal under these conditions. Activity figures of tens of thousands are common.

actuator, *n.* any electrically operated device that performs a mechanical action. The term is extensively used in control systems and ROBOTICS. An actuator can be a simple solenoid, or a very elaborate system of motors.

adder, *n.* a LOGIC CIRCUIT that provides the binary adding action that is summarized by the truth table in Fig. 2. An adder circuit that provides for a carry bit *into* the addition is called a FULL ADDER, and if this carry-in is not provided for, the device is called a HALF-ADDER.

address, *n.* a number that is used to activate a MEMORY LOCATION or a PORT connected to a MICROPROCESSOR. The microprocessor controls other parts of the system by using a set of connections called the ADDRESS BUS. Each line in an address bus links the microprocessor to each of the memory and port units in a system. When a set of binary signals is placed on the address bus by the microprocessor, this is used to locate one unique port or part of memory. Each address number therefore corresponds to one memory unit or one port. When a device is addressed by putting its address number on the bus, it can then be read from (data copied from the device to the microprocessor) or written

A	B	C_{in}	S	C_{out}
0	0	0	0	0
0	0	1	1	0
0	1	0	1	0
0	1	1	0	1
1	0	0	1	0
1	0	1	0	1
1	1	0	0	1
1	1	1	1	1

Fig. 2. **Adder**. (a) Circuit symbol. (b) Truth table for a two-bit full adder.

to (data copied from the microprocessor to the device).

address bus, *n.* the set of connections that carries binary ADDRESS numbers to all parts of a microprocessor system.

admittance, *n.* the reciprocal of IMPEDANCE. Symbol: **Y**; unit: SIEMENS (formerly mho). For circuits in which it is more convenient to work with currents than with voltages, the equation $\mathbf{Y} = G + jB$ is used rather than the more familiar $\mathbf{Z} = R + jX$. The symbol G is used for conductance (1/resistance), and B for susceptance (1/reactance). See COMPLEX NUMBER.

admittance gap, *n.* the hole in a WAVEGUIDE or CAVITY RESONATOR at which an electron beam and a resonant microwave signal can interact.

aerial (UK) or **antenna** (US), *n.* a transmitting or receiving device for radiated waves. The aerial acts as a form of MATCHING transformer for waves along a line and waves in space so that the maximum transfer of energy can be achieved.

Achieving high efficiency in an aerial system is of great importance both for transmitting and for receiving. Because of the very great differences in the wavelengths of radio waves at the extremes of the spectrum, aerials can take a great variety of shapes and sizes. For low radio frequencies, aerials take the form of long wires, well clear of the ground. For the VHF and UHF range, rod aerials, cut to tuned lengths, are used, and these may be of the YAGI type in order to be directional. At microwave frequencies, aerials consist of sections of launching WAVEGUIDES with parabolic reflectors. See also DIPOLE AERIAL, MARCONI AERIAL, RADIATION PATTERN, DIRECTIVITY.

aerial array, *n.* a set of aerials arranged to transmit or receive in one particular direction. This is done by using the correct spacing between aerials, and the correct phasing of signals, so that the waves from each separate aerial will reinforce each other in the chosen direction. A BROADSIDE ARRAY concentrates its energy in a direction that is at right angles to the line of aerials. An ENDFIRE ARRAY concentrates radiated energy in the direction of the aerial line. An array can be said to have a figure of gain as compared to a single element, and this figure is a good measure of both efficiency and directional qualities. See also MAJOR LOBE, YAGI, RADIATION PATTERN, DIRECTIVITY.

aerial current, *n.* the radio-frequency current in an aerial. This is measured as the ROOT MEAN SQUARE current at the carrier frequency at some point in the AERIAL FEEDER. For an UNTUNED AERIAL, the current is usually measured at the feeder connection, otherwise the current is measured at the voltage standing wave MODE, which is the maximum-current position.

aerial efficiency, *n.* the percentage power-radiation efficiency of an aerial. This is measured at the carrier frequency of radiation, and is the percentage of power radiated as compared to power supplied to the aerial. A low aerial efficiency implies a poor STANDING WAVE RATIO.

aerial feeder, *n.* the TRANSMISSION LINE that connects an aerial to a transmitter or to a receiver.

aerial gain, *n.* a measure of the efficiency of an aerial in comparison to a standard reference aerial. The efficiency is measured in terms of the power radiated or received as compared to the standard under the same conditions. For VHF and UHF aerials, the standard is a simple DIPOLE AERIAL. For lower frequencies, a notional 'infinite wire' standard is sometimes used, whose radiated or received energy figures are theoretically calculated.

aerial impedance, *n.* a COMPLEX NUMBER relating signal voltage to signal current at a point on the aerial. The aerial impedance will not be a constant, particularly for a TUNED AERIAL. The impedance is therefore usually measured at the aerial FEED POINT, and is often referred to as *feed-point impedance*.

aerial resistance or **radiation resistance,** *n.* a quantity obtained by dividing aerial power by the square of current. If the power figure is of radiated power, the resulting figure is of aerial radiation resistance. If the power figure that is used is of supplied power, then the resistance figure is of aerial resistance.

AF, see AUDIO FREQUENCY.

AFC, see AUTOMATIC FREQUENCY CONTROL.

afterglow, *n.* the light pattern that can be seen from the PHOSPHOR of a CATHODE-RAY TUBE screen after the electron beam has been cut off. For radar use, a long afterglow (of several seconds) is useful in allowing the tracks of moving objects to show up as a trail. For TV use, the afterglow must be short enough to avoid any appearance of trail. At the same time, some afterglow is desirable to avoid excessive FLICKER.

AGC, see AUTOMATIC GAIN CONTROL.

ageing or **burn-in,** *n.* the operating of a new component or circuit until its characteristics become stable. The term is usually applied to transmitting THERMIONIC VALVES and other HOT-CATHODE vacuum devices, in which small changes occur in the device characteristics during the first few hundred hours of life. This process can sometimes be speeded up by using more stringent conditions, such as raised voltage supply, higher input power, higher operating temperature, etc. A few types of PASSIVE COMPONENT can also benefit from ageing.

air-break switch, *n.* a switch whose contacts separate in air, as distinct from vacuum or oil.

air capacitor, *n.* a capacitor that uses air as its only DIELECTRIC. The device is used for some variable capacitors and for some high-voltage transmitter capacitors. See also VACUUM CAPACITOR.

air gap, *n.* any air-filled discontinuity in a material, particularly in MAGNETIC CORES.

Alcomax, *n. Trademark.* a magnetic material consisting of an alloy of iron, nickel, aluminium, cobalt and copper that has exceptionally high coercive force (see MAGNETIC HYSTERESIS). It is used mainly in making permanent magnets for loudspeakers and for MAGNETRONS.

aliasing, *n.* the effect produced when a signal is sampled too slowly, leading to a false result. When a varying analogue signal is measured or sampled at regular invervals, for example by an analogue-to-digital converter, SHANNON'S SAMPLING THEOREM states that the sample rate must be more than twice as fast as the rate of signal variation if aliasing is to be avoided. An illustration of the false results produced by aliasing can often be seen in films of stagecoaches, where the wheels appear to revolve slowly backwards. This is because the motion of the spokes is being sampled too slowly by the cine camera. For further details see Ref. 7.

alloyed junction, *n.* a JUNCTION (2) produced by depositing metal onto a piece of semiconductor material, which is then heated to form an alloy. The method was once used to produce germanium transistors that had better high-frequency characteristics than the normal diffused junction type.

all–pass network, *n.* a circuit that attenuates signals of all frequencies equally. Compare FILTER.

Alnico, *n. Trademark.* a magnetic material, an alloy of aluminium, nickel and iron (with copper and cobalt) that is used for permanent magnets.

alpha cutoff, *n.* the conventional limit of operating frequency for a transistor. COMMON–BASE CONNECTION of a transistor allows operation up to the highest possible frequency that the construction of the transistor allows. The alpha cutoff frequency is the frequency at which the voltage gain of the transistor in a common-base circuit has fallen to 0.707 of the voltage gain at lower frequencies.

alphanumeric, *adj.* (of a character set, code, or file of data) consisting of alphabetical and numerical symbols.

alternating current (AC), *n.* a current that flows in each of two directions alternately. The term usually implies that the time between current reversals is constant, so that the FREQUENCY of the current reversal is constant. The WAVEFORM of current plotted against time is also assumed to be symmetrical around zero and is usually a sinusoid. The term is normally reserved to denote the *mains power supply*. See also PULSE, MARK-SPACE RATIO.

alternator, *n.* a mechanical generator of ALTERNATING CURRENT. An alternator is fundamentally a coil of wire rotating in a constant magnetic field. If the connections to the ends of the coil are made through slip rings to ensure continuous contact, the waveform that is supplied will be alternating current.

For example, if a single-turn square coil with sides of length a is rotated at angular velocity ω about an axis perpendicular to a uniform magnetic field **B**, then the flux through the coil at time t will be

$$\phi = \mathbf{B}a \ \mathrm{Sin}\omega t$$

and the voltage generated at the terminals of the coil is

$$V = \frac{-\mathrm{d}\phi}{\mathrm{d}t} = -\omega\mathbf{B}a \ \mathrm{Cos}\omega t.$$

aluminized screen, *n.* a CATHODE-RAY TUBE screen whose brightness is increased by coating the PHOSPHOR with a thin film of aluminium, slightly spaced from the phosphor. Light from an excited part of the phosphor that would normally shine back inside the tube is thus reflected forward, increasing the total light output from the screen. The aluminium film must be thick enough to reflect efficiently, but not so thick as to absorb too great a proportion of the electrons that strike it.

AM, see AMPLITUDE MODULATION.

amateur bands, *n.* the SHORT-WAVE bands in the radio spectrum that are reserved for the use of licensed amateur operators. At one time, the short-wave bands were regarded as useless, and it was only the experiments of amateur enthusiasts that demonstrated that these bands were, in fact, the most efficient method of long-distance transmission that were available before the use of satellites. Governments then took possession of the short-wave bands, but selected parts were made available to amateurs in recognition of their achievements. Licensed amateurs continue to make many significant discoveries in radio communication.

AM/FM radio, *n.* a radio that can receive both AMPLITUDE MODULATED and FREQUENCY MODULATED signals.

ammeter, *abbrev. for* ampere-meter, a meter used for current measurements. For most purposes, ammeters use MOVING-COIL METER movements, shunted (see SHUNT) to the appropriate range. AC ammeters generally make use of RECTIFIERS along with moving-coil movements. THERMOAMMETERS (hot-wire ammeters) are used for radio-frequency current measurements, such as aerial current measurements.

amp, see AMPERE.

ampere (amp), *n.* the unit of electric current, defined in terms of the force between a pair of wires. Symbol: A. The definition imagines two infinitely long, straight, parallel wires of negligible diameter, suspended one metre apart in a vacuum, and with an identical current flowing in each wire. When the force between the wires is 2×10^{-7} newtons per metre length of wire, then the current flowing in the wires is one ampere. This definition is another way of stating that the BIOT-SAVART LAW is held to be the defining equation for magnetic FLUX DENSITY. The unit is named after André Marie Ampère (1775–1836), the French physicist and mathematician, who made major discoveries in the fields of magnetism and electricity.

ampere per metre, *n.* the unit of MAGNETIC FIELD strength. Symbol: **H**.

Ampère's law, see BIOT-SAVART LAW.

ampere-turn, *n.* the unit of MAGNETOMOTIVE FORCE (mmf) for a coil. The mmf of a coil is found by multiplying the number of turns by the current flowing. The size of magnetomotive force can then be related to the flux density by using the equation: mmf = reluctance × flux.

amplification, see GAIN.

Fig. 3. **Amplified Zener**. One form of amplified-Zener stabilizer, in which the transistor carries the stabilized current. The
Zener diode provides the stable base voltage for the
transistor. Another form of amplified-Zener circuit is shown
with the entry for SHUNT STABILIZER.

amplification factor, *n*. the absolute value of small signal
GAIN. The amplification factor for a valve or other device is
defined as change of output voltage divided by change of input
voltage, disregarding sign. The quantity has not been so widely
used for semiconductor devices.

amplified Zener, *n*. a form of VOLTAGE STABILIZER circuit. The
circuit uses a ZENER DIODE with a power transistor connected to
carry the main stabilizing current. See Fig. 3.

amplifier, *n*. a circuit that provides power GAIN. Amplifiers can
be classed as voltage amplifiers, current amplifiers, transconductance amplifiers or transresistance amplifiers, according to
their design and use. A voltage amplifier amplifies voltage
while providing a constant current, a current amplifier
amplifies current at a current voltage, and a transconductance
(or transresistance) amplifier is one where the output current
(or voltage) has a well-defined relation to the input voltage (or
current).

amplifier stage, *n*. a single section of an amplifier consisting of
several sections.

amplitude, *n*. the size of a wave at a given time. For a voltage
wave, this will mean the voltage, positive or negative, of the

13

wave at an instant. The peak amplitude is the amplitude measured from zero to one peak of the wave. The peak-to-peak amplitude (as measured by an oscilloscope) is the amplitude measured between the positive peak and the negative peak of the wave.

The term 'amplitude' is often reserved for the quantity A in

$$x = A\mathrm{Sin}\ (\omega t + \phi),$$

where x is the instantaneous amplitude at time t, A the peak amplitude, ω the ANGULAR FREQUENCY, and ϕ the PHASE ANGLE.

amplitude modulation (AM), a form of encoding that provides a means of carrying information by a radio wave. The AMPLITUDE of a high-frequency (radio) wave (see CARRIER 1) is increased or decreased by the amount of the amplitude of a low-frequency wave (audio or video). This results in the outline, or ENVELOPE, of the high-frequency wave taking the shape of the low-frequency wave. See also FREQUENCY MODULATION, SINGLE SIDEBAND, VESTIGIAL SIDEBAND.

AM, see AMPLITUDE MODULATION.

analogue circuit, *n.* a circuit whose output signal voltage is proportional to its input signal voltage, i.e. any circuit that, supplied with a varying input of suitable frequency, will produce an output whose voltage at any time bears a relationship to the voltage at the input.

analogue computer, *n.* a computer in which analogue voltages are used to represent quantities, and active circuitry such as amplifiers are used to represent mathematical operations. The analogue computer uses the AMPLITUDE of a wave to represent the size of a quantity, making linearity of amplification extremely important (see LINEAR AMPLIFIER). Mathematical actions, such as integration and differentiation, are represented by the correspondingly named electrical operations on a waveform. The basic circuit of the analogue computer is the OPERATIONAL AMPLIFIER, a very high-gain linear amplifier whose characteristics can be modified by using NEGATIVE FEEDBACK. Compare DIGITAL COMPUTER.

analogue/digital converter (ADC), *n.* a circuit that converts the analogue voltages or currents into digital (usually binary) numbers. The digital signal gives the amplitude of the analogue signal at one particular instant. One common way of achieving an A-to-D conversion is to measure the time taken for a steadily increasing voltage to equal the input voltage. This time is then converted into binary code. The rate at which conversions are carried out must be considerably greater than the frequency of the wave that is being sampled. See also QUANTIZATION, ALIASING.

AND, *n.* a logical operation in which a TRUE output is only given if two or more inputs are TRUE. See OPEN–COLLECTOR DEVICE.

AND gate, *n.* an electronic circuit whose action carries out AND logic. The output of the AND gate is TRUE (logic level 1) only when each input is simultaneously TRUE. See Fig. 4 (p.16).

anemometer, *n.* a wind-strength gauge. Electronic anemometers have largely replaced the older types for navigational purposes. The simplest system uses a TACHOGENERATOR driven by a propellor to measure wind speed, and a wind vane mounted on a potentiometer to transmit directional signals to the receiver. The advantage of electronic methods is that the distance between transmitter and receiver is unimportant.

angle modulation, *n.* a form of modulation in which the PHASE ANGLE of the CARRIER is affected by the amplitude of the modulating signal. Angle modulation is often used as a means of frequency modulation, and an angle-modulated signal can usually be demodulated by an FM radio receiver.

angle of flow, *n.* the fraction of a radio-frequency CYCLE for which current flows in an amplifying device. The term is used mainly for CLASS C transmitting stages. Conduction at all parts of the cycle corresponds to an angle of flow of 360 degrees, conduction for half of a cycle to an angle of flow of 180 degrees, and so on. Class C amplifiers normally have angles of conduction of considerably less than 180 degrees.

angular frequency, *n.* a wave frequency expressed in radians per second. One cycle of a wave is considered as the projection onto a line of one revolution of a circle, with one revolution tracing out the angle 2π. The angular frequency is therefore the frequency in hertz multiplied by 2π.

Fig. 4. **AND gate**. (a) Circuit symbol. (b) Truth table for the AND gate. If more than two inputs exist, the logic is that the output is 1 only if all inputs are 1.

anion, *n.* a negatively charged ION. The term is so called because such an ion will move, if free to do so, to a positively charged electrode or ANODE. Compare CATION.

anisotropic, *adj.* (of a material) having CHARACTERISTICS that depend on direction. A simple example is wood, in that the strength depends on grain direction. In electronics, the term is applied to crystals and to magnetic materials whose magnetic or electrical properties are different along different axes.

anode (UK) or **plate** (US), *n.* a conductor that is held at a positive potential. In electronics the term denotes an electron-collector in a vacuum device, such as a valve or cathode-ray tube.

anode current, *n.* the amount of electron current flowing from the electron source (CATHODE) to the anode. Since the conventional direction of current flow is from positive to negative, this is described as a current flowing from anode to cathode.

anodizing, *n.* the protecting of aluminium with a skin of oxide. This also serves as an electrical insulator, but is not a good heat insulator. Anodized aluminium surfaces can therefore be used as HEAT SINKS that also provide electrical insulation.

antenna, see AERIAL.

anticathode, see TARGET.

anticoincidence circuit, *n.* a form of XOR gate (see EXCLUSIVE OR) that has an output when there is a pulse at one input only, but no output when there are pulses at both inputs. The circuit can usually be adjusted to reject input pulses at the two inputs that are within a specified time apart. Such circuits are used in particle counters.

antihunting circuit, *n.* a part of the circuitry of a SERVO control system designed to damp out this oscillation around a set level. See DAMPED, HUNTING.

anti–interference aerial, *n.* a receiving aerial that is connected to the receiver by balanced TWIN CABLE or by COAXIAL CABLE. The aerial is placed well clear of man–made interference, and the link between the aerial and the receiver is designed so that it does not pick up any signals.

antijamming, *n.* any measure designed to reduce deliberate interference with electronic signals. This can include rapid changes of frequency, the use of DIGITAL coding or of very DIRECTIONAL AERIALS, or the use of satellite repeaters.

antinode, *n.* the point in a STANDING WAVE pattern that has maximum voltage amplitude. On a power transmission line or aerial, this is the point of minimum current and maximum resistance.

antiphase, *n.* a signal with a phase difference of 180°. The term is sometimes loosely used to mean *inverse* (see INVERSION), but the two are identical only for sine waves. See Fig. 5 on page 18.

antitracking, *n.* a silicone resin solution with good insulating properties. It is painted onto surfaces around a high–voltage connector to avoid leakage current, or TRACKING.

anti–transmit/receive (ATR) switch, *n.* the anti–TRANSMIT/ RECEIVE SWITCH in a RADAR waveguide. This is a device that open–circuits the transmitter waveguide during the reception period, thus steering the maximum amount of received energy into the receiver.

Compare TRANSMIT–RECEIVE (TR) SWITCH.

APC, see AUTOMATIC GAIN CONTROL.

aperiodic circuit or **nonresonant circuit,** *n.* an untuned circuit, i.e. any circuit that responds to a wide range of

Fig. 5. **Antiphase**. For the sine wave (a) a 180° phase shift is equivalent to inversion, but for the pulse waveform (b) this is not true.

frequencies without a noticeable resonance.

aperture distortion, *n*. the blurring of a TV picture due to the finite spot diameter of the electron beam. This makes a sharp transition from black to white or white to black in a TELEVISION CAMERA or PICTURE TUBE impossible to achieve.

aperture grille, *n*. a metal mask in a TV colour PICTURE TUBE that is etched with a pattern of narrow slits. The electron beams from the three guns of the colour tube cross over at a slit, and so strike the correct PHOSPHORS to achieve coloured light outputs. See Fig. 6.

See also COLOUR CRT.

apparent power, *n*. the figure of power that is obtained from multiplying voltage by current. For an alternating signal, this will be equal to true power only if the phase angle is zero, which will not be the case if the circuit contains inductive or capacitive devices. *True power* is obtained when apparent power is multiplied by the cosine of the phase angle. For further details see Ref. 8.

Appleton layer, see F LAYER.

array, see AERIAL ARRAY.

arc, *n*. a conducting path in air. This requires the air to be ionized, and is more likely to occur with DC than with low-frequency AC because at the zero-voltage portion of an AC wave, there will be no arc current, and the air can de-ionize in

(b)

(a)

Fig. 6. **Aperture grille**. (a) The shape of an aperture grille of a colour CRT. (b) The way in which the aperture causes the beams from the three electron guns to strike the correct phosphor stripes on the face of the CATHODE-RAY TUBE.

this time. An arc causes severe radio frequency interference, and also evaporation of metal from the conductors between which the arc takes place.

arcing, *n.* the appearance of an ARC when switch or other contacts open.

arcover, *n.* the appearance of an arc between two terminals with a large potential difference. Arcover is common in all high-voltage devices, such as X-RAY TUBES, CATHODE-RAY TUBES, transmitting valves, etc. Arcover is prevented by using insulation around high-voltage connectors, painting surfaces with ANTITRACKING material, and by the removal of dust and moisture.

arc suppression, *n.* any system for reducing ARCING. Switch contacts in DC circuits are arc-suppressed by using resistor-capacitor networks. For large switches, an airblast when the contacts open can be used to blow out the arc, or the contacts can be completely immersed in oil (*oil-quenched contacts*).

armature, *n.* any moving piece of SOFT MAGNETIC MATERIAL

19

such as the rotating part of an AC or DC generator or the moving part of a relay.

artificial aerial (UK) or **dummy antenna** (US), *n.* a network of PASSIVE COMPONENTS that acts as a load for a transmitter. The component values are chosen so that the network simulates the action of an aerial at the frequency of transmission, but with no radiation. The transmitter power is dissipated as heat, and the resistors in the aerial must be capable of dissipating this power. The use of an artificial aerial allows final adjustments and measurements to be made of a transmitter before connecting to its real aerial.

artificial line, *n.* a network of PASSIVE COMPONENTS that has the same characteristics as a TRANSMISSION LINE. See also LUMPED PARAMETER.

artwork, *n.* the DIAGRAMS that will be used to form the etch patterns for PRINTED CIRCUITS or INTEGRATED CIRCUITS. These will be reproduced photographically, with any reduction of scale that is needed.

ASCII, *n. acronym for* American Standard Code for Information Interchange, a number code used to represent letters, digits and punctuation marks. The code is widely used in computing.

aspect ratio, *n.* the ratio of width to height for a TV picture. A value of 4:3 is almost universal, but different values are usually standardized for ULTRA-HIGH DEFINITION TV systems.

assembler, *n.* a computer program that can translate commands into machine code for systems software. The commands must be written in assembly language, which uses simple mnemonic abbreviations for machine code instructions.

assembly, *n.* a set of components, usually on a single printed circuit board, that performs a distinct circuit action. The alternative to using assemblies is to have single-board construction.

astable circuit, *n.* a circuit which can be in one of two states, neither of which is permanently stable. Astable circuits are often used as oscillators. See also MONOSTABLE, BISTABLE, MULTIVIBRATOR.

astigmatism, *n.* a defect in an ELECTRON-OPTICS system in which the SPOT is elliptical rather than circular. Astigmatism in a CATHODE-RAY OSCILLOSCOPE tube causes the effect that vertical lines appear thicker than horizontal lines, or vice versa. Astigmatism in a TV CAMERA TUBE or receiver tube makes pictures appear to be out of focus in one direction.

asymmetrical waveform, *n.* a waveform that has no axis of symmetry, or that has a DC component so that its axis of symmetry is a DC voltage.

asynchronous, *adj.* (of a signal) being unsychronized to any other signal in a circuit. Compare SYNCHRONOUS; see also UNCLOCKED.

asynchronous counter or **serial counter,** *n.* a counter in which the input pulses are applied only to the first stage of the counter, and the output of each stage is used as the input for the following stage. If such a counter is incremented from, say, 0111 to 1000 in binary, the stages will not change simultaneously.

See also SYNCHRONOUS COUNTER.

attenuation, *n.* a reduction of signal power, the opposite of GAIN. Attenuation, like gain, is measured in decibels (dB). Attenuation of signals in circuits is caused by RESISTORS and any other energy-dissipating components.

attenuation band, *n.* the range of frequencies over which a FILTER attenuates signals.

attenuator, *n.* a circuit that attenuates a signal by a known amount. A switched attenuator uses a resistive LADDER network, and is calibrated in decibels. POTENTIOMETERS can be used as attenuators, but CALIBRATION is less easy. See Fig. 7 on page 22.

audio, *adj.* (of a device or frequency) making use of signals in the audio range of approximately 20Hz to 20kHz.

audio frequency (AF), *n.* the range of frequencies between about 15Hz and 20kHz. This corresponds to the range of sound wave frequencies that can be heard by a perfect human ear.

audiometer, *n.* an instrument used to measure acuity of human hearing. The older type used signals into earphones and required a response from the person being tested. This is not suitable for very young children, and later models have operated on a system that uses a pulse to set the eardrum into

Fig. 7. **Attenuator**. A simple attenuator using a chain of resistors.

resonance. The sound radiated by the resonating eardrum can then be picked up, recorded and analysed to give much more information about the ear than could be obtained by the earlier instrument.

audio signal, *n*. a SIGNAL that can be used to provide a sound when applied to a LOUDSPEAKER.

autodyne, *n*. an obsolete system of radio reception. The incoming carrier wave, amplified if necessary, is allowed to beat (see BEATING) with a LOCAL OSCILLATOR that is synchronized to the same frequency and phase. The BEAT NOTE extracted from this process is the original modulating frequency.

automatic control, *n*. any control system that uses electrical input signals to control a system without human intervention. The electrical signals into the controller will arise from TRANSDUCERS such as photocells, strain gauges, limit switches, level switches and so on. The output will usually consist of high-power supplies for electric motors, actuators, heaters and similar devices. Most control systems depend on the application of overall NEGATIVE FEEDBACK.

automatic frequency control (AFC), *n*. a system of LOCAL OSCILLATOR control in a frequency-modulated SUPERHETERO-DYNE receiver. The local oscillator is made voltage dependent, usually by making a VARACTOR diode part of the tuned circuit. At the demodulator, a DISCRIMINATOR circuit gives a DC voltage that varies according to the frequency of the IF signal. This DC voltage is connected (sometimes with a stage of amplification) to the varactor diode. If the receiver is perfectly tuned, this DC voltage should be zero. If not, then the voltage applied to the varactor diode will adjust the oscillator frequency until the receiver is in tune.

automatic gain control (AGC) or **automatic volume control (AVC)** or **automatic picture control (APC),** *n*. a system for counteracting input signal amplitude fluctuations in a radio–frequency signal. The scheme applies mainly to AM signals, and makes use of the DC level at the demodulator. This DC level is proportional to the amplitude of the carrier wave, and will vary as the carrier amplitude varies. By using this voltage to control the gain of several stages (usually RF and IF stages), the amount of IF signal at the detector can be made almost constant despite large variations in carrier amplitude.

automatic level control, *n*. a form of AUTOMATIC GAIN CONTROL for TV signals, in that the BLACK LEVEL of the picture is held at a constant level.

automatic noise limiter, *n*. a circuit that clips IMPULSE noise peaks from any signal. The circuit makes use of the principle of charging a capacitor to the peak signal voltage, and using this voltage to operate a CLIPPER. Any pulse of more than the peak amplitude is clipped.

automatic tracking, *n*. a form of automatic control for a radar aerial. This keeps the transmitted beam on the target while the range is computed. This is nowadays achieved electronically (by altering the phasing of signals to different parts of the aerial) rather than entirely by control of aerial movement.

automatic tuning, *n*. a form of AUTOMATIC FREQUENCY CONTROL that allows coarse setting by manual methods. If the receiver is put roughly into tune manually, the automatic system then takes over and completes the tuning process.

autotransformer, *n*. a transformer with a single winding having an adjustable secondary tapping. At mains frequency the device is used mainly for testing equipment that must operate with a range of supply voltages. Autotransformers are also in RF amplifiers functioning as tuned transformers.

avalanche, *n.* the uncontrollable breakdown of insulation, particularly of a gas or a SEMICONDUCTOR. An avalanche occurs in a gas when an ION is formed in a gas in which there is a strong electric field. The acceleration of the ion by the electric field can cause it to reach such speeds that collisions with gas molecules will generate more ions, which in turn are accelerated. This leads to total ionization of the gas in a very short time. The initial ionization can be triggered by a charged particle from a radioactive material, as in a Geiger–Müller tube, or by light or other radiation.

avalanche breakdown, *n.* a form of AVALANCHE effect in a SEMICONDUCTOR junction. Avalanche breakdown occurs in a reverse biased junction at a very sharply defined voltage level. The effect is used in the manufacture of voltage reference diodes. These diodes are usually named ZENER DIODES, but ZENER BREAKDOWN is not identical to avalanche breakdown, being more gradual.

AVC, see AUTOMATIC GAIN CONTROL.

avionics, *n.* the application of electronics to aviation. This covers all aspects of airborne radar, communications, control systems and on-board computers.

azimuth angle, *n.* the angle of tilt of a tape recording or replay HEAD. The head is at azimuth zero when the line of the magnetic gap is at 90 degrees to the line of motion of the tape. A tape recorded by a head with an azimuth angle error will replay poorly on a machine with a correctly aligned head. This is particularly important if the tape is used for digital signals. See Fig. 8.

azimuth error, *n.* an incorrect tape head AZIMUTH ANGLE that causes faint recording or replay.

Fig. 8. **Azimuth angle.** The azimuth angle for a tape head. Incorrect setting of this angle is very common, and causes muffled sound when a tape created on another machine is played.

B

back EMF, *n.* a voltage that is set up in opposition to a supplied voltage, for example the reverse ELECTROMOTIVE FORCE in an INDUCTOR when current changes, and the EMF developed in the ARMATURE coils of a DC motor when the armature revolves.

background count, *n.* the count of ionizing particles per minute in the absence of known radiating material. The background count is the natural count due to the Earth's own radioactivity, and also to the bombardment of particles from outer space. This background is irregular, varies considerably from one place to another, and very careful measurements are needed to distinguish it from any additional radiation from a weak radioactive source. See also IONIZATION.

background noise, *n.* the NOISE signal that is always present in any transmission.

back heating, *n.* an effect used in a MAGNETRON to continue electron emission. Electron emission is started by heating the CATHODE of a magnetron. When the magnetron is running, however, the path of many electrons causes them to return to the cathode. The bombardment of the cathode by returning (*back*) electrons causes heating, so that the auxiliary heating can be reduced or switched off.

back lobe, *n.* the pattern of strong radiation from a directional aerial that is in the reverse direction to the intended direction. See LOBE, RADIATION PATTERN.

back plate, *n.* the SIGNAL ELECTRODE of a TV CAMERA TUBE. The term originally denoted a metal plate that was used as an electron collector and located at the rear of the tube. For modern types of camera pick-up tube, such as the vidicon, the back plate is a conducting layer at the front of the tube.

back porch, *n.* the portion of the SYNCHRONIZING PULSE TV signal waveform that immediately follows the line sync pulse. On a monochrome signal, the back porch consists of 2.25 microseconds of BLACK LEVEL. On a colour signal, the COLOUR BURST of 10 cycles of subcarrier takes place in this time. This portion of subcarrier signal is used to synchronize the colour subcarrier oscillator in the receiver.

backward diode, *n.* a diode in which both regions are heavily doped (see DOPING). This has the effect of allowing the diode to conduct better in the reverse direction than in the forward direction, and with very small voltage drop. There is virtually no CARRIER STORAGE, so response speeds are very high. The backward diode is used for DEMODULATION, particularly of low-level microwave signals. See also TUNNEL DIODE.

backward-wave tube, *n.* a form of TRAVELLING-WAVE TUBE oscillator in which the electromagnetic wave travels in the opposite direction from the electron beam. See also CARCINOTRON.

balance, *n.* the symmetry or equality of signals. Stereo audio signals are said to be balanced in a stereo amplifier if they produce a sound that appears centrally between the loudspeakers when both channels are fed with the same signals. A waveform is said to be balanced about earth if the shape of the wave form is symmetrical with zero volts as the axis of symmetry.

balanced amplifier, *n.* an amplifier in which both a signal and its inverse are simultaneously amplified. The inputs and outputs of such an amplifier are balanced about earth (see BALANCE). The advantage is a very great immunity to interference from supply-line or radiated noise. See also PARAPHASE AMPLIFIER.

balanced line, *n.* a two-wire transmission line that carries signals balanced with respect to earth (see BALANCE). The wires of the line should have identical electrical characteristics.

ballast, *n.* a resistor that was used in early radio and electronic circuits to absorb supply SURGES. A ballast resistor was wired in series with a DC supply. Because the resistor ran hot, and had a large positive TEMPERATURE COEFFICIENT of resistance, any increase in current through the resistor caused an increase in its resistance value. This stabilized the value of current through the ballast. Tungsten-filament lamps were often used as ballast resistors.

balun, *n.* *acronym for Bal*anced-*Un*balanced transformer, a transformer designed to match an unbalanced line to a balanced line with minimum power loss. Its main use is to connect a (balanced) dipole aerial to an (unbalanced) coaxial feeder.

banana plug, *n.* an obsolete plug, once used for low-voltage connections. The banana plug has now been mainly superseded by the 4mm plug and socket.

band, *n.* **1.** a range of frequencies. **2.** in semiconductor theory, a range of permitted energy levels (see ENERGY BANDS).

band energy, see ENERGY BAND.

band-pass filter, *n.* a filter that allows a band of frequencies to pass, but rejects frequencies both above and below this range.

band-stop filter, *n.* a filter that stops a range of frequencies but allows signals of below or above this range to pass.

band switch, *n.* a manual switch for changing the tuning of a receiver or transmitter from one frequency range to another. This is usually done by changing the connections to inductors.

bandwidth, *n.* the range of frequencies in a band. For radio frequencies this is usually quoted in terms of the difference between the highest and the lowest frequencies in the band.

bank, *n.* a set of controls arranged together. The controls (switches, potentiometers, variable capacitors) may be mechanically or electrically connected so that all of them are altered by one control.

barrage reception, see DIVERSITY RECEPTION.

barrel distortion, *n.* the distortion of a TV picture in which the normally rectangular shape is distorted to one in which the sides are bowed outwards. Compare PINCUSHION DISTORTION.

base, *n.* one terminal of a BIPOLAR TRANSISTOR. For maximum voltage gain, the signal input will be to the base, and the output from the COLLECTOR. In some applications, the base is held at AC zero potential, and the signal input is to the EMITTER (1).

base level, *n.* the voltage level from which a PULSE starts and to which it returns. In most pulse-generating circuits the base level will either be earth or supply voltage level.

base stopper, *n.* a resistor of low value that is wired in series with the base of a TRANSISTOR in order to damp PARASITIC OSCILLATIONS. The base STOPPER is generally wired as close to the base terminal as is physically possible.

BASIC, *n. acronym for* Beginners All-purpose Symbolic Instruction Code, a high-level computing language, originally intended for teaching the skills of programming, but now a useful and very well-known language in its own right.

basic frequency, see FUNDAMENTAL FREQUENCY.

bass, *n.* the lowest pitched audio frequency notes in the region 15Hz to 200Hz (approximately). These frequencies are attenuated by the normal capacitor coupling in amplifier circuits, and the lower bass frequencies are not well reproduced by loudspeakers, particularly by small loudspeakers.

bass boost, *n.* a selective gain increase for the BASS frequencies. Bass boost is often used to compensate for the attenuation of bass frequencies in amplifier circuits and for the deficiencies of loudspeakers.

bass response, *n*. the relative gain of a device for the BASS frequencies, usually quoted in decibels relative to the response for a 1kHz signal.

battery, *n*. a group of identical devices connected so as to enhance one or more properties of an individual device. The term usually denotes a group of cells connected so as to provide either higher voltage or higher current than a single cell. Series connection provides voltage levels that are equal to the cell voltage multiplied by the number of series cells. Parallel connection allows higher currents to be delivered, because the total internal resistance is equal to the internal resistance of a cell divided by the number of cells.

baud, *n*. the unit of rate of serial transmission of digital signals along a pair of wires. One baud means one signal voltage or phase change per second. The unit is named after the pioneer telegraph engineer, J. Baudot (d. 1903). Calculating the rate of information transmitted at a given band rate is complicated by variations in the size of a BYTE and by the presence of start and stop BITS.

bayonet fitting, *n*. any form of locking connector that is attached by a plug-in and twist action.

beacon or **radio beacon,** *n*. the radio equivalent of a lighthouse. Signals sent out from a beacon transmitter are used for identification of the transmitter (*code beacon*), for location and guidance (*homing beacon*), and for more specialized purposes such as aircraft blind landing.

bead thermistor, *n*. a form of THERMISTOR in the shape of a small sphere with two leads.

beam, *n*. a confined path for radio waves or electrons. The term beam implies that the shape of the path is almost parallel-sided and straight.

beam angle, *n*. the angle of divergence of electrons emerging from the ELECTRON GUN of a CATHODE-RAY TUBE.

beam bending, *n*. a form of distortion in TV CAMERA TUBES. The electron beam scans over areas that are electrostatically charged by the action of light. The discharge current provided by the beam then constitutes the output video signal. The differences in charge, however, can cause the low-velocity beam to be deflected in the direction of more positive charge. The effect on the signal of this beam bending is to exaggerate the size of bright areas in the picture.

beam lead, *n.* a connection on a transistor or IC that is resistant to vibration. This is achieved by supporting the connection at the centre so that it is balanced.

beam power value or **beam tetrode,** *n.* a form of transmitting valve in which the electron flow from cathode to anode is formed into a beam by beam-forming plates. This results in lower losses than the use of an additional grid.

beam switching, *n.* a method of obtaining more than one TRACE from a single electron gun of a CATHODE-RAY TUBE. This is done by a very rapid alternation of vertical position of the trace so that to the eye more than one trace appears. The signals to the DEFLECTION PLATES are also switched at the same rate, making it appear that completely independent traces are being used.

beat frequency, *n.* a signal that is produced as a result of mixing two other signals. When two signals, frequencies f1 and $f2$, are mixed in a NONLINEAR device, the output contains these frequencies along with the sum frequency $(f1+f2)$ and the difference frequency $(f1-f2$ or $f2-f1$, whichever is positive). These sum and difference frequencies are both beat frequencies, but the difference frequency is the one that is normally used and referred to as a 'beat frequency'.

beat-frequency oscillator (BFO), *n.* a part of a receiver for CW (continuous wave, meaning morse code) signals that operates at a frequency slightly above or below the INTERMEDIATE FREQUENCY. The difference in frequencies is usually about 400Hz to 1kHz, so the beat frequency is an audio note. The BFO output is applied to the demodulator, so that morse signals sound as audio notes in the AF sections of the receiver. The term can also denote an audio SIGNAL GENERATOR that makes use of two radio frequency oscillators mixed so as to produce a wider range of beat signals.

beating, *n.* the production of signals from the mixing of higher frequencies.

beat note or **beat,** *n.* a signal produced by BEATING.

beat, see BEAT NOTE.

bel, *n.* a unit for comparing two power levels, equal to the logarithm to the base ten of the ratio of the two powers. Abbrevs: B, b. Named after Alexander Graham Bell, Scots-born US scientist. In electronics, power gain in bels is

$$\text{Log}_{10} \ \frac{P_2{}^2}{P_1{}^2}$$

where P_1 and P_2 are input and output powers respectively. A more convenient unit is the DECIBEL.

beta gain, *n.* the COMMON EMITTER current gain of a transistor.

beta ray, see ELECTRON BEAM.

BFO, see BEAT–FREQUENCY OSCILLATOR.

bias, *n.* a DC voltage applied to a device in order to control its linearity (see LINEAR). The output–input characteristic of most active devices is non–linear, and bias is used to select a position in the characteristic curve that will give reasonably linear results. Bias can also be used to provide deliberate nonlinearity, so that only the tip of a pulse, for example, will operate a circuit.

bidirectional transistor, *n.* a transistor in which the COLLECTOR and EMITTER regions have identical doping levels and geometry, so that the collector and emitter leads can be interchanged. Many small–signal transistors are reasonably bidirectional.

bifilar winding, *n.* a method of coil winding that reduces stray INDUCTANCE losses. The usual scheme is to wind both the primary and the secondary wires together round the core. See Fig. 9 on page 32.

bimetallic strip, *n.* a metal strip that will bend when its temperature changes. The strip is a composite of two metals with different expansivity values. The bending of the strip is normally used as a method of switching for thermostats, temperature limit switches, etc.

binary code, *n.* a system of representing numbers with only

primary   secondary

core

primary   secondary

Fig. 9. A **Bifilar winding**. The separate wires of the primary and the secondary windings are wound together onto the core.

the digits 0 and 1. The term can include systems such as Gray code and Excess-three code, but is normally restricted to denote 8–4–2–1 binary code in which the position of a digit in a number indicates its power of 2 significance.

binary number, *n.* a number expressed in BINARY CODE.

Biot-Savart law, *n.* the relationship between the amount of current flowing between two points and the MAGNETIC FLUX DENSITY that it creates. Formerly called *Ampère's law* in the UK. The law is stated in a form that is physically impossible to achieve, and only formulas deduced from the law can be tested.

The Biot-Savart law can be more fully explained by referring to Fig. 10. (Note that symbols in italic type, e.g. I, indicate a scalar; and that symbols in bold type, e.g. **B**, indicate a vector.) For any point P and any element *dl* of the current, the vector (cross) product $\mathbf{u}_T \times \mathbf{u}_R$ is perpendicular to the plane defined by the point P and the current I. The direction of the vector product is therefore that of the unit vector $\mathbf{u}_\theta$. The magnetic field produced at P by the element of current *dl* is a tangent to the circle of radius R that passes through P, is centred on the current, and is in a plane perpendicular to the current.

Fig. 10. **Biot-Savart law.** The law relates the flux density ΔB to the current I flowing in a minute element of conductor ds long. The flux density is calculated at a radius R from the wire, and the angle between the conductor and a line drawn from the element to the point at which the flux is considered is θ.

The total magnetic field **B** is the sum of the contributions made by each element, i.e.

$$\mathbf{B} = \frac{\mu_0}{4\pi} \ I \oint \frac{\mathbf{u}_T \times \mathbf{u}_R}{r^2} dl$$

The contributions from all terms in the integral have direction $\mathbf{u}_\theta$, and the total field **B** is also a tangent to the circle at P. Therefore it is only necessary to find the magnitude of **B**. As $\mathbf{u}_T$ and $\mathbf{u}_R$ are unit vectors, the magnitude of $\mathbf{u}_T \times \mathbf{u}_R$ is $\mathrm{Sin}\theta$. We can rewrite the equation above as:

$$B = \frac{\mu_0 I}{4\pi} \int_{-\infty}^{\infty} \frac{\mathrm{Sin}\theta}{r^2} \ dl$$

(where B is the magnitude of **B**), which can be solved to give the Biot–Savart law:

$$B = \frac{\mu_0 I}{2\pi R}$$

where R = radius. For further details see Ref. 10.

bipolar IC, *n*. a form of INTEGRATED CIRCUIT in which the transistors are bipolar (see BIPOLAR TRANSISTOR) rather than field-effect types.

bipolar transistor, *n*. a TRANSISTOR that makes use of two close-spaced JUNCTIONS(2) in a single CRYSTAL to form a p-n-p or n-p-n sandwich of layers. The central section is called the base, and the outer regions are the emitter and the collector. In general, the collector is of larger area than the emitter, otherwise the transistor construction is symmetrical.

With a steady voltage applied between the collector and the emitter, no current can flow unless a current is also flowing between the base and emitter. The collector–emitter current is very much greater than the base–emitter current, but is proportional to the base–emitter current over a very large current range. For the P-N-P transistor, the controlled current consists of holes, and the collector and base voltages are negative with respect to the emitter. The N-P-N transistor uses electrons as carriers, and operates with collector and base voltage levels that are positive with respect to the emitter. Compare FIELD-EFFECT TRANSISTOR.

bistable, *n*. a circuit possessing two stable states. The term usually denotes a FLIP-FLOP circuit which can be switched from one stable state to the other by a TRIGGER pulse. Compare STABLE CIRCUIT; see also MULTIVIBRATOR, MONOSTABLE STEERING DIODE.

bit, *n. abbrev. for* binary digit, i.e. one of the two possible digits, 0 or 1, in a BINARY NUMBER.

Bitter pattern, *n*. a method of investigating the magnetism of a material. A liquid that contains fine magnetic particles is applied to the surface of a magnetic material. The particles then form into a pattern that reveals how the material is magnetized.

black box, *n*. a method of treating the behaviour of a circuit or other device in which the internal construction is ignored, and only the inputs and outputs are considered. By treating a device as a 'black box' its effect in the circuit can be studied rather than its internal action. Components such as INTEGRATED CIRCUITS generally have to be treated as black boxes, because their internal construction is known in detail only to their manufacturers.

black level, *n.* a voltage level in a TV VIDEO SIGNAL that results in the electron beam being just cut off. Signals below this level cannot produce any effect on the screen of the cathode-ray tube.

blackout, *n.* a sudden loss of circuit gain. This is normally the result of nonlinear action that charges capacitors to CUTOFF bias levels. The cause of the nonlinear action is usually an excessive pulse input.

blanking, *n.* the suppression of an electron beam. This is normally done to prevent an unwanted display as, for example, when the FLYBACK part of a TIMEBASE is being traced.

blanking level, *n.* the voltage level in a video signal that corresponds to electron beam cutoff. See also BLACK LEVEL.

blasting, *n.* a severe distortion of an audio output caused by excessive input signal.

block diagram, *n.* an overall diagram for a system. A block diagram shows no circuit details. Each part of the circuit is shown as a block, with drawings of the waveforms in and out to illustrate the actions. In this way, the overall action is easier to understand, and a fault can often be isolated to one particular block. See also BLACK BOX.

blocked impedance, *n.* a form of IMPEDANCE found in an electromechanical TRANSDUCER. When a signal is applied to a loudspeaker or other electromechanical device, the measured impedance is greater than the electrical resistance of the coil windings. This is because of the power conversion to mechanical power. If the motion is prevented, the impedance changes to the lower value that is called the blocked impedance. Compare MOTIONAL IMPEDANCE.

blocking capacitor, *n.* a CAPACITOR whose main purpose is to pass signal frequencies between parts of a circuit that are at different DC levels without passing any DC current.

blocking oscillator, *n*. a form of OSCILLATOR that is used for
pulse generation. A blocking oscillator makes use of a capacitor
in the BIAS circuit. After one cycle of high-frequency oscillation, the capacitor is charged and switches off the oscillator
completely, so that no further oscillation can occur until the
charge has leaked away. The leakage is slow in comparison to
the time of oscillation, so the circuit generates pulses with a low
DUTY FACTOR. See Fig. 11. See also SQUEGGING.

Fig. 11. **Blocking oscillator**. A typical blocking oscillator
circuit. The time between pulses is determined by the values
of R and C, and the pulse width by the amount of feedback
and the characteristics of the transformer.

Bode diagram, *n*. a DIAGRAM in which logarithmic gain and
phase is plotted against logarithmic frequency for a filter,
amplifier or control system. The diagram is used to assess
frequency response and stability, particularly for control
systems. For further details see Ref. 9.

body capacitance, *n*. the CAPACITANCE of part of a circuit to a
nearby human body. Body capacitance is particularly trouble-

some when variable capacitors are operated, because the setting that is obtained when the hand touches the adjustor may not be correct when the hand is removed.

bolometer, *n.* a resistor for measuring radiated power, (particularly infrared radiation), that is blackened so as to absorb radiation. When the radiation is absorbed, the resistor is heated, and its resistance value changes. The change in resistance value is then used to calculate the amount of power absorbed.

bond, *vb.* to connect parts of a circuit so that they are at the same ELECTRIC POTENTIAL, usually earth potential. Bonding is reasonably straightforward for low-frequency circuits, but can be very difficult for high radio-frequency circuits, when the length of the bonding conductor can be an appreciable fraction of a wavelength.

bonding pads, *n.* the metal contacts around a semiconductor chip. The connections to the chip from each bonding pad are made through fine gold wires, and the bonding pads are in turn connected with more substantial wires to the pins of the chip.

booster, *n.* **1.** any device used to increase the power of a signal. **2.** a transmitter that is installed to increase signal strength in an area of poor reception. **3.** a carrier-frequency amplifier located at or near a receiver aerial to improve signal–noise ratio. **4.** a local power-supply transformer that is used to maintain voltage in a remote area.

bootstrapping, *n.* a system of POSITIVE FEEDBACK across an amplifying stage whose gain is always less than unity, so that oscillation is not possible. Bootstrapping circuits are used to simulate constant current conditions in TIMEBASES, and to increase the input impedance of amplifiers. See Fig. 12 on page 38.

bottoming, *n.* the DISTORTION of a signal because the signal voltage has reached earth level, or supply negative. An active device with a resistive load cannot provide an output voltage that rises above the level of the positive supply voltage or that falls below the level of the negative supply voltage, and distortion will be caused if the input signal is large enough to drive the output to these extremes.

Fig. 12. **Bootstrapping**. A typical bootstrapping circuit for a timebase. When the switch S1 opens, capacitor C starts to charge, and the voltage at the base of the transistor increases. Because the voltage at the emitter rises also and is coupled to the junction of R1 and R2 by the Zener diode, the voltage across R1 is constant, hence the current through it is constant. This results in a linear rise of voltage across C, a ramp signal, until the voltage rise ceases or the switch closes. In a practical circuit, the switch would be a transistor.

branch, *n.* a point where three or more connections join in, for example, a NETWORK of components.

breadboard, *n.* a temporary assembly for testing purposes. Breadboard circuits are often constructed on purpose-built plug-in boards, so that circuits can be constructed simply by plugging in ICs, transistors and passive components, with the minimum of wiring. See also PATCHBOARD.

break, *n.* an interruption in a CIRCUIT.

breakdown, *n.* a failure of insulation or other electrical characteristics. Breakdown of an active component generally means either (a) loss of gain, or (b) a short circuit between electrodes.

bridge, *n.* a form of measuring circuit. The simplest form of bridge circuit is the Wheatstone bridge, which consists of two potential dividers across a common supply (see Fig. 13). The condition for the potentials at the middle of the dividers to be identical is R1/R2 = R3/R4. This condition, the balance condition, is easy to identify if a sensitive current indicator is connected between the points, 'bridging' the gap. If three of the resistor values are known, then the fourth can be calculated. Alternatively, if one resistor in one arm is known, and the *ratio* of resistance values in the other arm is known, then the fourth resistance value can be calculated. The current indicator need not be calibrated, and the only requirement of it is that it should be sensitive. The bridge can, for example, be supplied with AC and headphones or an amplifier used as a detector.

Variations in the basic bridge, using complex impedances in place of the potential dividers, can be used for measuring capacitance, self-inductance, mutual inductance, and transformer ratios. For details of alternative bridge circuits, see Ref. 5.

Fig. 13. **Bridge**. The Wheatstone-resistor bridge circuit. This form of the circuit diagram shows the principle more clearly than the traditional diamond-shaped pattern.

bridge amplifier, *n.* a circuit that uses two sets of output stages that provide signals, one of which is inverted. The load, usually a loudspeaker, is connected between the amplifier outputs.

This is often used as a way of avoiding the use of an isolating capacitor between an amplifier output and a loudspeaker, since the steady voltage across the output terminals can be set to zero.

bridge rectifier, *n.* a full-wave rectifier circuit in which the rectifiers are connected in a bridge pattern, so that a different pair of rectifiers conducts for each direction of AC input.

broadband or **wideband,** *adj.* (of amplifiers and networks) capable of operation over a large range of frequencies. Typical broadband systems include VIDEO AMPLIFIERS for television, and the signal circuits of OSCILLOSCOPES.

broadcasting, *n.* the transmission of radio-frequency energy from an aerial so that the signals can be picked up by any receiver. Radiated signals should be distinguished from signals sent along cables or optical fibres which are delivered only to receivers that are connected to the cable.

broadside array, *n.* a set of aerials arranged to receive or transmit in a direction at right angles to the line of the aerials. See also AERIAL ARRAY.

brush, *n.* a carbon, wire filament or soft metal contact to a moving conductor, used on motors, servosystems, selsyns and rotary transformers.

brush discharge, *n.* a faint glow discharge surrounding a high-voltage conductor. The brush discharge is particularly strong around points and sharp edges, and causes severe radio-frequency interference.

BSI, *abbrev. for* British Standards Institution, an association (founded 1901) that establishes and maintains standards for units of measurement, technical terminology, etc.

bubble memory, *n.* a form of magnetic memory for computers using microscopic zones (bubbles) of reversible field inside a magnetic material to store information.

bucket brigade, see CHARGE–COUPLED DEVICE.

buffer, *n.* **1.** an isolating unity-gain amplifier. **2.** a temporary memory in a computer.

buffer memory, *n.* a part of computer memory that is used to gather up data into convenient bundles. For example, data that is to be recorded on disk is often gathered into units of 256 bytes before being recorded. Replay from a disk may also be stored temporarily in a buffer.

bug, *n.* a fault in a circuit or in a computer program.

build-up time, *n.* the time needed for circuit current to reach its normal level.

buncher, *n.* the electrode of a KLYSTRON that causes the steady electron stream to form into groups (bunches) the electrons separated by spaces.

buried layer, *n.* a base layer of high-conductivity SEMICONDUCTOR. The layers of a transistor or IC are fabricated on top of this buried layer, that is then used for electrical and thermal connections.

burn-in, see AGEING.

burst, *n.* a few cycles of signal. See COLOUR BURST.

bus, *n.* **1.** a set of connections to several devices. A *power bus*, for example, is a set of conductors that carries DC supply to several devices. **2.** in computing, a set of lines that connects all the main components such as microprocessor, memory chips and ports. See also ADDRESS, DATA BUS.

bush, *n.* a form of bearing or insulator through which a shaft of cable is taken.

Butterworth filter, *n.* a filter that produces a flat PASS BAND response at the expense of steepness in the transition region between pass band and STOP BAND. This is known as a *Butterworth response*. The amplitude response is given by

$$\frac{V_{\text{out}}}{V_{\text{in}}} = \frac{1}{[1 + (f/f_c)^{2n}]^{\frac{1}{2}}}$$

where n is the order of the filter, f the frequency, and f_c the cutoff frequency. See also CHEBYSHEV FILTER. For further details see Ref. 2.

by-pass, *adj.* (of a component) providing a shunt for signals. A *by-pass capacitor*, for example, shunts unwanted signals to earth.

byte, *n.* a group of (usually eight) BITS representing a single character.

C

cable, *n.* an insulated wire or a set of insulated wires bound together (see INSULATOR). The individual wire CONDUCTORS in the cable are usually stranded, and the whole cable is reasonably flexible, so that it can be laid into ducts. The term can denote a single SIGNAL conductor, such as the COAXIAL CABLE for a TV aerial, or a complex set of conductors like the cable that links a TV camera to its control unit. Most cables incorporate some protection for the conductors, such as metal sheathing.

calibration, *n.* the checking of a measuring instrument against a standard. The action is performed on instruments such as voltmeters and, particularly, CATHODE-RAY OSCILLOSCOPES, whose characteristics may drift with time.

calibration pips, *n.* a built-in form of timebase CALIBRATION for CATHODE-RAY OSCILLOSCOPES, using short pulses generated by a crystal-controlled oscillator (see CRYSTAL CONTROL). By pressing a calibration switch, these calibration pips can be shown on the display, and used to check the accuracy of the timebase.

call sign, *n.* a set of letters and numbers that is used to identify a transmitter. The system is used in the UK mainly by amateur operators, and by the users of radio links. In the US and many other countries, even entertainment radio stations are required to broadcast a call sign at intervals.

camera tube, *n.* a device that produces a VIDEO SIGNAL from an optical image. Camera tubes rely on either photoemissive or photoconductive effects to convert light intensity patterns into electrostatic charge patterns (see PHOTOELECTRIC EFFECT, PHOTOCONDUCTIVE CELL). A scanning electron beam then discharges these patterns, and the discharging current forms the output video signal, as the beam scans. A camera-control unit provides the scanning signals for the camera, and also adds the correct BLACK LEVEL and the SYNCHRONIZING PULSES to the video output so that it can be used for studio monitors and ultimately transmitted. See also IMAGE ORTHICON, VIDICON.

cancellation circuit, *n.* a technique used in radar circuitry to remove FIXED RETURNS. In a radar system that allows only moving objects to be noted, the pulses returned from fixed objects have to be cancelled. This is done by using a DELAY LINE. The pulse from an object is compared with the pulse from the previous scan. If the pulses coincide, the object is nonmoving, and the cancellation circuit removes it by adding an inverted signal.

canned, *adj.* **1.** (of a portion of a circuit) being protected against electrostatic or magnetic fields. A SCREENING can around a coil reduces the chances of pick–up of interfering signals, and also reduces the field around the coil which can affect other components. The can will, however, lower the Q FACTOR of the coil. **2.** a slang term for recorded, as in *canned music*.

capacitance, *n.* the property of a system that enables it to store electrostatic charge. The capacitance of an isolated conductor is defined as the slope of the graph of potential plotted against charge. Symbol: C; unit: farad. An object is said to have a capacitance (C) of one farad if it can store one coulomb of charge (Q) at a potential of one volt. Capacitance can be written $C = Q/V$, and is measured in unity of coulombs per volt. In practice the farad is too large a unit, and microfarads (10^{-6}), nanofarads (10^{-9}) and picofarads (10^{-12}) are used. See also CAPACITOR.

capacitive coupling, *n.* a circuit that transfers signal through a CAPACITOR.

capacitive load, *n.* a load that behaves like a combination of resistor and capacitor. This implies that the phase of voltage lags the phase of current. If the load were purely capacitive, the phase angle would be 90 degrees, but there would be no power dissipation.

capacitive reactance, *n.* the ratio of signal voltage to current for a capacitor. This quantity decreases as the frequency is increased, with the relationship $X = 1/\omega C$, where X is reactance in ohms, ω is angular frequency (equal to $2\pi f$), and C is capacitance in farads. For a pure capacitor (with no series or parallel resistance and no inductance), the phase of current leads the phase of voltage by 90 degrees. See also IMPEDANCE.

capacitive tuning, *n.* the altering of the tuning of a RESONANT CIRCUIT by varying the CAPACITANCE. This involves using a variable capacitor or a variable inductor.

capacitor, *n.* a passive circuit component with CAPACITANCE. A capacitor is formed from a pair of conducting surfaces separated by a layer of insulator. A capacitor made from a pair of parallel conducting plates of area S separated by a distance d, with the gap between the plates filled by a dielectric of relative permittivity ϵ_r, will have a capacitance C given by

$$C = \frac{\epsilon_r \epsilon_o S}{d}$$

where ϵ_o is the permittivity of free space. The form of construction affects the amount of capacitance that can be achieved in a reasonable bulk, the stability of capacitance value, and the voltage that can be applied across the conductors (plates). The voltage-variable capacitance across a semi-conductor junction can also be used in the form of a VARACTOR. See also CERAMIC CAPACITOR, ELECTROLYTIC CAPACITOR, FOIL CAPACITOR, MICA CAPACITOR, MOS CAPACITOR, PAPER CAPACITOR, PLASTIC–FILM CAPACITOR.

capacitor microphone, *n.* a microphone in which the transducer is a CAPACITOR. The microphone consists of a metal backplate placed adjacent to a conducting diaphragm. The diaphragm is electrostatically charged, so that when it vibrates, the voltage on the diaphragm will vary as the capacitance varies. This variation of voltage constitutes the output signal. The microphone tends to be bulky if reasonable sensitivity is required, and needs a polarizing voltage to supply the charge to the diaphragm. The ELECTRET microphone is a more modern version.

capstan, *n.* the rotating tape-drive spindle of a tape recorder. The capstan consists of an accurately ground cylindrical rod that rotates at a constant speed. The tape is sandwiched between the capstan and a rubber pinchwheel, so that the constant speed rotation of the capstan causes a constant linear motion of the tape. Any irregularity of the capstan or of its bearings will cause irregular tape speed, which will in turn cause WOW or FLUTTER to appear on signals retrieved from the tape.

carbon microphone, *n.* a microphone formerly used for telephones, now obsolete.

carbon resistor or **carbon–composition resistor,** *n.* the most common and the cheapest construction of resistor. This uses a mixture of graphite and clay (the same mixture as is used for pencils), baked and moulded into a casing in contact with metal caps that are attached to the wire leads. The TOLERANCE range of resistance for a batch is large, and the stability of resistance value is not high. For most purposes this type has now been replaced by metal or carbon FILM RESISTORS.

carcinotron or **crossed–field tube,** *n.* a form of TRAVELLING-WAVE TUBE that is used as a microwave oscillator. It is distinguished by the use of crossed electrostatic and magnetic fields, and a circular beam path. It is also classed as a form of BACKWARD-WAVE TUBE because the electromagnetic wave motion is in the reverse direction as compared to the electron beam motion.

carrier, *n.* **1.** a radio-frequency sine wave that can be modulated (see MODULATION) and used to carry information. Also called radio wave. **2.** an ELECTRON, HOLE, or ION whose movement causes the flow of current.

carrier frequency, *n.* the frequency of an unmodulated carrier wave.

carrier storage or **charge storage,** *n.* the storage of charge in the form of excess CARRIERS near a semiconductor JUNCTION. The significance of carrier storage is that when the bias across the junction is reversed, current will flow as a result of these carriers recombining. This means that a junction will continue to pass current until some (short) time after applying a reverse bias.

carrier suppression, *n.* a form of radio MODULATION. The carrier is modulated, giving a set of signals that consists of carrier and sidebands. The carrier is then suppressed by filtering or by adding an inverse carrier signal, leaving only the sideband(s). The effect of carrier suppression is to increase very greatly the power efficiency of the transmission. Another effect is to confine reception to receivers that are equipped to replace the missing carrier.

cascade, *n.* a number of devices connected in series so that the output of one stage serves as the input of the next.

cascode, *n.* a form of amplifier circuit that has high output impedance and very large degree of isolation between output and input. In BIPOLAR TRANSISTOR form, the cascode consists of a COMMON EMITTER stage directly coupled to a COMMON BASE stage. See Fig. 14.

Fig. 14. **Cascode**. A cascode circuit using a pair of bipolar transistors. Q_1 is a grounded-emitter amplifier with R_{load} as its collector resistor. Q_2 is interposed in the collector path to prevent Q_1's collector from swinging, while passing the collector current through the R_{load} unchanged. V_4 is a fixed-bias voltage. The cascode is an excellent HF amplifier.

catcher, *n.* the electron-collecting electrode of a KLYSTRON.

catching diode or **clipping diode,** *n.* a diode that is used to limit the amplitude of a waveform.

cathode or **emitter,** *n.* the electron–emitting part of a THERMIONIC VALVE. In transmitting valves, this consists of a winding of tungsten wire that is electrically heated to a very high temperature. An obsolete form of triode valve used a low-temperature cathode that consisted of a coating of oxides of calcium, strontium and barium deposited onto a nickel tube. This was heated to a working temperature of around 1000K by a molybdenum filament inside the nickel tube. The filament was insulated by a coating of aluminium oxide (alumina). The cathode of a cathode-ray tube consists of a flat-topped nickel cylinder that is heated by an internal filament. The oxide coating is on the flat top of the cylinder.

cathode follower, *n.* an obsolete form of valve circuit with very high input impedance and low output impedance. The transistor equivalent is the EMITTER FOLLOWER or source follower. Nowadays, follower circuits are most usually made using operational amplifiers.

cathode-ray oscilloscope (CRO), *n.* the instrument that is used for measurements on waveforms and pulses. Often shortened to *oscilloscope*. The oscilloscope is based on a CATHODE-RAY TUBE that uses ELECTROSTATIC DEFLECTION. The horizontal plates of the tube are supplied with a sawtooth TIMEBASE waveform that causes the electron beam to sweep across the face of the tube at a constant speed and return (flyback) very rapidly. The beam is automatically brightened during sweep, and blanked during flyback. The waveform that is to be measured is amplified and applied to the Y-deflection plates.

The combination of waveform and timebase produces a graph picture of the wave, showing the amplitude and time between wave peaks. By having both the timebase and the amplifier calibrated, the peak-to-peak amplitude and the time between wave peaks can be measured for any wave that can be displayed. More advanced facilities include delayed triggering, second timebase, and multiple traces.

cathode-ray tube (CRT), *n.* an electron beam display device. Sometimes shortened to *tube* (but note that in the US, *tube* means any thermionic vacuum device). All cathode-ray tubes make use of the emission of electrons from a hot CATHODE, the formation of emitted electrons into a beam by ELECTRON LENSES, and the emission of light from a material, the PHOSPHOR, that is struck by electrons. In addition, all cathode-ray tubes must provide for the beam to be deflected in any direction across the face of the tube.

The two main types of cathode-ray tube are INSTRUMENT TUBES used for measurement purposes, particularly in CATHODE-RAY OSCILLOSCOPES, and PICTURE TUBES, used for TV and radar.

cation, *n.* a positively-charged ION. The term 'cation' is used because a positively-charged ion is attracted to a negatively-charged electrode, or CATHODE. Compare ANION.

cavity resonator, *n.* a MICROWAVE tuned circuit. The cylindrical cavity can be considered as a coil with one turn that is tuned by stray capacity, but it is more realistic to regard it in terms of the dimensions of a wavelength as related to the circumference of the cavity.

CAZAMP, *n. acronym for* Commutating Auto-Zeroing Amplifier, a device consisting of a pair of MOSFET OPERATIONAL AMPLIFIERS and a number of FET switches (see FIELD–EFFECT TRANSISTOR) contained within a single package. At any given time one amplifier is being zeroed (having its input-offset voltage removed) while the second amplifier behaves as a normal operational amplifier and amplifies the signal. The operational amplifiers switch roles periodically via the FET switches, and the effect is that drifts due to input offsets are effectively cancelled out.

CB, see CITIZEN'S BAND.

CCD, see CHARGE–COUPLED DEVICE.

CCIR, *abbrev. for* Comité Consultatif International des Radiocommunications, the international standardizing committee for radio and television.

CCITT, *abbrev. for* Comité Consultatif International Telegraphique et Telephonique, the international standardizing committee for telegraphs and telephones.

Ceefax, *n. Trademark.* a form of TELETEXT service broadcast by the BBC. Identical technically to the ITV ORACLE service.

cell, *n.* any device that has an electric output. A *voltaic cell* is a generator of voltage from chemical effects, and such cells are used for low-voltage supplies, or when joined to make BATTERIES (1), for higher voltages. Light-sensitive cells, or PHOTOCELLS, provide a voltage output when illuminated.

centimetric wave, *n.* a wave whose wavelength is less than a metre and more than a centimetre.

central processing unit (CPU), *n.* the main working unit of a computer that carries out the actions of the program.

centre tap, *n.* a connection to the centre of a transformer winding.

ceramic capacitor, *n.* a capacitor that is formed by metallizing two parallel surfaces of a ceramic slab. The range of CAPACITANCE can vary from a few picofarads to several nanofarads. Ceramic capacitors often have capacitance values that can change as the applied voltage is altered, and can suffer from comparatively large energy losses. They are best used as bypass capacitors for radio frequencies, and should when possible be avoided in oscillator circuits.

cermet, *n.* a ceramic-metal composite material. The cermet is very hard, but with a RESISTIVITY that makes it suitable for manufacturing POTENTIOMETERS.

channel, *n.* **1.** in radio communication, a specified frequency or frequency band used for signals. **2.** in a FIELD-EFFECT TRANSISTOR, the conducting path between the source and the drain whose conductivity is controlled by the gate.

channel stopper, *n.* a heavily doped layer in an INTEGRATED CIRCUIT that prevents the formation of unwanted FIELD-EFFECT TRANSISTOR channels.

characteristic, *n.* a relationship or set of relationships between a number (usually a pair) of quantities. These are usually shown graphically with one quantity plotted against another, and with a different graph line representing each value of a third quantity. See Fig. 15 (p.50). For example, a set of characteristics for a TRANSISTOR may show the output current plotted against input current for a range of different output voltages.

characteristic impedance, *n.* the impedance of a correctly terminated line or any other network with two input and two

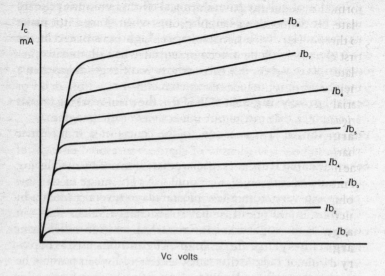

Fig. 15. **Characteristic**. A typical set of transistor characteristics. In this example, collector current I_c is plotted against collector voltage V_c, for various values I_b of base current.

output terminals. See ITERATIVE IMPEDANCE.

charge, *n.* the fundamental property of the electron (negative charge) and proton (positive charge). The recognizable and measurable feature of charge is that one charge will exert force on any other charge. The relationship was discovered by Charles Coulomb, after whom the modern unit of charge is named. One COULOMB (which equals 6.24184×10^{18} electrons) is the charge which, one metre from an equal charge in a vacuum, repels it with a force of 8.9874×10^9 newtons.

charge carrier, *n.* any moving particle that is charged. The term denotes electrons, holes and ions that move under the influence of an electric field. The movement of a charge carrier constitutes current. Current is defined as rate of flow of charge in units of coulombs per second, i.e. $I = dQ/dt$. See also RESIDUAL CURRENT.

charge–coupled device (CCD), *n.* **1.** a charge-storage memory device. The CCD is based on a set of MOS capacitors formed in sequence on a chip, and with a common (earth) plate. By connecting adjacent groups of three capacitor plates to three-phase CLOCK signal lines, a charge that is placed on the first capacitor can be moved in sequence to each of the other plates on the chip. This forms a type of FIRST-IN/FIRST-OUT memory that is used mainly as a SHIFT REGISTER, time-delay or serial memory. A serial CCD of this type is also called a *bucket brigade*. **2.** a form of semiconductor TV camera device.

charge density, *n.* a measure of the concentration of electric charge. The surface density of charge is measured in terms of the number of COULOMBS of charge per square metre of surface. A more practical unit is microcoulombs per square metre. The volume density of charge is measured in terms of coulombs or microcoulombs of charge per cubic metre of volume.

charge storage, see CARRIER STORAGE.

charge-storage diode or **snap-off diode** or **stop-recovery diode,** *n.* a diode that can be used as a pulse generator. The stored charge allows the diode to conduct for a brief time after applying reverse voltage. This causes the reverse voltage across the diode to remain low until all the charge carriers have been absorbed, following which the reverse voltage rise is very fast. This fast voltage rise, limited by the CAPACITANCE across the diode and the supply impedance, constitutes the leading edge of a pulse that is terminated when the diode conducts again.

charge-storage tube, see STORAGE TUBE.

charge-transfer device, *n.* any form of INTEGRATED CIRCUIT that operates by switching charge from one capacitor to another. See also CHARGE-COUPLED DEVICE.

chart recorder, *n.* an electromechanical device used for making a permanent record of a waveform. The input signal amplitude operates a pen drive so that the position of the pen on a paper chart indicates instantaneous signal amplitude. The chart may be in the form of a roll that is driven past the pen at a steady slow rate. By using several separately controlled pens, a number of quantities can be plotted on one chart. For high speed measurements photosensitive paper may be used, with a point light source instead of a pen.

Chebyshev filter, *n.* a filter that allows limited passband ripple to occur but gives a steeper transfer function in the transition region between PASS BAND and STOP BAND. The amplitude response of a Chebyshev filter is given by

$$\frac{V_{out}}{V_{in}} = \frac{1}{[1 + \epsilon^2 C_n{}^2(f/f_c)]^{\frac{1}{2}}}$$

where C is a polynomial of degree n, ϵ is a constant, f_c is the corner frequency, and f the frequency. For further details see Ref. 2.

chip, *n.* the small slice from a SEMICONDUCTOR wafer on which a transistor or integrated circuit is fabricated.

chip-select pin, *n.* an input pin for a DIGITAL IC. The chip-select pin allows the complete chip to be enabled or disabled according to the logic voltage on the pin. This allows, for example, different areas of memory to be activated in a computer.

choke, *n.* an obsolete term for INDUCTOR, particularly a large inductor with a magnetic core.

choke coupling, *n.* the use of an INDUCTOR as the load for an amplifying stage.

chopper, *n.* a circuit that converts a steady input voltage by regular switching into a square wave. This was originally done mechanically (using a *vibrator*), but is now achieved with MOS transistors or ICs. The chopped voltage can then be amplified using AC amplifier techniques. DC – DC transformers can be made by using a chopper, amplifier and rectifier system.

chrominance signal, *n.* the portion of a TV signal that carries colour information. The TV signal has to permit compatibility, meaning that the same signal can be used by both MONOCHROME and COLOUR TELEVISION receivers. The monochrome, or LUMINANCE, signal is transmitted normally, and the colour information is added in the form of a chrominance signal that is modulated onto a SUBCARRIER. A monochrome receiver does not demodulate this subcarrier, and thus uses only the luminance signal. The effect of the subcarrier on the monochrome receiver is to cause a fine bar pattern that is not visible at normal viewing distances. A colour receiver can demodulate the subcarrier, recover the chrominance signals and make use of them, mixed with the luminance signal, to provide three separate signals for the three ELECTRON GUNS of the COLOUR TUBE.

circuit, *n*. a path for electric current, consisting of a current path through ACTIVE COMPONENTS or PASSIVE COMPONENTS. See also GAIN, FILTER, MODULATION, DEMODULATION, SWITCH, OSCILLATION, and GATE.

circuit breaker, *n*. a form of overload switch used in place of a FUSE to interrupt a circuit when excessive current flows or when a voltage surge occurs. The circuit breaker is magnetically operated, and can be manually reset.

circuit diagram or **schematic** (US), *n*. a diagram that shows a circuit in symbolic form. There is a standard symbol for each component, showing the connections. In a circuit diagram, a current path is shown as a line that joins components. Some diagrams also show input and output waveforms at points in the circuit. Components in the diagram may be labelled with an identifying letter and number (such as R234, C122) and usually also with their value. Compare WIRING DIAGRAM.

circuit element, *n*. any one COMPONENT in a circuit.

citizen's band (CB), *n*. a portion of the radio frequency range that is set aside for amateur users who do not hold an amateur licence. The main CB band is a part of the 28m band, though there are also UHF allocations. CB originated in the US and became very popular with long-distance drivers in particular. A strong following in the UK was instrumental in obtaining allocation of bands, but the results were disappointing. The short range of permitted transmitters, together with the undisciplined behaviour of many users, killed off the original CB craze for all but a few genuine enthusiasts.

clamp, *vb*. to force a signal voltage level to a particular voltage at a selected time. Clamping is particularly important in a VIDEO waveform, because the 30% voltage level of the video signal is the BLACK LEVEL. If this is not at the correct voltage when applied to the ELECTRON GUN, correct black level will not be achieved. At the time when the signal is at black level, then a clamp provides a low-resistance path to the correct voltage level. The clamp is then released for the remainder of the signal.

clamping diode, *n.* a diode used to prevent a signal from exceeding certain voltage limits. The diode is connected between the signal and a reference voltage so that, if the signal exceeds the reference voltage, current flows through the diode and the signal voltage is 'clamped'. More elaborate circuits can be devised, using a BRIDGE connection of diodes with the connecting path opened by using pulses to bias the diodes.

class A, *n.* the linear operating mode of an amplifier. An amplifier is operating in class A if current flows in the amplifying device for each and any part of the input signal waveform. The amplifying device is never CUTOFF and never bottomed (see BOTTOMING). The mode is used in particular for audio voltage amplifiers, some audio output stages, and some RF amplifiers (for frequency-modulated signals).

class AB, *n.* the class of amplification (GAIN) in which the amplifying device can be CUTOFF or bottomed (see BOTTOMING) for a small part of the signal waveform. The mode is used for some audio output stages and in RF amplifiers.

class B, *n.* the class of amplification (GAIN) in which the amplifying device passes no current for half of the signal input wave. This system can be used for audio output if a matching device is used to handle the other half of the wave. It can also be used for RF amplification with a tuned load, because the natural oscillation of the tuned circuit will provide the missing section of output signal.

class C, *n.* the class of amplification (GAIN) in which the amplifying device is CUTOFF for more than half of the signal waveform. The mode is used for high-efficiency RF amplifiers in transmitters, CW or amplitude modulated. The load is always a tuned circuit whose resonance will supply the missing part of the waveform.

class D, *n.* the class of amplification (GAIN) in which the amplifying device is based on a pulse-modulation amplification system. Pulses at high frequency have their width modulated by a low-frequency (usually audio) waveform. The pulses can be amplified with no regard to linearity, and demodulation is achieved by any low-pass filter, even by direct coupling to a loudspeaker. The system requires good pulse handling, and early examples were not competitive with conventional analogue amplifiers.

C layer, *n.* the lowest layer of the IONOSPHERE, approximately 40 to 60km above the surface of the Earth.

clear, *vb.* **1.** to reset a LOGIC output voltage to zero. **2.** to empty a computer memory and fill it with null characters.

clipper or **peak limiter,** *n.* a circuit that removes part of a waveform. A peak clipper is typically a biased diode circuit that will conduct when a signal peak exceeds the bias level. This can be used for limiting the amplitude of the wave peaks. Clippers are extensively used in speed-quality radio transmitter circuits to prevent OVERMODULATION. Another application is to remove peaks caused by the effects of IMPULSE NOISE on FM or TV signals. See Fig. 16.

Fig. 16. **Clipper.** A simple peak clipper circuit using in this example a Zener diode.

clock, *n.* a circuit that generates pulses at precisely controlled intervals. Used in connection with logic gates and counters of the SYNCHRONOUS type, and particularly in computer circuits. Clock circuits generally consist of QUARTZ CRYSTAL controlled oscillators along with pulse-shaping circuits.

closed circuit, *n.* **1.** a complete electrical circuit through which current can flow when a voltage is applied. **2.** closed, i.e. wire-transmitted, TV and radio systems.

clutter, *n.* unwanted signals in a radar system. Clutter consists of the signal echos from such things as ocean waves, ploughed fields, buildings and other irregularities that are not radar targets. An *anticlutter circuit* is one that conceals such signals by making use of the fact that the signals always recur at the same times. By submitting a freshly received signal and a delayed signal to an ANTICOINCIDENCE CIRCUIT, the fixed signals of clutter can be removed, though this may also remove slowly-changing signals from slowly-moving targets.

CML, see CURRENT–MODE LOGIC.

CMOS, *abbrev. for* complementary metal-oxide semiconductor, an INTEGRATED CIRCUIT structure that uses series combinations of n–channel and p–channel FIELD–EFFECT TRANSISTORS in each device. The important feature of CMOS construction is the very low power consumption, along with the ability to operate on low supply voltages. For computing purposes, the older CMOS ICs operate rather too slowly to be of use as processors, but CMOS memory with battery backup is sometimes used as a form of nonvolatile memory, and modern CMOS designs are capable of higher speed operation. High-speed CMOS versions of microprocessors are available for small computers.

coaxial cable, *n.* a type of shielded cable for conducting signals. The signal carrier is stranded or single-core wire that is insulated. This insulated sleeve is surrounded by a braided wire covering, forming the outer earthed conductor of the cable. This braiding is, in turn, covered by a tough outer insulator. Coaxial cable is used extensively in TV (RF and video) connections. The CHARACTERISTIC IMPEDANCE is normally around 50 to 75ohms. By using solid inner wire, with insulating beads, the capacitance per metre and the loss per metre of the cable can be made very low. Compare TWIN CABLE.

coercivity or **coercive force,** *n.* the amount of magnetic field strength that has to be applied to a magnetized material in order to reduce the flux density of the material to zero. When the field is removed, the magnetic material will have a remanent (see REMANENCE) flux density. See MAGNETIC HYSTERESIS.

coherent oscillator, *n.* an oscillator whose bursts of waves are all in PHASE, such as light and microwave oscillators of the LASER and MASER type respectively.

coil, *n.* an INDUCTOR formed by a winding of wire or other conducting material into a shape with circular, square, elliptical or other cross-sections. The conductors must be insulated from each other, and the coil is used either for its INDUCTANCE or to generate a MAGNETIC FIELD.

coincidence circuit, *n.* a circuit that delivers an output when two inputs coincide. A pulse coincidence circuit will deliver an output pulse when two input pulses (to separate terminals) arrive at the same time. A voltage coincidence circuit (or *voltage comparator*) provides an output when the voltage levels at the two inputs are identical, or within a preset range of each other.

coincidental half-current switching, *n.* a method of using MAGNETIC CORES as computer memory elements. The magnetic characteristic graph shapes of the cores are approximately rectangular, and the magnetic state can be reversed by applying a known current. If each signal through one of a number of wires laced through the core consists of a current of about half the critical level, then one single signal cannot change the core magnetism. The magnetism will be changed only if two wires carry current signals in the same direction, hence the term 'coincidental half-current switching'.

cold-cathode emitter, *n.* an electron EMITTER (1) that requires no artificial heating. *Cold emission* of electrons is achieved by using a high value of electric field near the cathode. See also FIELD EMISSION.

cold emission, see COLD-CATHODE EMITTER.

collector, *n.* the CARRIER collecting electrode of a transistor. Carriers that flow from the EMITTER(1) through the BASE region end up in the collector region. The total rate of flow of charge into this region constitutes the collector current.

colour burst, *n.* the 10 cycles of sine wave that are used to synchronize the colour oscillator in a TV receiver. These cycles of sine wave are at the colour SUBCARRIER frequency, and are placed in the BACK PORCH of the line sync signal.

colour code, *n.* the internationally standardized code that is used for marking resistors and, to a lesser extent, capacitor values. For details of the code, see the Appendix.

colour CRT, *n.* a CATHODE-RAY TUBE that can display a range of colours. The most familiar type uses a set of three colour-emitting PHOSPHORS that are laid down as fine vertical stripes on the face of the tube. Three separate electron guns are arranged in line, and a metal grille, the APERTURE GRILLE, is placed close to the screen. The effect of the apertures in the grille, one aperture for each group of three colour phosphor stripes, is to shield each phosphor stripe from the electron beams of two of the electron guns. In this way, the beam from one gun can reach only the green phosphor, the beam from the second gun can reach only the red phosphor, and the beam from the third gun can reach only the blue phosphor. By controlling the relative beam currents of the three guns, any colour and any brightness that the system is capable of can be obtained.

colour fringe, *n.* a surrounding of unwanted colour at the edge of an image. This can be caused by MOIRE-PATTERN effects (often called strobing) when a striped image is being viewed. It can also be caused by poor CONVERGENCE of electron guns, by undesired magnetization of tube electrodes, or by other faults. It can be particularly troublesome around monochrome images on COLOUR TELEVISION tubes.

colour killer, *n.* a switching circuit within a COLOUR TELE-VISION receiver. The colour killer switches off the colour demodulator circuits when no colour burst is being received. This avoids the possibility of random noise signals being interpreted as colour signals and causing COLOUR FRINGES on monochrome images.

colour saturation, *n.* a measurement of the intensity of colour. A saturated colour primary would be 100% red, green or blue. Mixing white (itself a mixture of red, green and blue) with a saturated colour produces an unsaturated colour. For example, a 50% saturated blue would consist of 50% blue and 50% white light.

colour television, *n.* the production of coloured images on a TV screen. The COLOUR TELEVISION SYSTEM must be compatible, i.e., capable of providing acceptable pictures on a MONOCHROME receiver. This is done by adding the colour signals to the normal signal that would be used by a monochrome receiver. The signals from the camera are processed into a luminance signal, the normal signal for a monochrome receiver, and two difference signals. A colour difference signal is the signal voltage that results from subtracting the luminance signal from a colour signal, and in the UK PAL system, these colour difference signals are written as **R-Y** and **B-Y**. In this nomenclature, **Y** represents the luminance signal, **R** the red signal and **B** the blue signal. These colour difference signals are modulated onto a subcarrier that in turn is modulated onto the main vision signal. At the receiver, the colour TV circuits will separate out the subcarrier signals, and generate a local subcarrier from an oscillator that is synchronized to the COLOUR BURST in the BACK PORCH of the line sync pulse. By using two synchronous demodulators (see SYNCHRONOUS DETECTION), the colour difference signals are demodulated, and are then mixed with the luminance signal to provide three separate colour signals, red, green and blue. These are then used to operate the three electron beams of the colour TV tube.

colour television system, *n.* the method that is used to carry the colour difference signals to a COLOUR TELEVISION receiver. The main systems are NTSC (US), PAL (most of Europe) and SECAM (France and USSR). The differences between the systems hinge on the methods of modulation of the subcarrier, and the way in which phase shift errors can be avoided.

Colpitts oscillator, *n.* a crystal-controlled oscillator circuit whose distinguishing feature is a POTENTIAL DIVIDER that uses capacitors. See Fig. 17 on page 60. See also HARTLEY OSCILLATOR.

common-base connection or **grounded-base circuit,** *n.* a transistor connection in which the base is maintained at signal earth. The signal input is to the emitter and the output is taken from the collector. The common-base connection offers unity current gain, moderate voltage gain, and good high-frequency characteristics. It is used mainly for impedance transformation

Fig. 17. **Colpitts oscillator**. One form of the Colpitts oscillator circuit, distinguished by its use of a capacitive voltage divider to obtain the feedback signal.

(low input, high output impedances) and for radio frequency amplifier stages.

common–collector connection, see EMITTER FOLLOWER.

common–emitter connection or **grounded–emitter connection,** *n*. a transistor connection in which the emitter is maintained at signal earth. This connection features very large current and voltage gain figures, with medium impedance input and output. It is the most common type of transistor circuit connection. See Fig. 18.

common–mode rejection, *n*. a measure of the noise rejection of a differential amplifier. In a differential amplifier, the difference between a pair of inputs is amplified. A common–mode signal is one that is applied with the same phase to both inputs of the amplifier, and it should result in a very small output signal. The common–mode rejection ratio is the ratio, expressed in decibels, of the response to a differential signal to

Fig. 18. **Common-emitter connection**. A typical common-emitter amplifier stage, shown here in the form of an audio-voltage amplifier.

the response to a common–mode signal when both are applied at equal amplitude. The rejection ratio can be very large, of the order of 100dB., for some ICs.

commutator, *n.* a form of reversing switch, usually the mechanical rotary switch connected to coils in the armature of a motor.

compact disc, *n.* a method of sound or video recording that uses a reflective or transparent plastic disc and a laser. The signals are converted into DIGITAL form, and used to switch a laser beam on and off while the beam is being guided over the surface of a spinning metal disc. This produces a pattern of pitting on the surface that carries the information of the signals and this master disc can be used to print copies. These copies are compact discs, and their signals can be played back with a system that uses a low-power laser. See also SOUND REPRODUCTION.

compander, *n.* a combination of COMPRESSOR and EXPANDER. Many audio systems, notably recording systems, cannot cope with a large amplitude range, the DYNAMIC range of the signal. This can be remedied by using a NONLINEAR amplifier to compress the volume range before recording or transmitting. The volume range is then restored later by another nonlinear amplifier that expands the range again. The system is useful only if the compression and expansion can be very closely matched. A compander system called DBX is successfully used as a tape-noise reduction system for domestic cassette recordings. The system is also used in some broadcasting applications (not in the UK), and has been suggested as a method of overcoming the unsatisfactory reception of FM Radio 3 in many parts of the UK.

comparator, *n.* **1.** (also called *voltage comparator*) a circuit (usually based on an OPERATIONAL AMPLIFIER) that gives a positive output when

$$V_{in1} > V_{in2}$$

a negative output when

$$V_{in1} < V_{in2}$$

and a zero output when

$$V_{in1} = V_{in2}$$

2. a device that compares two binary bytes and gives TRUE logical outputs to indicate whether one binary value is greater, less or equal to the other.

compensated attenuator, *n.* an attenuator that is designed to operate over a large frequency range. A resistive attenuator does not provide the correct attenuation ratios for high-frequency signals. This is because of the STRAY CAPACITANCE across the resistors. By using low value resistors, and by wiring capacitors in parallel with the resistors (which also provide the correct division ratio), the attenuator can be compensated for strays, and so operate over a wide bandwidth.

compensating leads, *n.* a set of dummy leads used as balancing RESISTORS. In measurements which involve small changes in resistance values the behaviour of connecting leads may interfere with the measurement. The leads may, for example, interfere because their resistance changes with temperature. By using a second identical pair of leads physically close, but electrically connected to the other part of the bridge, these changes can be compensated for.

complementary transistors, *n*. a pair of transistors of opposite (bipolar) type, one a P-N-P TRANSISTOR, the other an N-P-N TRANSISTOR, or opposite CHANNEL MOS types. The two are often used in series circuits, and require to be closely matched in their characteristics. The complementary bipolar pair is often used as an audio CLASS B output stage, and the MOS equivalent is the basis of CMOS ICs. See also TOTEM-POLE CIRCUIT.

complementer, a circuit whose output is the inverse of its input. See INVERTER.

complex number, *n*. any number of the form a + bi, where a and b are real numbers and $i = \sqrt{-1}$ (electronics engineers generally use j rather than i, as the latter may be mistaken for 1). Complex numbers include real and imaginary numbers. When describing AC circuits it is necessary to use complex numbers to describe the magnitude and phase of a voltage or current. A complex number can be represented as a point on a diagram (known as an *Argand diagram*) as shown in Fig. 19 on page 64. Real numbers (such as DC voltages) appear as points along the x-axis. Complex numbers can appear anywhere on the diagram, and are defined in terms of a real part 'a' and a complex part 'b' in the form $\mathbf{c} = a + ib$, where $i = \sqrt{-1}$, and **c** = complex quantity. The magnitude of **c** is $\sqrt{(a^2 + b^2)}$, and its phase is ArcTan (b/a). For further details see Ref. 5.

component, *n*. any separately packaged unit of a CIRCUIT with its own connecting leads. See ACTIVE COMPONENT, PASSIVE COMPONENT.

composite conductor, *n*. a multiwire conductor, using different metals. One common type is a copper-steel composite that is used for suspended power lines. The steel contributes little to the conductivity of the line, but most of its strength.

composition resistor, see CARBON RESISTOR.

composite signal, *n*. a VIDEO signal that contains all the

Fig. 19. **Complex number**. See main entry.

necessary components for a receiver. A video signal from a camera very often consists only of the video portion from each colour pick-up tube. The LUMINANCE signal has to be formed, and the colour difference signals modulated on to the colour SUBCARRIER. The SYNCHRONIZING PULSES are then added, along with the COLOUR BURST to give the complete composite signal ready to be modulated onto the video carrier.

compressor, *n.* a circuit that reduces the dynamic range of a signal. The action is achieved by a nonlinear stage whose gain reduces as the signal amplitude increases. See also COMPANDER.

computer, *n.* any device that operates on data in accordance with a preset program of instructions. See ANALOGUE COMPUTER, DIGITAL COMPUTER.

conditionally stable, *adj.* (of an amplifier or servofeedback circuit) being capable of oscillating only under certain conditions. This means that the circuit will not break into oscillation unless some condition is violated. A common condition is that the load of an amplifier shall be resistive or inductive, never capacitive. An amplifier that can be used with any load without any trace of oscillation is said to be *unconditionally stable*.

conductance, *n*. the inverse of RESISTANCE. Symbol: *G*; unit: SIEMENS. See also MUTUAL CONDUCTABLE.

conduction, *n*. the transmission of energy by particle movement. Electrical conduction in most metals is the result of free-electron movement, but positive holes are present in significant numbers in some metals and are sometimes the main current carriers. Conduction in gases and in liquids is by movement of IONS. In liquids (mostly water solutions), the ions are surrounded by water molecules and are slow-moving. In gases, the ions can be rapidly accelerated so as to move fast enough to ionize any molecules that they strike, causing total ionization. See also BREAKDOWN.

conduction angle, *n*. the fraction of a cycle during which a device (usually a transmitting valve or transistor operating in CLASS C) conducts. One cycle represents an angle of 360 degrees, and the fraction of the cycle for which the valve or transistor conducts is multiplied by 360 to obtain the conduction angle.

conduction angle control, *n*. a method of using a THYRISTOR to regulate an ALTERNATING CURRENT supply. In this system, the point in the cycle at which the thyristor fires can be controlled, and the thyristor is switched off by the zero-voltage part of each cycle. For a half-wave of AC, then, the thyristor can be on for a maximum of 180 degrees, and a minimum of zero. Full cycle control can be obtained using more than one thyristor, or by the use of a TRIAC.

conduction electrons, *n*. the electrons in a solid that are free to move within the material, so providing CONDUCTIVITY.

conductivity, *n*. the inverse of RESISTIVITY. Symbol: κ; unit: siemens per metre. The conductivity of a material measures the ease with which electric current will pass through the material.

conductor, *n*. a material with good CONDUCTIVITY, for example, a metal, or semiconductor that has a large density of free CARRIERS.

cone, *n*. the part of a loudspeaker that vibrates to produce sound waves. The cone is normally conical in shape, and is made of stiff material. Materials such as paper, plastics, metal and composites have been used at various times, but stiffened paper is the most widespread material. The cone is attached to the VOICE COIL and this in turn is held by the SPIDER in the gap of the magnet.

conjugate, *adj*. (of impedance values) being equal when the resistance portions are equal and the reactive components are equal and opposite (one inductive, the other capacitive).

constantan, *n*. an alloy of nickel and copper used in manufacture of resistors that gets its name from having an almost constant resistance value as temperature changes. In other words, the TEMPERATURE COEFFICIENT of RESISTIVITY is unusually low. Since the resistivity value is fairly high for a metal alloy, fairly large value wire-wound resistors can be made of constantan without the need to use very long lengths or impracticably small diameters of wire. Used also in conjunction with pure copper in THERMOCOUPLES.

constant–current source, *n*. a source of current that remains constant despite fluctuations of load. The main requirement for a constant current source is high output impedance, so that the current is determined by the source impedance rather than by the load impedance.

constant–K filter, *n*. a type of FILTER design in which the product of series impedance and shunt impedance is constant and equal to the square of the characteristic resistance. See CHARACTERISTIC IMPEDANCE.

constant–voltage source, *n*. a very low impedance source that can maintain a constant voltage across a varying load.

contact, *n*. a point or area where two materials touch. When the materials are both conductors, current can be made to flow across the contact. Unless the conductors are joined by high pressure, welding or soldering, the resistance at this point, the CONTACT RESISTANCE, may be high. For two different metals in contact, there will usually be a potential (a few tenths of a volt DC) that is called the *contact potential* or *contact voltage*. This contact potential is temperature-variable, so the contact can be used as a THERMOCOUPLE.

contact breaker, *n*. an electromechanical protective device for CIRCUITS. The action of the contact breaker is to interrupt a supply when a fault condition, usually excessive current flow, arises. Once the contact breaker has operated, it will have to be reset by hand to allow resumption of supply. See also OVERCURRENT TRIP.

contactor, *n.* a form of relay for switching large currents. A contactor is designed with a larger mechanical movement than a relay, and with a parallel movement of contacts rather than the normal hinged-arm movement of a relay.

contact resistance, *n.* the resistance between materials that are in CONTACT.

contact voltage, see CONTACT.

contrast, *n.* the ratio of intensities of lit and unlit parts of a picture. The contrast of a TV signal is determined, within limits, by the AMPLITUDE of the video signal. The contrast control of a TV receiver or monitor is the video GAIN CONTROL.

control electrode, *n.* the electrode that controls current flow between other electrodes. The control electrode of a bipolar transistor is the BASE, which controls current flow between emitter and collector. The controlling parameter in this example is base current. For a MOSFET, the controlling electrode is the gate, and its voltage controls the current between source and drain. For a transmitting valve, the controlling electrode is the grid, the voltage of which controls current between cathode and anode. The grid voltage can be positive or negative with respect to the cathode voltage, and when the grid voltage is positive, grid current will flow.

convergence, *n.* the meeting of the three electron beams of a COLOUR TELEVISION tube. The three beams should converge and cross over at the APERTURE GRILLE.

conversion gain ratio, *n.* a figure of merit for a FREQUENCY CHANGER, equal to the ratio of output power at the changed frequency to input power at the original frequency. The figure is usually expressed in decibels.

converter, *n.* any device that converts electrical energy from one form to another. An INVERTER (1) changes DC into AC. The circuit that changes from AC to DC is normally known as a POWER PACK. The term can also denote a *frequency converter*. This is a circuit that beats signals together to form a new signal frequency (see BEAT NOTE MIXER). An *impedance converter* allows signal impedance to be matched to load IMPEDANCE (see COMMON–COLLECTOR CONNECTION, EMITTER FOLLOWER). See also TRANSDUCERS.

cooling, *n.* the dissipation of heat energy. For solid materials such as TRANSISTORS, cooling relies firstly on conduction to transfer heat energy from the semiconductor to external materials such as cooling fins or metal blocks. The fins then convect heat (with a small amount of radiation), and blocks can be water-cooled. Cooling for transmitting valves can be by radiation or convection. Radiation-cooled valves use a glass envelope, and the heat of the anode is allowed to radiate away. Larger valves use metal envelopes that can be water cooled, steam cooled, or forced-air cooled.

coplanar transistor, *n.* a form of TRANSISTOR construction in which the electrodes are all on the surface of the SEMICONDUCTOR.

copper, *n.* a metal element universally used for low-resistance connections. Copper is used for wire, cable, and printed-circuit tracks.

copper–oxide rectifier, *n.* a type of RECTIFIER that uses copper/copper-oxide JUNCTIONS. Formerly used in low-voltage supplies (particularly chargers for secondary cells) until replaced by silicon. Copper-oxide rectifiers have a low forward voltage drop, and are still used as meter-movement protection devices.

core, *n.* see MAGNETIC CORE (1).

core loss, *n.* the loss of energy from an inductor or transformer caused by the core. The two factors that cause loss are EDDY CURRENTS and HYSTERESIS. Eddy currents are caused by induction of voltages across parts of the core, and can be minimized by shaping the core, particularly with air gaps. Hysteresis loss is caused when the magnetism of the core is changed, and can be minimized only by careful choice of material and operating conditions.

core store, *n.* a computer memory system that uses MAGNETIC CORES. Each core, about 2mm diameter, is threaded by perpendicular wires that magnetize the core in one direction or the other. The two directions of magnetization correspond to logic states 0 and 1. See COINCIDENTAL HALF–CURRENT SWITCHING.

core-type transformer, *n*. a transformer that is wound onto a core so that the core is surrounded by the winding. The alternative is the *shell-type transformer* in which the magnetic material surrounds the windings.

correlator, *n*. a circuit with which a waveform can be detected amid surrounding noise because of the periodic nature of the waveform.

cosmic noise, *n*. the radio frequency noise that has its origins in space.

coulomb, *n*. the unit of electric charge. Symbol: C. The coulomb is that charge which, when it is placed one metre from an equal charge in a vacuum, repels it with a force of 8.9874×10^9N. It is named after Charles Augustin de Coulomb (1736–1806), French physicist. The coulomb is a rather inconveniently large quantity for everyday use, so the microcoulomb ($= 10^{-6}$C; symbol: μC) and the picocoulomb ($= 10^{-12}$C; symbol: pC) are more commonly used. The coulomb can also be defined as the quantity of electricity transported in one second by a current of 1 ampere.

The definition of the coulomb is expressed in terms of Coulomb's law, which states that the force (**F**) between two charges Q_1 and Q_2 at a separation of d metres in a vacuum is given by

$$\mathbf{F} = \frac{Q_1 Q_2}{4\pi\epsilon_0 d^2}$$

where ϵ_0 is the PERMITTIVITY OF FREE SPACE and F is in newtons.

counter, *n*. a digital circuit that gives an output which is the total of the number of pulses that have been applied to the input. A digital counter may indicate the count on a digital display, an analogue counter may present it as a meter reading. Many counters display the COUNT RATE, that is the number of pulses per second. Counters are used as frequency meters, and also to count the conduction pulses for detectors of radioactivity such a GEIGER–MÜLLER TUBES.

countermeasures, *n*. any electronic method of combatting enemy RADAR or communications or for counteracting JAMMING.

count rate, *n.* the rate of arrival of pulses, the terms of pulses per second. See COUNTER.

coupling, *n.* the passing of a signal from one stage to another. *Direct coupling* implies that the signal and its DC level are passed. *AC coupling* means that the DC is blocked, and only the alternating part of the signal is passed. *Tuned coupling* is used to pass one particular frequency or band of frequencies; the opposite is *broadband* or *aperiodic coupling*. See also CRITICAL COUPLING, INTERSTAGE COUPLING.

coupling coefficient, *n.* a measure of the effectiveness of a tuned COUPLING. The coefficient is defined as the ratio of coupling impedance to the geometrical average of impedances on each side of the coupling. The quantity is measured rather than calculated in most cases.

coupling loop, *n.* a small inductor that is used to pick up a sample of a signal.

CPU, see CENTRAL PROCESSING UNIT.

critical coupling, *n.* the point of maximum transfer of SIGNAL between two RESONANT CIRCUITS. As the COUPLING between two tuned circuits is increased, the graph of amplitude plotted against frequency for the output rises in a steep peak at the resonant frequency (see RESONANCE). This peak is at its maximum at the point of 'critical coupling'. See Fig. 20. See also OVERCOUPLING.

critical damping, *n.* a resistive circuit loading which is just sufficient to prevent oscillation in a resonant circuit. If a resonant circuit is loaded by a resistor in parallel or in series, the resistor will dissipate energy and discourage oscillation. The effectiveness of this resistor can be seen if the circuit is briefly pulsed and the output viewed on an oscilloscope screen. If the damping is low, the circuit will oscillate freely, or 'ring'. As the damping is increased (lower value of parallel resistance, or higher value of series resistance), the oscillations die away more quickly. Eventually, the shape of the output takes the form of a single cycle with no subsequent oscillation. This is the point of 'critical damping'.

Fig. 20. **Critical coupling**. The effect of coupling between two tuned circuits, showing critical coupling, undercoupling and overcoupling.

CRO, see CATHODE-RAY OSCILLOSCOPE.

crosscoupling, *n.* an undesired coupling between circuits, usually inductive circuits. Crosscoupling can be reduced by shielding and good earthing. See also EARTH LOOP.

crossed-field tube, see CARCINOTRON.

crossmodulation or **intermodulation,** *n.* the unwanted modulation of one frequency by another. The effect occurs mainly in audio circuits and in wideband circuits in which a range of signal frequencies will be present. In audio circuits, crossmodulation causes noticable distortion when the signal contains both a bass note and a treble note. Nonlinearity in an amplifier stage causes the bass note to modulate the treble note, so that the sound from the loudspeaker gives the effect of a treble note whose loudness is rising and falling at the rate of the bass frequency.

crossover frequency, *n.* a value of frequency that represents the transition between the pass band and the stop band of a FILTER.

crossover network, *n.* a network in loudspeaker systems. It is very difficult to design a magnetic type of loudspeaker that will cover the whole audio-frequency range satisfactorily. Because of this, high-quality loudspeaker systems contain a unit, the

71

WOOFER, that is designed to give optimum reproduction of the lower notes, and another unit or units (TWEETER) that works best at high frequencies. The output from the amplifier then has to be divided so that the lower notes are fed to the woofer, not to the tweeter, and the higher notes are fed to the tweeter and not to the woofer. The filter network that carries out this action is called the 'crossover network'. At its simplest (which regrettably, it often is) it consists of a capacitor and a large-value iron-cored inductor. See also DIVIDING NETWORK.

crosstalk, *n.* interference between communications so that each channel receives some signal from the other. This can be due to unwanted coupling between telephone lines, between nearby amplifier circuits, or between different carrier frequencies. Crosstalk between different radio channels is often due to nonlinearity in some stage. This can occur when one transmitter is very close and is overloading the first stage of a receiver. The amount of crosstalk is usually specified in decibels.

CRT, see CATHODE–RAY TUBE.

crystal, *n.* a solid material in which the components, usually ions (see IONIZATION), are arranged in a precise geometrical pattern to create rigidity and hardness, the ability to be cleaved easily along certain directions leaving a perfect plane surface and, in many cases, useful electrical properties. QUARTZ CRYSTALS are used in oscillators, crystals of silicon for the manufacture of TRANSISTORS and INTEGRATED CIRCUITS, and crystals of materials such as barium titanate in TRANSDUCERS.

crystal control, *n.* the use of a vibrating QUARTZ CRYSTAL to control the frequency of a sine wave oscillator. The crystal acts as a form of tuned circuit with an exceptionally high Q-FACTOR (30,000 or more). This stabilizes the frequency of the oscillator, and can also be used to produce a very pure sine wave, free from HARMONICS. For highest stability, the crystal must be cut in a certain way, and contained in a thermostatically-controlled enclosure, the crystal oven.

crystal counter, *n.* a device for detecting IONIZING RADIATION. Several types of crystalline substances are affected when they are struck by radioactive particles. Some crystals emit a flash of light for each particle, and this light can be detected by a photocell, giving an electrical pulse. Another method is to separate an electron from a hole in a semiconducting crystal, which will make the material momentarily conductive. In either case, the resulting electrical pulse can be amplified and applied to a counter.

crystal filter, *n.* a form of filter that uses a quartz crystal in place of a tuned circuit. This allows a very narrow band of frequencies to be accepted or rejected.

crystal microphone, *n.* a form of microphone that employs a PIEZOELECTRIC crystal. The sound waves vibrate the crystal, causing a varying voltage to be generated between conducting electrodes on the surface.

current, *n.* the rate of flow of electric CHARGE. Symbol: *I*. Current is usually measured in AMPERES. The ampere is equivalent to the rate of flow of one COULOMB per second.

current amplifier, *n.* an amplifier whose output signal current is much greater than its input signal current. If the voltage signal levels are unchanged, or if there is also voltage gain, the current amplifier acts also as a power amplifier.

current density, *n.* **1.** the amount of current flow per unit cross-sectional area of a conductor. **2.** a measure of radiated energy, such as from a radio beam.

current feedback or **series feedback,** *n.* the FEEDBACK of a signal that is proportional to the current output.

current gain, *n.* the ratio of output current to input current for an amplifying device.

current limiter, *n.* any device that will not permit the current in a circuit to exceed some fixed value. A resistor is a simple form of current limiter, but the term is usually reserved for a circuit that is part of a constant voltage power supply. The function of the circuit is to limit the current to a safe level in the event of the load becoming a short circuit.

current-mode logic (CML), see EMITTER-COUPLED LOGIC.

current source/sink ability, *n.* a measure in amps or millamps (normally specified by the manufacturer) of the ability of a device to provide (source) or accept (sink) current without causing failure. See also FAN-IN, FAN-OUT.

current transformer, *n.* a step-up TRANSFORMER whose low-impedance primary winding is connected in series with an AC supply line. The secondary voltage of the transformer is then proportional to the primary current. This secondary voltage can be rectified and used to drive a meter (an *instrument transformer*) that is scaled in terms of primary current. A development of the idea uses a clamp as the primary winding. When the clamp is placed over an insulated cable, the meter reading shows the current passing. This is one of the few methods of measuring current without breaking the circuit.

cutter, *n.* a device used in the preparation of a master recording on disc. The sound signals from the master tape are applied to an electromagnetic cutter head that carries a stylus. The vibrations of the stylus cut a groove of modulated width in the material of the master disc. This disc is then used to prepare a number of moulds, and these are in turn used in stamping vinyl copies, the conventional audio records. The whole process is being superseded by the COMPACT DISC system (see RECORDING OF SOUND).

cutoff, *n.* the BIAS point at which current just ceases in control devices such as CATHODE-RAY TUBES, transistors and valves. The *cutoff voltage* of a CRT is the (negative) value of voltage between grid and cathode that will *just* cause the electron beam to disappear.

cuttoff frequency, *n.* **1.** a value of frequency at which the gain of an amplifying device is noticeably reduced. **2.** a frequency at the edge of a filter pass band at which the attenuation suddenly increases, usually taken as the point where the signal is attenuated −3dB. **3.** the frequency beyond which the gain of a transistor rapidly drops because of its construction. Once again, the −3dB point is usually selected.

cutoff voltage, see CUTOFF.

cutout, *n.* an automatic overload switch that will open under excess current or dissipation conditions. The cutout may reset automatically after a time delay, or have to be reset manually. TV receivers often contain thermal cutouts that have to be reset by resoldering two spring-loaded contacts. A high-current cutout is called a CONTACT BREAKER.

cycle, *n.* a complete alternation of voltage or current. Typically, this may start at zero, rise to a positive maximum, reverse, pass through zero and rise to a negative maximum, then return to zero again. A complete cycle is often represented by 360° or by 2π radians.

cylindrical winding or **solenoidal winding,** *n*. a coil wound on a cylindrical former. The coil can be single or multilayer, and if the length is much greater than the diameter, it is a fairly straightforward matter to calculate the SELF-INDUCTANCE value in the absence of magnetic material. NOMOGRAMS are available for finding the number of turns of wire of a given gauge in order to achieve a stated inductance value.

D

daisychain, *vb*. to connect (digital) devices so that a pulse will affect the first device in a series string that is enabled (see ENABLING), and that device in turn will affect the next in line. An example is leading-zero suppression in a digital display, so that, for example, the number 7.4 is not displayed as 00007.4. The zero-suppression pair of connections in each display unit are daisychained. When a number is displayed, a zero in the first display (the most-significant digit) will be suppressed, and a pulse will be sent to the next display. This process will continue until a display is reached which is not displaying a zero. The daisychain ends there, and no other zeros will be suppressed.

damped, *adj*. (of a RESONANT CIRCUIT) being prevented from OSCILLATION. A resonant circuit is damped by a load of any type, such as a PARALLEL resistor. An undamped resonant circuit (which never exists in practice) would oscillate indefinitely after any stimulus. In practice, quartz crystals with no external damping can execute several thousand oscillations after being excited. Increased damping (a smaller value of parallel resistor) causes the amplitude of the oscillations to decrease. At critical damping, a pulse input produces a single cycle of output, with no subsequent oscillation. Damping can also be applied to mechanical oscillations, either mechanically, for example, using dashpots and oil, or electromagnetically. Compare OVERDAMPED, UNDERDAMPED, CRITICAL DAMPING.

damping factor, *n.* a measurement of the effectiveness of damping (see DAMPED), i.e. the ratio of the AMPLITUDE of one OSCILLATION to the amplitude of the following oscillation. The logarithm of this measurement is also used, and is called the LOGARITHMIC DECREMENT.

dark current, *n.* the current that flows in an unilluminated PHOTOCELL. This current can arise from molecular-scale defects in the photosensitive material or structure, and limits the usefulness of the photocell at low light levels.

dark spot, *n.* a point on the PHOSPHOR or a CATHODE-RAY TUBE that is insensitive, and does not shine when struck by electrons. A dark spot may be due to POISON in the phosphor, to ion bombardment, or to burn-out through having the beam current steadily on the spot over a long period.

Darlington pair, *n.* a form of compound EMITTER FOLLOWER circuit for transistors. The circuit has very high current gain, but its voltage gain is limited by the finite value of resistance between the collector and the base of the first transistor. See Fig. 21.

dashpot, *n.* a mechanical damping device that consists of a small pot filled with oil. A cylinder floating in the oil is connected to the mechanical system whose motion is to be DAMPED.

data bus, a set of connections that carries voltage levels representing binary digits (see BINARY CODE) to all parts of a computer system.

dB or db, see DECIBEL.

dbx, *n. Trademark.* a very effective COMPANDER system. The system is used for tape-hiss suppression on domestic cassette recorders and for increasing the signal-to-noise ratio for FM receivers (not in the UK).

DC, see DIRECT CURRENT.

DC restoration, *n.* the restoration of the correct DC level in a signal that has been transmitted by radio, or passed through a

Fig. 21. **Darlington pair**. The circuit can be obtained in prefabricated form as a single device.

capacitor. A VIDEO SIGNAL, for example, that has been passed through a capacitor, will not have its BLACK LEVEL at zero volts, and the voltage of the black level will vary with the ratio of light to dark in the signal. The DC position of the black level can be restored by clamping (see CLAMP), or more simply by a DC restoration circuit.

See DC-RESTORING DIODE.

DC-restoring diode, *n.* a diode used in a DC-RESTORATION circuit along with a capacitor to establish the correct BLACK LEVEL of a VIDEO signal.

See Fig. 22 on page 78.

dead-beat, *adj.* (of a meter movement) being critically damped to avoid OSCILLATION. This means that when the meter movement is connected in a circuit, the needle will not oscillate around a steady value, but move steadily to that value. If the movement is OVERDAMPED, the needle may take an irritatingly long time to reach its final value.

dead time, *n.* the time for which a device is disabled following

input   output

Fig. 22. **DC-restoring diode**. The principle is that the diode will, in this example, conduct when the signal voltage is negative, charging the capacitor so as to restore a voltage level close to zero. The resistor ensures a time constant that will permit the capacitor voltage to be discharged slowly compared to the time between pulses. The forward voltage of the diode is ignored here; in practice it would cause the baseline of the output to be at about −0.6V.

some event. Many detectors of radioactivity are unable to detect another particle for a short time following the arrival of a particle, and this time is the 'dead time' for the detector. Some electronic circuits exhibit a dead time following an overload.

debouncing circuit, *n*. a CIRCUIT that is used to suppress multiple pulses from a switch. When a mechanical switch is closed, the contacts will bounce open again, and may bounce several times. This causes the closure of a switch to generate a set of voltage pulses. If the switch is part of a counter circuit, the excess pulses have to be suppressed, and this is done by a circuit connected across the switch. A typical circuit uses the RS FLIP-FLOP.

debunching, *n*. the separation (due to mutual repulsion) of bunched (see BUNCHING) electrons in a beam because of their CHARGE. Debunching affects dense electron beams, and particularly 'packets' of electrons in KLYSTRONS.

deca- or **dec-,** *prefix*. denoting ten.

decade counter, *n.* a counter that displays in the familiar scale of ten, as distinct from a BINARY CODE or HEXADECIMAL SCALE display.

decay time, *n.* the time needed for a voltage to decay below a defined threshold. The decay time is often measured from the 90% to the 10% amplitude levels.

decibel (dB or **db),** *n.* the unit of comparative power, one tenth of a BEL. For voltages V_1 and V_2 across equal impedances, the decibel ratio is defined as $20\log_{10} V_2/V_1$.

decoder, *n.* a demodulator for PULSE CODE MODULATION transmissions.

decoupling, *n.* the process of shorting unwanted signals to earth. A decoupling CAPACITOR can be used to remove unwanted high frequencies, and an INDUCTOR can be used to decouple unwanted low frequencies.

decrement, *n.* **1.** the reduction of a count by one. **2.** Also called *logarithmic decrement.* a measurement of damping (see DAMPING FACTOR).

de-emphasis, *n.* a circuit technique used in FM radio reception. The audio signal is pre-emphasized (see PRE-EMPHASIS) before modulation, and the de-emphasis circuit is a form of LOW-PASS FILTER that restores the normal audio signal spectrum.

definition, see RESOLUTION.

deflection coils, *n.* COILS used to supply magnetic fields for the BEAM deflection of a TV or radar CATHODE-RAY TUBE. The coils are shaped to wrap tightly around the neck of the tube, and are fed with a sawtooth *current* waveform to cause beam deflection. The voltage waveform across the coils takes the form of a large pulse at the moment when current is switched off, and this is utilized in an energy-recovery circuit, returning power to the supply and also generating the EHT voltage for the FINAL ANODE of the tube.

deflection defocusing, *n.* a fault of an electron optical system that results from the fact that a beam that is focused when aimed at the centre of the screen or target will be out of focus at the edge. The cure is dynamic focusing, in which part of the deflection waveform is added to a focus current in a coil.

deflection plates, *n.* a method of applying ELECTROSTATIC DEFLECTION to an instrument CATHODE-RAY TUBE. The plates are usually shaped in a diverging pattern to avoid being struck by the beam. The sensitivity of the tube will be proportional to the length of the plates.

deflection sensitivity, *n.* a measure of the effectiveness of a deflection system. For ELECTROSTATIC DEFLECTION, this is measured as the amount of beam deflection at the screen per volt applied between the deflection plates at a given acceleration voltage. The deflection sensitivity is inversely proportional to the accelerating potential between CATHODE and FINAL ANODE. For a magnetically-deflected tube, the deflection sensitivity is not internally fixed, because the deflection coils are external. The tube manufacturer may quote deflection sensitivity in terms of millimetres of deflection per unit flux density. In this case, deflection sensitivity is inversely proportional to the square root of accelerating potential.

defluxer, *n.* a demagnetizing device. Most defluxers consist of a MAGNETIC CORE with a large air gap and a coil that is connected to AC mains. The large AC field can be applied to a magnetized material to force the material to undergo the hysteresis cycle. If the material is then pulled slowly away from the defluxing coils, the magnetism will go through ever-decreasing peaks until it reaches zero.

deformation voltage, *n.* the voltage between the electrodes of a PIEZOELECTRIC crystal when a force is applied to the crystal.

degree, *n.* a unit of angle or of temperature.

delay, *n.* a time interval, or a voltage bias. The delay time for a pulse circuit is the time that is needed for an input pulse to produce an output. See also DELAYED AGC.

delayed AGC, *n.* an AGC (AUTOMATIC GAIN CONTROL) voltage that is applied against a BIAS. This causes the AGC to be ineffective until the signal strength has reached some preset level. In this way, small signals will benefit from the full gain of the RF and IF stages of the receiver.

delay equalizer, *n.* a network that corrects the distortion of wideband signals that have passed through a DELAY LINE.

delay line, *n.* a circuit or system that causes a deliberate time delay to a signal. Delay lines may be made from COAXIAL or TWIN CABLES. An alternative is to use a LUMPED PARAMETER line, consisting of a capacitor-inductor ladder network. For delays of more than a fraction of a microsecond, ACOUSTIC DELAY LINES are more practical. For digital circuits, bucket-brigade and CHARGE-COUPLED DEVICE delay lines are used. See also CANCELLATION CIRCUIT.

delta-star transformer, *n.* a form of TRANSFORMER for AC power circuits. A three-phase supply network with no neutral line may be transformed in this type of system to a three-phase and neutral supply.

demodulation, *n.* the recovery of a modulating waveform from a modulated CARRIER. For AMPLITUDE MODULATION, this can be achieved by using a diode and capacitor to rectify the carrier. For frequency modulation, the FOSTER–SEELEY DISCRIMINATOR or RATIO DETECTOR has been used, but ICs that use pulse-counting techniques are now more common. Phase-sensitive SYNCHRONOUS DEMODULATION is used for colour TV CHROMINANCE SIGNALS, and various methods are used for the many forms of pulse modulation, ranging from a simple low-pass filter to elaborate decoders.

demodulator or (formerly) **detector,** *n.* any circuit that accomplishes DEMODULATION.

demultiplexer, *n.* a circuit that separates signals that have been transmitted in combined form by a MULTIPLEXER. A *digital multiplexer* is a digital circuit that accepts binary signal inputs on a number of lines, and has as outputs a number of single lines. These output lines are numbered, and the one that is at low voltage (a logical FALSE) corresponds to the binary number on the input lines. The remaining outputs are at higher voltage (logical TRUE).

depletion layer, *n.* the region in a SEMICONDUCTOR around a JUNCTION. In the region close to a P-N JUNCTION, the number of free carriers is lower than in the remainder of the material because they combine and eliminate each other. This is the 'depletion layer'. Its size can be increased by reverse-biasing the junction, and decreased by forward-biasing. See also VARACTOR.

depletion mode, *n*. the operation of a FIELD–EFFECT TRANSISTOR with reverse bias. A depletion mode FET will pass maximum current at zero bias, and the effect of bias is to reduce the channel current. Compare ENHANCEMENT MODE.

deposition, *n*. the laying down of one material on top of another. See METALLIZING.

depth of modulation or **modulation factor,** *n*. a factor (for AMPLITUDE MODULATION of a carrier) equal to amplitude of modulating signal divided by amplitude of unmodulated signal. The depth of modulation is usually expressed as a percentage, and is an index of the efficiency of the modulating process. When the depth of modulation approaches 100%, the distortion of the signal will be very large, but when the depth of modulation is low, 20% or less, the SIGNAL–TO–NOISE RATIO will be poor.

derating, *n*. a reduction in operating RATINGS under some conditions. For example, the maximum voltage that can be applied to a transistor may have to be reduced when the temperature is increased or when high-frequency signals are used.

desoldering, *n*. the removal of soldered connections. This can be done using solder-braid, which removes solder by capillary action. A more suitable method for extensive use is a desoldering gun which sucks up molten solder, using either a built-in or a separate hot iron to melt the solder. Desoldering is particularly important if working ICs are to be removed. For faulty ICs, it is easier to cut all the pins and then remove them with a soldering iron and pliers. It is, however, good practice to mount all ICs in sockets so that they can be easily removed if necessary.

destructive read, *n*. a reading of memory that destroys the contents of the memory. MAGNETIC CORE (2) stores are subject to destructive read because the reading is carried out by pulses that will set the direction of magnetization to the logic 0 direction. This causes no effect on a read wire when the core is already at the 0 condition, but will induce a pulse when the core is at logic 1 and then is changed to logic 0. The core must then be rewritten to logic 1 by another circuit if the content of the memory is not to be lost.

detached contact system, *n.* a method of indicating RELAY action in CIRCUIT DIAGRAMS. The coil of the relay is shown in the part of the circuit where it is wired. The contacts are then shown in whatever circuit they switch, and these may be illustrated on a separate page of the circuit. The correspondence of the coil and its contacts is shown by label numbers. See Fig. 23 on page 84.

detector, *n.* **1.** an old term for DEMODULATOR. **2.** a device that detects subatomic particles.

detune, *vb.* to adjust a tuned circuit so that it is not in resonance with an input signal.

deviation, *n.* **1.** the difference from a standard value in error measurement and assessment. **2.** in FREQUENCY MODULATION, the difference between the modulated frequency and the carrier centre frequency at any instant.

device, *n.* an electronic COMPONENT or small group of components (ASSEMBLY) that carries out an action.

diac, *n.* a form of DIODE that conducts in either direction. The diac is an insulator for low voltages in either direction, but it will break down for a critical voltage and can pass currents in either direction. Diacs are used mainly in the triggering circuits of TRAICS and THYRISTORS.

diaphragm, *n.* a thin vibrating sheet used in MICROPHONES to convert a sound wave into a mechanical movement that will then be converted into an electrical signal.

dichroic mirror, *n.* a colour-selective mirror consisting of a thin film of material on a flat glass plate. The thin film must have a refractive index very different from that of glass. The thickness of the film is arranged to make use of interference effects so the film acts as a mirror for only a selected range of wavelengths.

dielectric, *n.* an INSULATOR, particularly in a CAPACITOR. The PERMITTIVITY of an insulating material was formerly known as the *dielectric constant*.

dielectric heating, *n.* the process of heating an INSULATOR by making it the DIELECTRIC in a capacitor that is supplied with

Fig. 23. **Detached contact system**. The Fig. shows the relay coil and its contacts separately, using identification letters and numbers so that the two can be associated. This system makes it easier to draw circuits containing relays.

high-frequency signals. Heat is generated because of a form of electric hysteresis. See also INDUCTION FURNACE.

differential amplifier or (formerly) **long-tailed pair,** *n.* an AMPLIFIER that has two inputs. The output of a differential amplifier is proportional to the voltage or current difference between the inputs. See also COMMON–MODE REJECTION.

differential capacitor, *n.* a CAPACITOR with two sets of static plates and one set of moving plates. The moving plates can be adjusted so that their capacitance to either set of fixed plates is increased or decreased.

differential resistance, see INCREMENTAL RESISTANCE.

differential winding, *n.* a winding on a TRANSFORMER that can be used as a form of control by passing a current that opposes the current in the main coil.

differentiating circuit, *n.* a CIRCUIT based on an OPERATIONAL AMPLIFIER with capacitive input and resistive feedback, that carries out the mathematical operation of differentiation, i.e., $V_{out} = dV_{in}/dt$. When a voltage step is applied to a differentiating circuit, the output of the circuit is the differential of a function that is an impulse. The effect of a differentiating circuit on any waveform apart from a sine wave is to produce a signal with sharp spikes whenever the input waveform changes rapidly. The effect on a sine wave is to produce a cosine wave.

diffused junction, *n.* a semiconductor JUNCTION (2) that has been produced by DIFFUSION.

diffusion, *n.* a method of creating a semiconductor JUNCTION by heating the pure semiconductor material in contact with a DOPING impurity. The doping impurity is in the form of a gaseous compound, and the semiconductor is heated to a temperature just below the melting point. At this temperature, atoms of the doping material that strike the surface of the semiconductor are able to travel (diffuse) into the semiconductor, forming a junction.

digital, *adj.* (of an electronic component or circuit) operating with a small number of voltage levels, usually two. When two levels only are used, they are described, no matter to what voltage they correspond, as level 0 (FALSE) and level 1 (TRUE). Because only two easily-distinguished voltage levels are used, most of the forms of distortion that affect analogue waveforms become irrelevant.

digital circuit, *n.* a circuit whose inputs and outputs can take only two levels, referred to as (logic) 0 and (logic) 1. The word logic is often omitted.

digital computer, *n.* a computer that acts on numbers in BINARY CODE. Any type of information can be coded into number form, and the digital computer can carry out actions of selecting, storing, retrieving and arranging the coded information. A particular advantage of the digital computer is that the programming can also be in number codes, so no circuit adjustment is required, whereas ANALOGUE COMPUTERS require HARDWARE alteration.

digital counter, *n.* a CIRCUIT that counts the number of pulses that arrive at its input. The counting is achieved using digital circuits (usually FLIP-FLOPS), and may be displayed in binary or denary figures, or even as a meter reading. The input pulse must be of a level that will operate the counter.

digital voltmeter (DVM), *n.* a voltmeter that measures a voltage level by counting the number of small voltage steps needed to reach that level. The digital voltmeter generates a waveform that consists of a STAIRCASE VOLTAGE wave of (typically) one millivolt steps. The steps are counted in a COUNTER, and the count stops and is displayed when the staircase waveform voltage becomes equal to the applied voltage. The sequence automatically repeats several times per second so that varying voltages can be tracked.

digitizer, *n.* any device that can convert a measurement into the form of a binary number. The easiest methods usually involve a TRANSDUCER to convert the quantity being measured into a voltage, and then a circuit like that of the DIGITAL VOLTMETER to obtain a binary number count.

DIL (dual–in–line) package, *n.* a method of packaging an INTEGRATED CIRCUIT by attaching the chip to a plastic or ceramic slab that has a set of pins at 0.1 inch spacing along each side. The standard distance between the lines of pins is 0.3″ for the smaller packages and 0.6″ for the larger types (such as microprocessors).

DIN, *n. acronym for* Deutsche Industrie Norm, the German equivalent to BSI, the standard applied to a system of plugs, sockets and cables widely used for audio signals.

diode, *n.* a COMPONENT that allows current to pass in only one direction between its two connectors. The direction in which current passes is the forward direction, and the voltage that causes current flow is the forward voltage. A reverse voltage does not cause current to flow unless the voltage is high enough to cause diode BREAKDOWN. Virtually all of the diodes in use nowadays are semiconductor diodes, using either point contact or junction construction. See also GUNN DIODE, IMPATT DIODE, TUNNEL DIODE, ZENER DIODE, LIGHT–EMITTING DIODE, PHOTODIODE.

diode forward voltage, *n.* the VOLTAGE across a DIODE when it is conducting in the normal forward direction. This voltage is decided mainly by the semiconductor material from which the diode is constructed. Typical figures are 0.55V for a silicon diode, and 0.15V for a germanium diode.

diode pump, *n.* a form of pulse-counting CIRCUIT that produces an output voltage which is proportional to the number of input pulses.

diode reverse voltage, *n.* a VOLTAGE applied across a DIODE in the reverse, nonconducting, direction.

diplexer, *n.* a CIRCUIT that allows the transmission of two signals along one wire or channel without interference.

dipole, *n.* **1.** any system of two equal and opposite elements such as a pair of equal and opposite electric CHARGES. **2.** see DIPOLE AERIAL.

dipole aerial or **dipole,** *n.* an AERIAL that consists of two conducting rods arranged in line but electrically separate. The rods are of equal length, cut to a definite fraction of the wavelength of the signal that is to be received or transmitted. A very common size is half a wavelength, meaning half of the wavelength on the conductor rather than half of the free-space wavelength. For the lower range of frequencies, the dipole is more likely to consist of wires, possibly parallel sets of wires, rather than rods. The signals are applied to, or received from, the dipole halves in ANTIPHASE. See Fig. 24 on page 88.

dip-soldering, *n.* a mass-production SOLDERING method. PRINTED CIRCUIT BOARDS have their components inserted, and the solder side of the board is coated with flux. The whole surface of the board is then dipped into a bath of molten solder. The level of the solder is maintained so that solder does not run onto the component side of the board, but comes in contact with all the joints on the underside. Where dense packing of printed-circuit lines is used, solder-repelling varnish is coated between lines to prevent solder 'bridges' from causing unwanted short circuits.

direct coupling, *n.* the connecting of the output of one amplifier STAGE directly to the input of another. Direct coupling implies no DC blocking components such as capacitors or transformers, so the DC level is also being amplified. Some designs attenuate the DC level by using resistors or ZENER DIODES in the coupling.

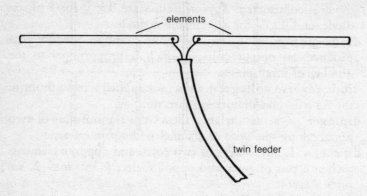

Fig. 24. **Dipole aerial**. See main entry.

direct current (DC), *n.* a steady current in one direction such as is provided by a CELL, a dynamo, or from the smoothed output of a rectifier circuit.

directional aerial, *n.* an aerial that transmits or receives signals in one preferred direction. A simple DIPOLE AERIAL is not particularly directional, but it can be made so by adding REFLECTOR and DIRECTOR elements. See Fig. 25. See also YAGI AERIAL.

direction finding, *n.* the measuring of the direction of the transmitter of a radio frequency SIGNAL. The oldest method (*loop direction-finding*) involves the use of two aerials in combination, one vertical whip and one rotating loop. A rotating loop aerial will give maximum signal when its axis points to the source of signal, but this occurs at two positions of the loop. By comparing the phase of the loop signal with a signal from a fixed aerial, the correct direction of the two can be found.

Modern direction-finding methods make use of precisely timed signals sent to and from satellites, and do not involve the geometrical arrangement of aerials.

directivity, *n.* the ability of an AERIAL system to transmit or receive in one particular direction.

director, *n.* a rod element added to a DIPOLE AERIAL. Director rods are placed in the desired direction of transmission or

Fig. 25. **Directional aerial**. The directors of a directional aerial are located between the signal source of a (receiving) aerial and the dipole. The arrangement of the reflectors is also shown here. The whole set constitutes a YAGI AERIAL.

reception. They consist of conducting rods, but are not electrically connected to the dipole, or to any signal. The distance of each director from the dipole, or from the previous director, and the overall length of the director, must be theoretically calculated with a formula.

direct wave, *n.* the wave path from TRANSMITTER to RECEIVER along the earth's surface. A direct wave is possible only if the transmitter and receiver are reasonably close, approximating to 'line of sight' conditions. The wave that is received as a result of reflection from the ionosphere is known as the SKY WAVE.

disc, *n.* **1.** a flat plastic disc for the recording of sound. The conventional LP disc is made of vinyl, and hot-stamped with an impression of the sound pattern. The COMPACT DISC uses a form of digital recording and requires a laser-reading system. See also RECORDING OF SOUND. **2.** an alternative spelling of DISK.

discharge, *n.* the removal or neutralization of electric CHARGE. An electrostatic charge on a material may be discharged by connection to earth or by IONIZATION of the surrounding air. An ionized gas passes current by movement of oppositely charged ions in opposite directions, and this is called a GAS DISCHARGE.

discrete, *adj*. (of a device) forming a separate component rather than part of an INTEGRATED CIRCUIT.

discriminator, *n*. **1.** a circuit that demodulates a frequency-modulated or phase-modulated signal (see DEMODULATION). **2.** a circuit that selectively passes pulse inputs of some particular amplitude range.

disc winding, *n*. an old method of coil winding in which the coil is wound as a flat disc. Such coils can be seen on radios of the later 1920s and early 1930s.

disk or **disc,** *n*. a thin flat circular plastic sheet coated with magnetic material for the storage of computer data. See also FLOPPY DISK.

displacement current, *n*. the CURRENT that flows as a result of charge displacement in an INSULATOR. Displacement current is responsible for the REACTANCE of a capacitor and for the TRANSMISSION of electromagnetic waves in space.

display, *n*. any device that presents information as an image. Thus CATHODE-RAY TUBES and digital SEVEN-SEGMENT DISPLAY devices are displays, but meter readings are not.

dissipation, *n*. the loss of power from a system, either in the form of heat, or as electromagnetic radiation.

distortion, *n*. an unwanted change of signal waveshape as, for example, on a received TV picture. See also CROSSOVER NETWORK, DELAY, DEVIATION, FREQUENCY, HARMONIC, INTERMODULATION, NONLINEAR, PHASE DISTORTION.

distributed capacitance, *n*. the CAPACITANCE that exists between conductors rather than contained in a capacitor. A pair of transmission lines will have capacitance to each other. This value is not located in one place or as one component, but is present distributed along the length of the line (the value of capacitance is often quoted per metre of length). Similarly the windings of a coil have capacitance to each other that is distributed rather than lumped (see LUMPED PARAMETER).

distributed inductance, *n*. self-INDUCTANCE or mutual inductance that cannot be localized in a component. A conductor will have a value of inductance, for example, that is distributed along its whole length. The inductance is often quoted per metre.

disturbed-sun noise, *n.* the additional radio-frequency noise that is the result of sunspot or other eruptions in the sun.

divergence angle, *n.* the angle between the sides of a BEAM. A beam of electrons that is required to have parallel sides will usually diverge because of the repulsion between electrons.

diversity reception or **barrage reception,** *n.* a system of reception that uses several aerials or channels to carry the same information. The principle is to overcome interference or fading by making use of the strongest of the signals at any given time. The most common type is in the form of a multiple-diversity AERIAL system, using many aerials spread over a large area. The receiver then automatically selects the aerial that provides the largest signal at the desired frequency. Another form of diversity is *frequency diversity*, which uses transmissions on several different frequency bands, with the receiver switched to the strongest signal at any time.

divider, *n.* a CIRCUIT that carries out a reduction of a circuit quantity. A *potential divider* uses (typically) two resistors to reduce a voltage by a calculable amount. A *frequency divider* changes an input frequency to a lower value that is an exact submultiple of the original (half, third, tenth, etc.). Modern frequency-divider circuits make use of digital systems.

dividing network, *n.* a form of DIVIDER that separates signals on the basis of frequency. This will use potential divider circuits that contain reactances rather than pure resistors. See also CROSSOVER NETWORK.

division ratio, *n.* the ratio of output signal to input signal for an ATTENUATOR or POTENTIOMETER.

D layer, *n.* the layer in the IONOSPHERE that is located approximately between 60 and 90km above the earth's surface. This layer reflects mainly the lower radio frequency signals.

Dolby system, *n.* *Trademark.* a well-known and widely used noise-reduction system for tape, particularly cassette tape. The principle is based on the fact that TAPE HISS is much more noticeable on low amplitude outputs. These are selectively boosted on recording, and attenuated on replay. The system is therefore a companding system (see COMPANDER). For professional use, the Dolby A system breaks the audio waveband into several sections, and carries out the companding action for each section. The simpler Dolby B system that is widely used for prerecorded tapes confines the Dolby action to the higher frequency signals only. The later Dolby C system for domestic use is more effective and covers a wider range.

donor, *n.* an impurity material that provides free electrons to a semiconductor. Compare ACCEPTOR.

doping, *n.* the adding of a DONOR or ACCEPTOR impurity to a pure semiconductor.

Doppler effect, *n.* (originally) the apparent change of sound frequency when either the source of sound, the receiver, or both, are in motion. In sound, Doppler effect can be due to an increase of sound wave velocity when the source is moving. Electromagnetic waves travel at a constant rate in free space, and the Doppler effect for electromagnetic waves is due to changes in the wavelength of the signal caused by movement of source or receiver.

Doppler radar, *n.* a RADAR system that relies on the change of echo frequency caused by a moving target. This is a sytem that is used for low-level navigation, and also in the radar speed meters used by police.

dot generator, *n.* a form of signal generator used for COLOUR TELEVISION. The correct adjustment of a CATHODE-RAY TUBE, particularly a colour tube, is checked by connecting a dot generator to the receiver. This produces a pattern of dots that should be white and evenly spaced. Any irregularity in the spacing of the dots points to timebase or deflection coil faults, and any trace of colour fringes indicates gun CONVERGENCE faults.

dot matrix, *n.* a method of displaying letters or digits as a pattern of dots. The method is used mainly in computers both for CATHODE-RAY TUBE displays and for printing on paper.

double-base diode, see UNIJUNCTION.

double-beam CRT, *n.* a CATHODE-RAY TUBE that has two independent electron guns, producing two traces on the screen. The guns are usually interconnected so that the same TIMEBASE is applied to both guns, which also share focus and brightness circuits. The Y-PLATES are independent so that the two traces can display different signals. The double-beam tube is particularly useful for displaying phase differences between sine waves and time differences between pulses. Formerly, split-beam guns were made that used a single gun, but which split the beams after the focus electrode. This provides two-beam operation, but with the disadvantage that one signal is displayed in inverted form. Some oscilloscopes simulate double (or multiple) beam action by BEAM SWITCHING.

double-pole switch, *n*. a form of SWITCH that has two unconnected contact sets which are mechanically but not electrically connected, so that two separate circuits can be switched simultaneously.

double-sideband transmission, *n*. the TRANSMISSION of both of the SIDEBANDS that are generated by conventional amplitude modulation. Broadcast radio transmissions other than FM use double-sideband transmission with full carrier amplitude.

double-superhet receiver or **triple detection receiver,** *n*. a SUPERHETERODYNE RECEIVER with two conversion stages. The system is often used for receivers that have to cover a very wide range of input frequencies, such as a 'communications' receiver. One IF will be a high-frequency one, 10MHz to 30MHZ, and the second IF will be at the conventional 470kHZ. The system allows narrow-band reception, good selectivity, and no risk of FREQUENCY PULLING of the local oscillators.

double-throw switch, *n*. a switch with two closed (on) positions in addition to the open position. A *single-throw switch* is a switch with one closed (on) position in addition to the open position.

double-tuned circuit, *n*. a CIRCUIT that contains two inductors that have mutual INDUCTANCE and that are each part of a tuned circuit.

down-converter, *n*. a frequency changer circuit whose output is at a lower frequency than its input. The term usually denotes a converter from SHF or MICROWAVE frequencies to normal TV frequencies, as, for example, direct reception through a dish from a satellite.

down-counter, *n*. a digital counting circuit whose output count number decreases for each input pulse.

drain, *n.* the charge-collecting electrode of a FIELD–EFFECT TRANSISTOR.

drift, *n.* **1.** a free movement of a beam of electrons that is not being acted on by an accelerating field. Such electrons will drift with a steady velocity. See DRIFT SPACE, KLYSTRON. **2.** an unwanted change in quantities such as the frequency of an oscillator or the voltage output of a supply. Drift often occurs in the first few minutes after switching on, and is mainly due to heating of components.

drift space, *n.* a part of an electron–beam tube that is free of magnetic or electrostatic fields that would act on the moving electrons. There are no accelerating fields in this region, so each electron in a beam will continue with the velocity that it had as it entered this space. This allows bunching to occur (see BUNCHER).

driven aerial, *n.* an AERIAL that is directly connected to a transmitter or receiver. An example is the dipole of a YAGI.

driver, *n.* a CIRCUIT that provides power. A *line driver* provides output signal power at an IMPEDANCE that matches a trans-mission line, so that power can be transmitted along the line. A *bus driver* is a DIGITAL CIRCUIT that provides current amplifica-tion for the data or address signal outputs of a microprocessor, so allowing a large number of connections to be made to the bus (see FANOUT). A *driver stage* in an audio amplifier is the STAGE that supplies signal to the output stage.

driver of loudspeaker, *n.* the electromagnetic part of a loudspeaker, consisting of VOICE COIL and magnet.

driver transformer, *n.* a TRANSFORMER that is connected as a DRIVER. The term usually denotes a transformer that allows a single-ended transistor stage in an audio amplifier to provide signals to a complementary pair, or to a more complex single-ended push–pull circuit.

driving impedance, *n.* the IMPEDANCE of a driven CIRCUIT, usually a line, or a power-absorbing electromechanical system. A loudspeaker, for example, has a driving impedance that is composed of its coil resistance and its MOTIONAL IMPEDANCE.

droop or **sag,** *n.* the reduction of voltage level of a pulse top. A square pulse ought to have a pulse top that is of constant voltage. If this voltage decays towards zero, it is said to droop, and the amount of droop is the difference between the ideal voltage level and the true level at the end of the top section. See Fig. 26.

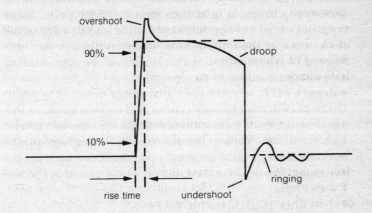

Fig. 26. **Droop**. The droop of a pulse shape. The Fig. also illustrates other faults such as rise-time, overshoot, undershoot and ringing.

dropin, *n.* a piece of nonmagnetic material on a tape. A dropin is caused by contamination, and will result in a momentary loss of signal when the tape is replayed.

dropout, *n.* a piece of tape with missing magnetic coating. Signal cannot be recorded on a dropout section, so this also results in loss of recorded signal.

dropper, *n.* a resistor that dissipates power by heating and reduces circuit voltage. The term usually denotes a resistor in a circuit that is fed by DC mains.

dry joint, *n.* a faulty soldered connection. A dry joint occurs when the SOLDER has not been hot enough, has not been applied to the joint for long enough, or when the flux has not burned off completely. In a dry joint, there is a high resistance between each metal and the solder, and the joint may also be a RECTIFYING CONTACT.

DTL, *abbrev. for* diode-transistor logic, an obsolete system once used for logic ICs.

D-type flip-flop, *n.* a form of IC FLIP-FLOP that has a CLOCK input and a data input. The data input (the D of the title) is normally disabled until the clock pulse arrives. When a clock pulse arrives, data present at the D input is transferred to the device output, and is held until the next clock pulse. Some types of D-type flip-flop will LATCH at the leading edge of the clock, some at the trailing edge, some on the top. An *edge-triggered* D-type is a flip-flop that latches on one edge, leading or trailing according to the design.

dual-gate FET, *n.* a form of signal-mixer device. The FIELD-EFFECT TRANSISTOR channel is controlled by two gates, so that signal on either or both gates will affect the channel current. This forms an excellent mixing circuit for high-frequency receivers, because there is virtually no connection between the two gates. The device is used to a very large extent in FM and TV receivers.

dual-in-line (DIL), see DIL PACKAGE.

dubbing, *n.* the mixing of recorded sound SIGNALS to form a single signal. The process is commonly used with multitrack recording methods, in which each instrument has its own microphone and provides a separate recording track. Dubbing allows the sound engineers more control over the sound of a recorded performance, but may produce results that are quite unlike any live performance.

dummy antenna, see ARTIFICIAL AERIAL.

dummy load, *n.* a power-absorbing circuit that acts like a LOAD and is used for test purposes. A loudspeaker, for example, can be replaced by a resistor of the correct value (about 8ohms) and power rating. This will not allow the effects of MOTIONAL IMPEDANCE to be simulated, but does allow testing of such features as the power-frequency characteristics.

duplex, *n.* a two-way simultaneous signalling operation such as a telegraph system in which messages can be sent over the lines in both directions at the same time. Compare HALF-DUPLEX, SIMPLEX.

dust core or **powdered-iron core,** *n.* a form of magnetic core for an indicator. A dust core is made from powdered magnetic material bound by a resin. The dust is itself an insulator so that EDDY CURRENTS cannot flow, and the main source of losses is HYSTERESIS. Dust cores are used in coils for frequencies in the range 100kHz to 100MHz, but the materials used for high-frequency signals need to be carefully selected.

duty cycle, *n.* a series of repeated operations, such as a SYSTEM that is pulsed on and off (see PULSE).

duty factor or **duty ratio,** *n.* the ratio of on-time within a duty cycle to total duty-cycle time for a DEVICE.

DVM, see DIGITAL VOLTMETER.

dynamic, *adj.* (of a SYSTEM) using under working conditions with changing or varying SIGNALS applied. A dynamic measurement, for example, means a measurement on a circuit that is operating with a signal input, as distinct from a measurement made with no signals, or even with power switched off.

dynamic convergence, *n.* the CONVERGENCE of a set of electron beams when scanned. For a COLOUR TELEVISION tube, the static convergence means that the three electron beams of the guns strike the correct phosphor stripes at the centre of the tube. When the tube is scanned, however, the convergence may not be correct at the edges. This is a dynamic-convergence problem, and is solved by applying correcting signals, derived from the timebase waveforms, to the convergence coils.

dynamic memory, see DYNAMIC RAM.

dynamic RAM (DRAM), a form of semiconductor MEMORY in which each BIT is stored as CHARGE on a semiconductor CAPACITOR. The charge leaks away unless regenerated by special REFRESH circuits, but the principle can be used to construct single chips with very large memory storage.

dynamic range, *n.* the available range of output signal from a device. The lower limit of output is set by the noise level, and the upper limit by BOTTOMING or SATURATION. The dynamic range is usually quoted in decibels.

dynamic resistance, *n.* **1.** the resistance of a parallel resonant circuit at the resonant frequency. **2.** the resistance of any device measured with AC of a stated frequency.

dynamic tracking, *n.* a method of improving VIDEO CASSETTE RECORDER performance. Conventional video recorders use revolving heads that scan across the moving tape at high speed. Because of mechanical tolerances, there must be a 'guard band' of unrecorded tape between recorded bands. If the recording and replay head is mounted on a PIEZOELECTRIC transducer, it is possible to lay down much more closely spaced tracks, and to follow any track by tiny adjustments of the head position, achieved by a servofeedback system. This was pioneered by Philips for their eight-hour play video cassette system, now abandoned.

dynamo, *n.* a generator that uses a rotating coil (rotor) and a magnetic field (stator). By convention, a dynamo picks up current from the coils by using a COMMUTATOR and brushes. This gives an output that is, for a single coil, the same as that from a FULL-WAVE RECTIFIER. If slip rings are used for making connections, the machine is described as an ALTERNATOR.

Nowadays, it is more common to use a magnetic rotor fed with DC, and to take the AC from the stator to a rectifier system to obtain DC. Such a system is easier to control by electronic methods, using the electronic system to control the current to the rotor.

dynode, *n.* an ELECTRODE that acts as a multiplier of electrons. When a fast-moving electron strikes a material, it may be reflected, absorbed, or cause SECONDARY EMISSION. If the accelerating potential is in the region of 200V to 2,000V, then secondary emission is more common. This means that for each electron incident on the surface, more than one electron will be emitted. For some materials, notably elements such as caesium that are also photoelectric emitters, the number of secondary electrons per primary electron is high, of the order of three to seven.

A dynode consists of a metal mesh or perforated plate that is coated with a material that has a high secondary-emission ratio. When an electron beam strikes this dynode, the beam leaving the dynode is much denser in electrons than the beam striking. In other words, the beam current has been amplified. This form of amplification is virtually noiseless, and so is used extensively in photoelectric devices such as photomultipliers as a way of obtaining very great sensitivity.

dynode chain, *n.* a series chain of resistors with a dynode fed from each junction of two resistors. This chain ensures that the correct relative accelerating voltages are applied to each dynode in a chain of, typically, four to eight dynodes.

E

EAROM, *n. acronym for* Electrically Alterable Read–Only Memory. This is a form of NONVOLATILE computer memory, the contents of which can be altered by electrical signals while connected in a circuit.

earphone, *n.* a miniature electrical sound TRANSDUCER. The earphone is designed to be used in contact with the ear, so comparatively good sound quality can be achieved with none of the complications of loudspeaker enclosures, and with much lower power levels.

earth or **ground,** *n.* any zero–voltage point. The earth itself is taken as being of zero voltage because its potential is not greatly affected by small changes of charge.

earth bonding, *n.* the making of a connection to earth. This is often done by burying a metal plate in the earth and connecting to this. An alternative is to use metal waterpipes, but care must be taken to connect to a pipe that passes through the ground. Pipes for central heating and hot water supply should not be used. The use nowadays of plastics for water and other pipes means that very great care is needed in earthing equipment, particularly transmitters. Electrical circuits are commonly 'multiple–earthed', meaning that all pipework and other metal is bonded to a common earth that is also used for the AC supply earth.

earth capacitance, *n.* the CAPACITANCE of any point in a circuit to the earth. If this capacitance is variable, it may lead to tuning errors in RF receivers.

earth current, *n*. a CURRENT flowing to or through the earth. A current will flow to the earth if an insulation fault develops in earthed equipment. This type of fault should cause fuses to blow, or earth-leakage contact breakers (ELCBs) to open. Currents can also flow through the earth, and may cause electrolytic corrosion of metals, including EARTH-BONDING plates.

earth fault, *n*. an insulation breakdown that causes current to flow to earth.

earth-leakage contact breaker (ELCB), *n*. a safety device that replaces the use of FUSES in many AC supply systems. The ELCB operates by balancing the live line current and the return (neutral) line current. Any imbalance must be due to earth current, and causes the breaker to trip, opening the circuits. The ELCB can be manually reset after the fault is cleared. An ELCB should be used in conjunction with any mains-operated equipment that is used out of doors or in damp conditions.

earth loop, *n*. a cause of unwanted FEEDBACK of signal that is caused by using separated earth connections in a circuit. The currents flowing between the two earth points result in a potential difference that provides the unwanted feedback signal.

earth plane or **ground plane,** *n*. a sheet of metal that is earthed or (particularly in a battery-operated circuit) used as an earth. The surrounding metal on a printed circuit board is often used as a form of earth plane.

earth potential, *n*. the zero potential (see ELECTRIC POTENTIAL). All potentials on earth are measured relative to the potential of the earth, which does not change rapidly.

earth return, *n*. the return half of a CIRCUIT in which a wire is used for the first half. An earth return was used in early morse-code TELEGRAPHY.

eccentric line, *n*. a COAXIAL CABLE type of line in which the inner electrode is not central.

E-cell, *n*. an electrolytic timer that is cheap to construct and can be used to indicate service intervals. The principle of the device is based on the electrolytic deposition of a metal spike, with the length of the metal spike indicating the time for which current has flowed.

ECH, see EDDY CURRENT HEATER.

echo, *n*. a reflected wave of sound or electromagnetism. The return beam of a RADAR system is called an echo. TV signals, particularly on UHF, can be reflected by metal objects, and cause disturbing effects. For example, if an echo is strong, and not too far out of line from the main signal direction, it will cause a second image on the TV receiver screen. This is particularly noticeable if the echo signal is delayed, because this causes the second image to be displaced. An echo image of this type is termed a *ghost*. Ghosting is dealt with by using more DIRECTIONAL AERIALS, or by shifting the aerial position. Ghosting can also be caused by a long and incorrectly terminated transmission line (see TERMINATION).

echo sounding, *n*. the location of underwater objects by using RADAR methods with sound waves in water.

ECL, see EMITTER COUPLED LOGIC.

eddy current, *n*. an unwanted current flowing within the iron core of a transformer, causing energy loss. Eddy currents are caused by voltages induced by the varying magnetic field around a transformer. They can be reduced by dividing the transformer core into a number of thin plates or laminations. See also EDDY CURRENT HEATER.

eddy current heater (ECH) or **induction heater,** *n*. a method of heating metal objects without making physical connections. The object is surrounded by or placed near a coil in which a large current of high-frequency signal is flowing. The induced eddy currents will then heat the metal. Metals can be heated in a vacuum in order to remove absorbed gas, or melted by using an ECH. Eddy current heating often occurs in TRANSFORMERS as an unwanted effect.

edge connector, *n*. a connector that is formed as part of a printed circuit board. The metal at the edge of the board is shaped into a set of strips, each strip connected to some part of the circuit. Connections are made by a plug that grips the board and uses metal springs to make contact with each strip.

edge effect, *n.* the existence of a nonuniform, rapidly changing electric field at the edge of a capacitor plate.

effective resistance, *n.* the RESISTANCE to AC measured by the dissipated power. By measuring power and dividing by the square of current, or by dividing the square of voltage by power, a figure of resistance is obtained. This may not correspond to DC resistance value, because it includes a resistance equivalent for power lost by eddy currents, hysteresis, etc.

effective value, *n.* **1.** a value of some quantity measured under operating conditions. **2.** the ROOT MEAN SQUARE value of an alternating quantity.

efficiency, *n.* the percentage conversion of energy. The efficiency of the power-amplifier stage of a radio transmitter is the output power as a percentage of the DC supply power (*input power*) to the stage.

EHF, *abbrev. for* extremely-high frequency, millimetric waves in the wavelength range 1mm to 10mm.

EHT, *abbrev. for* extra-high tension e.g. high-voltage supplies for CATHODE-RAY TUBES, CAMERA TUBES, DYNODE CHAINS, and radio TRANSMITTERS. Any voltage higher then 1,000V is in the EHT range. See also HIGH TENSION.

EIA, *abbrev. for* Electronic Industries Association (UK).

elastoresistance, *n.* the change of electrical resistance with stress. Stretching a film of a conductor will lengthen the specimen and also cause its cross section to decrease. Both of these effects will also cause the resistance to rise. The effect is used for stress measurement in STRAIN GAUGES.

E layer or **Heaviside layer** or **Kennelly-Heaviside layer,** *n.* the layer in the IONOSPHERE that lies approximately between 90 and 150km above the Earth's surface. It reflects the medium-frequency range, and was one of the first of the ionospheric layers to be identified. Oliver Heaviside (1850–1925) predicted the possibility of the ionosphere, and Arthur Kennelly (1861–1939) proved the existence of the layers and measured their heights by using RADAR techniques.

ELCB, see EARTH-LEAKAGE CONTACT BREAKER.

electret, *n.* a permanently-charged insulating material.

Electrets are made by allowing molten plastics to solidify in a large electric field, and have been used in the construction of capacitor microphones and gramophone pick-ups.

electric axis, *n.* the direction in which the maximum potential difference is developed when a PIEZOELECTRIC crystal is stressed.

electric eye, see PHOTOCELL.

electric field, *n.* a field of force surrounding a charged particle within which another charged particle experiences a force. The intensity of the electric field at a point is equal to the force-per-unit charge placed at that point. The symbol for electric field is **E**, where

$$\mathbf{E} = \frac{\text{Force}}{\text{Charge}} = \frac{\mathbf{F}}{Q}.$$

Q = charge and is measured in coulombs. $\mathbf{F}$ = force and is measured in newtons per coulomb.

electric potential or **voltage,** *n.* a measurement of the electrical equivalent of height. Symbol: V; unit; VOLT. The potential at a point is usually measured as POTENTIAL DIFFERENCE from EARTH POTENTIAL, and is defined as the amount of work done per unit CHARGE when a charge is removed from that point to infinity. Potential and particularly potential difference is easily measurable, unlike charge.

electroacoustics, *n.* the study of devices that work with electric and sound signals, including MICROPHONES, LOUD-SPEAKERS and all forms of sound TRANSDUCERS, including ULTRASONIC transducers.

electrocardiograph (ECG), *n.* an instrument for displaying and recording heart currents. The operation of the heart, like any other muscle, is controlled by small electrical signals that can be picked up on probes and displayed on a CATHODE-RAY TUBE or on a chart recorder. An electrocardiograph normally uses BALANCED AMPLIFIERS because of the very small voltages that are being picked up. Earthing (see EARTH) is very important, because any fault current transmitted to the probe electrodes would be fatal.

electrode, *n.* a conductor in an electronic device that is at some

ELECTRIC POTENTIAL and which can collect or emit charged particles.

electrodynamic, *adj.* (of an electrical device) operated by the mechanical forces arising from magnetic fields due to wires carrying CURRENTS, particularly in coil form.

electroencephalograph, *n.* an instrument that detects and displays the voltage waveforms of the brain. For general techniques, see ELECTROCARDIOGRAPH.

electroluminescence, *n.* the giving out of light from a material when an ELECTRIC FIELD is applied. Materials that are electroluminescent will give out light when subjected to an alternating electric field, using a construction like a capacitor with one transparent plate. The effect has fallen out of widespread use because of the short operating life of the material.

electrolysis, *n.* the effect of the flow of IONS in a molten or dissolved solid. By immersing a pair of conducting plates in the material, one positive (the anode), the other negative (the cathode), the ions can be collected. The combination of ion collection with chemical changes can be a very valuable source of pure materials, including some elements that cannot be prepared in any other way (aluminium, for example). See also CATION, ANION.

electrolyte, *n.* a liquid that conducts because of the presence of IONS. Conducting liquids include molten salts, and water solutions of acids, salts and alkalis. Some ionic materials such as liquid ammonia also form ionic solutions.

electrolytic capacitor, *n.* a CAPACITOR that provides very large capacitance values in a small volume. The simplest electrolytic capacitor consists of aluminium sheets sandwiching a piece of blotting paper that has been soaked in aluminium perborate. Applying a voltage to this arrangement causes a thin film of insulating oxide to form on one sheet, and it is the large capacitance across this film which is utilized. The capacitance value can be increased by increasing the area of one plate by perforating it and folding it. The capacitor is sealed to avoid evaporation of the electrolyte liquid.

Though high values of capacitance can be achieved, there is

always a comparatively large leakage current. The capacitor is POLARIZED (1), which means that the voltage must always be applied to it with the same polarity as was originally used to form the insulating layer. Failure to observe this can lead to explosive failure. The voltage that can be permitted across the capacitor is also low, and very few electrolytic capacitors can be used at DC voltage levels of over 500V. The capacitors are also temperature sensitive, and the voltage rating must be drastically reduced when high ambient temperatures are present. Many specifications for military equipment, or equipment that is to be used under a wide range of environmental conditions, do not permit the use of electrolytic capacitors.

electrolytic polishing, *n*. a method of obtaining a very high polish by electrolytically filling up any irregularities on the surface of a metal. The metal forms the ANODE in an electrolytic cell.

electromagnet, *n*. a magnet that has a high FLUX DENSITY value only when current flows through coils. Any coil of wire will act as an electromagnet, but the effect is greatly enhanced when a core of FERROMAGNETIC material such as soft iron, a SOFT MAGNETIC MATERIAL, is used.

electromagnetic deflection, *n*. the deflection of an ELECTRON BEAM such as a CATHODE–RAY TUBE beam by electromagnets. The neck of the tube is surrounded by a set of coils. When a current of SAWTOOTH WAVEFORM flows in the coils, the beam is deflected to form a linear TIMEBASE. Two pairs of coils are used to form a TV RASTER scan. For RADAR use, a radial scan is used, and this is usually done using three coils at 120 degree angles. The phase of the sawtooth current in the three coils is controlled so as to alter the position of the end of each scan.

electromagnetic focusing, *n*. the focusing of an ELECTRON BEAM by electromagnets. This is now unusual, because modern TV receiver tubes use electrostatic focusing. Electromagnetic focusing was used on early designs, and for some radar tubes.

electromagnetic induction, *n*. the production of a POTENTIAL DIFFERENCE by changing MAGNETIC FLUX. A potential difference will be produced between two points if the magnetic flux at right angles to a line drawn between the points changes.

If the two points are joined by a conductor, the potential difference can be measured and used. This is the basis of generators, alternators or dynamos. The size of potential difference is equal to the rate of change of flux (Faraday's law), and its polarity is such that if current flowed, it would set up a flux change in the reverse direction (Lenz's law). If no conductor is present, the changing magnetic flux causes an electric field.

electromagnetic lens, *n.* a lens for ELECTRON BEAMS produced by using coils to form a magnetic field that will focus the electron beams. An electromagnetic lens is easier to work with than an ELECTROSTATIC LENS when very high energy electron beams are used, as in electron microscopes and some electron beam tubes.

electromagnetic radiation, *n.* the radiation of energy in the form of varying electric and magnetic fields (static fields do not cause wave radiation). Radiation is a consequence of the laws of electrostatics and of electromagnetism that are gathered together in MAXWELL'S EQUATIONS. The fundamental cause of electromagnetic radiation is the acceleration of charged particles, so that any alternating current is capable of causing radiation. In practice, radiation is achieved efficiently only for frequencies that are of the order of 100kHz upwards. Light is one form of electromagnetic radiation. See ELECTROMAGNETIC SPECTRUM.

electromagnetic spectrum, *n.* the range of known and possible electromagnetic waves. This range extends from very long waves, low frequency, at 100kHz or even less, up to very short wavelengths (high frequencies) such as x-rays and gamma radiation. The spectrum includes all known radio waves, including many that cannot at present be easily generated or detected, infrared, light, ultraviolet and all of the wave frequencies that arrive from outer space. See ELECTROMAGNETIC RADIATION.

electromagnetism, *n.* MAGNETISM caused by electric CURRENTS. The term is commonly used to denote magnetism caused by the passage of electric currents through coils of wire, but magnetism produced by any moving charge such as in a radiated wave, or even permanent magnetism, is electro-magnetism.

electrometer, *n*. a form of VOLTMETER with a very high input resistance. The term was once used to denote electrostatic voltmeters, but is now applied to FET and valve voltmeters that can be used to measure potential differences across very high resistances.

electromotive force (emf), *n*. the voltage of a source of electrical energy. The term POTENTIAL DIFFERENCE is usually reserved for the voltage across a device that is dissipating electrical energy.

electron, *n*. a stable, negatively charged elementary particle orbiting the positive nucleus of an atom. The number of electrons in a neutral atom is equal to the number of positive PROTONS in the central nucleus (equivalent to the atomic number of the element). The charge of an electron is 1.6022×10^{-19} coulomb; this charge is of equal magnitude but opposite sign to that of a proton. Electrons have a very small rest mass (9.1096×10^{-31} kilogram, 1836 times smaller than that of a proton), and can easily be detached from atoms (leaving IONS) in a vacuum and accelerated to high speeds. The movement of electrons (as for any charged particles) is what we call electric CURRENT. Solid conductors are materials in which some electrons (the conduction electrons) are only very loosely attached to atoms and will move readily through the solid material.

electron beam or (formerly) **beta ray,** *n*. a large number of electrons flowing in the same direction in a confined path. An electron beam is achieved by using ELECTROSTATIC FIELDS to accelerate electrons away from a source, and either electrostatic or magnetic fields to form the scattering electrons into a beam. See also ELECTRON LENS.

electron gun, *n*. an arrangement of an electron-emitting CATHODE and ELECTRON LENSES that forms an ELECTRON BEAM. The device is used in CATHODE-RAY TUBES.

electron-hole pair, *n*. the charged particles produced by heating or DOPING a SEMICONDUCTOR. The pure (intrinsic) state of semiconductors is almost free of charged particles that can move. By heating, or by the addition of doping impurities, electrons can be released, leaving gaps in the structure of the materials (HOLES). These holes behave like charged particles, with positive charge and an apparent mass approximately equal to the mass of the electron. Since there must be a hole for each free electron, these particles always exist in pairs in a semiconductor.

electronic device, *n.* any device that achieves its effect by directly controlling the movement of ELECTRONS or HOLES. The electrons may be moving in a vacuum, in a solid or in a gas, and their movement can be accompanied by the movement of holes or ions.

electronic memory, *n.* a form of MEMORY in which writing, storage and reading are electronic (see ELECTRONIC DEVICE). The storage action can use CHARGE storage (electrostatic memory), the switching of an electron flow between devices (flip-flop static memory) or magnetization of a magnetic material (as in a core store).

electronics, *n.* **1.** the science and technology concerned with the development, behaviour and application of devices that use moving electrons, ions or holes. **2.** the circuits and devices of a piece of electronic equipment.

electronic switch, *n.* a SWITCH with no moving parts. The switching is carried out by acting on the electrons (or other CARRIERS) with FIELDS (electric or magnetic). This makes the switching very fast, with no problems of contact or wear.

electronic tuning, *n.* the changing of the FREQUENCY of a tuned circuit without mechanical intervention. Electronic tuning by means of VARACTOR diodes is extensively used for FM radio and TV receivers.

electron lens, *n.* a set of ELECTRODES or coils that can focus an ELECTRON BEAM. The electrons from a CATHODE are accelerated through a hole at the end of a grid cylinder that is at a negative potential. The shape of the fields at this aperture cause the electron paths to cross over, with a point of minimum diameter. This is the start of a beam, and the diverging paths of the electrons from this point are then controlled either by using ELECTROSTATIC FIELDS or by using MAGNETIC FIELDS.

electron microscope, *n.* an instrument for viewing images of very small objects. The microscope is based on the principle that a fast-moving particle will exhibit some of the properties of a wave, so that an ELECTRON BEAM behaves like a short-wavelength light beam. The electron beam can be arranged to pass through the specimen or to be reflected from it. Greater resolution is achieved by this means than is possible optically, because the wavelength of an electron beam is much shorter than that of light.

The *transmission electron microscope* (*TEM*) allows the electrons to pass through the specimen, and the resulting image is viewed on a fluorescent screen. Considerable experience is needed if the images are to be correctly interpreted.

The *scanning electron microscope* (*SEM*) uses TELEVISION techniques, scanning the electron beam across the object and picking up the scattered, reflected and secondary electrons from the surface. These returned electrons are then used to form a TV-type of output signal. Microscopes of this type yield an image that is much easier to interpret, and which looks like the image seen through an optical microscope.

electron multiplier, *n.* a set of DYNODES arranged to multiply the number of electrons in a beam at each dynode stage. The principle is used particularly in photoelectric devices as a way of noiseless amplification.

electron optics, *n.* the study of the control of ELECTRON BEAMS. Electron optics includes the production, focusing, deflection and use of electron beams.

electronvolt, *n.* the amount of energy acquired by an electron accelerated by one volt. Symbol: eV. A useful unit for measuring small energy changes, equal to 1.6×10^{-19} joules. See also WORK FUNCTION.

electroplating, *n.* the deposition of metals from a solution onto a conductor. The object that is to be coated is suspended from wires in a bath of an acid or alkaline solution that contains salt of the metal that is to be used for coating. A bar or sheet of the coating metal (the anode) is also immersed in the solution, not touching the object that is to be coated. The two are then connected to a supply, the anode to the positive pole, using a low voltage, typically four to eight volts. By movement of ions and chemical actions, metal is dissolved from the anode and deposited onto the object that is to be coated. Electroplating is used extensively for coating metal objects with gold, silver, chromium, nickel and other metals.

electrostatic, *adj.* of, concerned with, producing, or caused by electric CHARGES and ELECTRIC FIELDS at rest.

electrostatic deflection, *n.* the deflection of an ELECTRON BEAM that occurs when electric fields are applied between metal plates. The beam is deflected in the direction of the more positive plate. See DEFLECTION SENSITIVITY.

electrostatic field, *n.* the ELECTRIC FIELD that acts with force on an electron or ion. An electrostatic field exists around any charged particle, and around any conductor that is connected to a potential.

electrostatic focusing, *n.* the focusing of an ELECTRON BEAM by passing it through shaped metal electrodes at different potentials. The aim is to create a SADDLE-SHAPED FIELD to converge a diverging beam so that it will focus on some target, such as a PHOSPHOR screen.

electrostatic induction, *n.* the production of electric CHARGE on an object, conductor or nonconductor, because of another charge. Electrostatic induction is caused by the separation of electrons from atoms under the influence of an electrostatic field from another charge or potential.

electrostatic lens, *n.* an assembly of metal electrodes at different ELECTRIC POTENTIALS. The fields that are set up will cause an electron beam to be converged or diverged, just as an arrangement of glass lenses will affect a beam of light. Compare ELECTROMAGNETIC LENS; see also SADDLE-SHAPED FIELD.

electrostatic loudspeaker, *n.* a loudspeaker whose operating principle is the deflection of a charged membrane by electrostatic forces. The technique is used for very high quality sound reproduction, as in the famous QUAD units.

electrostatic precipitator, *n.* a method of removing dust in, for example, an air-conditioning system. Air is forced through a metal mesh that is maintained at a very high DC potential (several kV). Dust particles, which are usually charged, are attracted to the mesh, which can be cleaned at intervals by switching off the potential. Precipitators of this type also generate ions, which some people believe affect the wellbeing of users of the conditioned air either adversely (positive ions) or beneficially (negative ions).

electrostatic separator, *n.* a method of separating powders of insulating materials that are falling or moving along a belt. The principle is to apply a very strong ELECTROSTATIC FIELD so that materials with different permittivity values experience different amounts of force, and take different paths.

electrostriction, *n.* the movement of the atoms of a material caused by ELECTROSTATIC FIELDS. This means that the materials will expand or shrink by a very small amount when the field is applied or removed.

element, *n.* a material made up of identical atoms.

emf or **EMF,** see ELECTROMOTIVE FORCE.

emission, *n.* the release of electrons from a material. The term usually denotes the release of electrons into a vacuum from a metal under the influence of heat (THERMIONIC EMISSION), light (PHOTOEMISSION) or electric fields (FIELD EMISSION). For emission to be achieved, each electron must acquire an amount of energy greater than the binding energy that holds it in place. Electrons in semiconductors are not emitted from the material, only displaced.

emitter, *n.* **1.** the electrode in a semiconductor device from which electrons or holes pass to another layer of the material. **2.** another term for CATHODE.

emitter-coupled logic (ECL) or **current-mode logic (CML),** *n.* a fast-acting form of logic circuit used in computing. The ECL circuit makes use of TRANSISTORS that are connected at the emitters to a common LOAD. The load is such that the current through it is constant. Small changes of bias voltage at the bases of the transistors will cause current to be switched from one transistor to the other. The voltage that is needed for switching can be very small, and the amount of current that is switched can be comparatively large, allowing STRAY CAPACITANCES to be rapidly charged or discharged. An

Fig. 27. **Emitter-coupled logic**. With inputs A and B at zero, Tr_3 conducts. When either A or B or both is high, transistor Tr_1 or Tr_2 or both will draw current at the expense of Tr_3. This will cause the voltage at the collector of Tr_3 to rise. This is an elementary OR-gate.

ECL device can usually be switched at rates of up to 200MHz. See Fig. 27.

emitter follower or **common–collector connection** or **grounded–collector connection,** *n.* a circuit that has high input IMPEDANCE and low output impedance. The load is placed in the emitter circuit, and the input signal is applied to the base. Because the base–emitter voltage of a transistor varies only very slightly when a small signal is applied, the emitter voltage follows the base voltage very closely, hence the name. The circuit is used extensively as a BUFFER and a DRIVER for loads with high stray capacitance. The use of emitter followers as buffers has largely been superseded by the introduction of OPERATIONAL AMPLIFIER followers. See Fig. 28.

enabling, *adj.* (of a circuit or device) allowing to act normally. A circuit can be disabled by, for example, removing or

Fig. 28. **Emitter follower**. This is a current amplifier, with a voltage gain of less than unity. In the Fig., base-bias resistors have been shown, but a more common method is to direct-couple the base to the previous stage.

reversing BIAS so that an input signal is ineffective. Digital devices are often provided with an enable input to activate/deactivate them as required.

encoder, *n.* a device that produces an output in electronic form corresponding to some measurement. The output is usually in digital signal form. For example, a shaft–position encoder is a form of TRANSDUCER that produces different digital outputs corresponding to different angular positions as a shaft rotates.

endaround shift, see ROTATION.

endfire array, *n.* an AERIAL array in which the aiming direction is along the line of aerials rather than at right angles to the line.

energy band, *n.* a permitted range of energy values for particles in a solid. An energy value within this range is called the *band energy*. In single atoms, each electron has a definite amount of energy, its energy level, and no intermediate levels of energy are found. When atoms are closely spaced, as in solids, these permitted energy levels merge into bands, so that electrons can take any of a range of energy values. The arrangement of energy bands in a material, and whether bands are full (one electron exists with each possible level of energy), empty (no electrons with any of the permitted levels of energy), or part-filled, determine whether a material is an insulator, semiconductor or conductor.

enhancement mode, *n.* a mode of operation of some types of FIELD-EFFECT TRANSISTORS. A FET that needs enhancement mode biasing will pass little or no current in the absence of a positive BIAS voltage, and a bias voltage has to be applied in order to pass working current. Compare DEPLETION.

envelope, *n.* the outline of the amplitude peaks of a modulated radio wave. This envelope shape should be of the same shape as the wave that is being used to modulate the radio frequency.

epitaxial transistor, *n.* a (PLANAR) transistor that has been formed by EPITAXY. This means that a layer of lightly doped material has been deposited on to a heavily doped main collector region. The use of this extra layer allows better collector-base BREAKDOWN characteristics, while the heavily doped region permits a low-resistance collector connection, and good THERMAL CONDUCTIVITY.

epitaxy, *n.* the growth of other layers on the surface of a SEMICONDUCTOR crystal, usually from a gas. The layers will be of doped or INTRINSIC material, and the importance of the process is that the added layers maintain the same crystal structure as the underlying crystal, so that the whole structure behaves as one crystal. Epitaxy has been the main process for creating transistors and integrated circuits for many years. However, it is being superseded by ION-IMPLANTATION for some specialized purposes.

EPLD, *abbrev. for* erasable-programmable logic device, an assembly of identical gate and inverter circuits whose interconnections can be established by programming and can be reprogrammed. An EPLD is a form of UNCOMMITTED LOGIC ARRAY.

epoxy resin, *n.* a plastic resin with exceptionally good insulating characteristics. The value of epoxy resins is that many of them are particularly easy to use in coating or moulding applications. Most of these resins can be obtained as 'two-pack' types, consisting of a viscous resin and a liquid setting agent. The two are mixed just before use, and the setting time depends on the mixture ratios and on temperature.

EPROM, *n. acronym for* Erasable Programmable Read-Only Memory, a semiconductor-memory integrated circuit (or chip) for computer use in which the data is held semi-permanently. An EPROM can only be erased by shining an intense ultraviolet light through a transparent quartz window in the chip. Once it has been erased, data can be stored in an EPROM, and will be retained even when no power is supplied to the chip.

equalization, *n.* a form of controlled DISTORTION. The best example is the treatment of audio signals for disc recording. The bass signals are reduced in amplitude, because otherwise the amplitude of the groove wave would be too great. Similarly, the amplitudes of high-frequency signals are boosted, because the disc noise is mainly in this region. After transcribing (converting back into electrical signals), the bass amplitude has to be boosted and the treble attenuated in order to recover the correct signal balance.

equalizer, *n.* any circuit that carries out EQUALIZATION. The term is used also to denote circuits that will selectively boost or attenuate parts of the audio spectrum. Equalizers are used in professional applications to overcome studio problems of boom or 'deadness'. The device is sometimes called a *graphics equalizer*, particularly when the control panel shows the effect of the controls on a frequency response graph.

equivalent circuit, *n.* an arrangement of simple electrical COMPONENTS that is electrically equivalent to a complex CIRCUIT. The equivalent circuit is used for calculation purposes, and makes use of simple real components (like resistors, inductors and capacitors) along with idealized components (signal voltage or current generators). By representing a complex device such as a transistor voltage amplifier with an equivalent circuit which may, for example, contain a voltage generator and a few resistors, it is possible to calculate gain and other features closely enough for practical purposes. See also NORTON'S THEOREM, THEVENIN'S THEOREM.

equivalent resistance, *n.* a single resistance value that has the same effect as a number of other RESISTORS or power-dissipating components. A circuit may, for example, contain RESISTANCE and INDUCTANCE. Its equivalent resistance value will allow calculation of total power dissipated in all the parts of the circuit, including the resistance of the inductor, and the impact of any effects like motional impedances. The use of an equivalent resistance is particularly suited to the treatment of the inputs and outputs of ACTIVE COMPONENTS.

erase, *vb.* to remove data from a memory store, usually semiconductor memory, but also magnetic media such as tapes or disks.

erase head, *n.* a tape recorder head that is used to erase tapes or disks immediately prior to recording. The erase head uses a comparatively large gap and is fed by a high-amplitude high-frequency signal. The effect is to take each part of the tape through a large number of HYSTERESIS cycles, gradually reducing the peak amplitude so that the magnetic particles are left unmagnetized.

etching, *n.* the dissolving of material by a chemical process, particularly with acids. Etching is used to produce printed circuit boards (using solutions of materials such as ferric chloride), and in the production of transistors and integrated circuits.

excitation, *n.* the addition of energy to a system, for example signals that form an input for a system such as an amplifier or oscillator.

exclusive–OR (XOR) gate, *n.* a form of LOGIC GATE giving a logic comparison. The OR GATE produces an output 1 if any or all of its inputs are at logic 1. The XOR gate excludes the case of more than one level 1 input, so that the XOR gate output is 1 if only one input is at level 1. See Fig. 29.

expanded sweep, *n.* a TIMEBASE for a CATHODE–RAY OSCILLO-SCOPE in which the timebase amplitude can be greatly increased. This allows the effect of time-magnification, so that a small part of a waveform can be examined in greater detail without the need to switch to another timebase speed and resynchronize.

expander, *n.* a circuit that increases the dynamic range of a signal. The action is achieved by a NONLINEAR stage whose gain increases as the signal amplitude increases. See also COMPANDER.

(a)

A	B	Q
0	0	0
0	1	1
1	0	1
1	1	0

(b)

Fig. 29. **Exclusive-OR gate**. The two-input exclusive-OR gate symbol (a) and truth table (b). The logic of the gate is that the output is 1 only for one single input equal to 1.

F

facsimile (fax), *n.* the TRANSMISSION of text or diagrams on paper by line or radio. Formerly done by electromechanical methods, but nowadays achieved by computing techniques. The material to be transmitted is scanned and each unit area shape generates a BINARY CODE which is transmitted. At the receiver, each code operates a set of needles in a DOT-MATRIX printer, producing the same pattern that existed in the transmitted material.

fader, *n.* a form of ganged ATTENUATOR, normally using one single control. A fader allows one signal to be reduced to zero amplitude smoothly while another signal is increased from zero to normal amplitude.

fading, *n.* the reduction of CARRIER (1) signal strength at a receiver. Fading is usually caused by interference between waves that arrive at the receiver by different routes. At least one such path must be caused by reflection of a wave by the

117

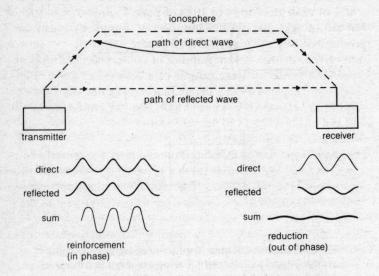

Fig. 30. **Fading**. Fading of a signal is due to the phase differences between the direct wave and its reflection from the ionosphere, or between one reflection and another.

IONOSPHERE, and the reflecting height of the ionosphere is continually shifting. Because of this, waves at the receiver produce a resultant which can be of low or high amplitude according to the phase angle between the arriving waves. See Fig. 30. Fading is counteracted by DIVERSITY reception and by the use of AUTOMATIC GAIN CONTROL.

failure rate, *n.* a measure of the unreliability of a component or system. The failure rate is measured in terms of the number of failures per thousand hours operation, or thousands of on/off cycles, whichever is more appropriate. For some systems using integrated circuits, the failure rate may be immeasurably small (for example, no system may have failed during testing), so failure rates then have to be computed on the basis of ACCELERATED LIFE TESTS under unnatural conditions. Compare RELIABILITY; see also MEAN LIFE.

fall time, *n.* the time taken for the amplitude of a pulse to reduce to a predefined level, usually measured as the time from 90% of peak amplitude to 10% of peak. Compare RISE TIME.

fan-in, *n*. the maximum number of inputs that can be connected to a LOGIC CIRCUIT. Compare FAN-OUT.

fan-out, *n*. the maximum number of LOGIC CIRCUIT inputs of the same family that the output of a device can drive. This quantity is decided by the current that is available at the output, and by the capacitance at each input. Fan-out can be increased by the use of BUFFERS. Compare FAN-IN.

farad, *n*. see CAPACITANCE.

Faraday cage, *n*. a metal box or mesh screen that is earthed to prevent electrostatic INTERFERENCE between circuits inside the cage and circuits outside. Large Faraday cages are used in testing transmitters or, conversely, to test equipment that might be affected by interference.

fast-recovery diode, *n*. a diode in which normal forward-biased operation resumes rapidly following a period of reversal. Ordinary diodes suffer from CARRIER-STORAGE effects, which make the shut-off comparatively slow. For use with microwave signals, SCHOTTKY DIODES or diodes fabricated from compound semiconductors such as GALLIUM ARSENIDE, must be used.

fault current, *n*. a CURRENT, usually large, that flows because of a circuit fault, usually a failure of insulation.

FCC, *abbrev. for* Federal Communications Commission, the regulating body for radio broadcasting in the US.

feedback, *n*. the return as part of the INPUT to an AMPLIFIER of a signal that is obtained from the OUTPUT. If the signal that is fed back is in phase, the amplifier is supplying part of its own input. This makes the effective GAIN very much higher, and will cause oscillation if the gain of the amplifier is greater than the loss of the network that connects the output with the input. If the feedback signal is in antiphase, the feedback is negative. This lowers gain, but also reduces noise and distortion caused by the amplifier. An amplifier that has NEGATIVE FEEDBACK is also stabilized against changes caused by alterations in the characteristics of components such as transistors or resistors. When the amount of negative feedback is very large, the only components that noticeably affect the gain are the resistors or other components in the feedback loop itself. The use of negative feedback is a very important feature of the design of LINEAR AMPLIFIERS. See also POSITIVE FEEDBACK.

feedback control loop, *n*. a feedback LOOP used in a control system. The control system may contain mechanical, thermal, hydraulic or optical components, and these are therefore included as part of the feedback loop.

feeder, *n*. a line that carries radio power from a transmitter to an AERIAL system.

feedthrough, *n*. a form of connection that passes through a material. The device is often used as a type of component, such as a feedthrough CAPACITOR. A feedthrough capacitor consists of a pin that is surrounded by a coaxial capacitor, creating a comparatively large capacitance between the pin and the body of the capacitor. The device is used to decouple connections that pass out of or into a circuit through a metal panel.

femto-, *prefix* denoting a submultiple equal to 10^{-15}.

ferrite, *n*. a brittle crystalline material made from oxides of iron and other metals, used as an electrically-insulating magnetic material.

ferromagnetic, *adj*. (of a material) exhibiting the same type of magnetic behaviour as iron, a characteristic of magnetic materials that have high PERMEABILITY.

See also HYSTERESIS LOOP.

FET, see FIELD–EFFECT TRANSISTOR.

fibre optics, *n*. the use of highly transparent glass fibres to carry light signals. The light beams are prevented from escaping from the material by total internal reflection. Because a light beam is an electromagnetic wave with a frequency in the range of 10^{14}–10^{15}Hz, huge amounts of information can be carried on one beam.

field, *n*. **1.** a part of space in which a force effect acts. In an ELECTRIC FIELD, a force can be detected on any charge. In a MAGNETIC FIELD, a force will be detected on any magnetic material, or on a wire that carries current. **2.** (in TV) a half-frame of a picture, see RASTER.

field coil, *n.* a coil that is used to generate a magnetic field by passing current through.

field control, *n.* the adjustment of MAGNETIC FIELD in an electric motor or AC generator. Field control is used to adjust motor speed or AC generator output voltage.

Fig. 31. **Field-effect transistor**. See main entry.

field–effect transistor (FET), *n.* a form of transistor in which current flow through a CHANNEL (2) is controlled by means of a GATE (1). Contacts are made on the two end faces of a bar of silicon which is called the *channel* (the *n-channel* if doped with N-TYPE impurities, and the *p-channel* if doped with P-TYPE impurities). The contacts are called the *source* and the *drain* respectively. Supposing that the channel is of the n-type, a p–type region will be diffused into the centre of the silicon bar as shown in Fig. 31, where the shaded area represents the channel. If a voltage is applied between the source and the drain as shown, electrons will be injected into the channel at the source and be collected at the drain.

Around the p–n junction formed between the gate and the channel, a DEPLETION LAYER will form. The presence of this depletion layer narrows the effective width of the channel as far as current carriers (electrons in this example) are concerned. If the gate is made negative with respect to the source, the width of the depletion layer increases, reducing the drain–source current. Thus voltage on the gate controls the current through the device.

If a FET with a p-channel is used, the arguments above still apply, but all voltages must be reversed.

The device described above is known as a *junction FET* (*JFET*). It should be noted that the gate of an n-channel JFET cannot be made positive or conduction will occur from the gate to the channel. A JFET can therefore only be operated in DEPLETION MODE.

If a thin layer of silicon oxide is interposed between the gate and the channel, the gate may be made positive (for n-channel devices) with respect to the channel without gate conduction occurring. This has the effect of widening the gate and reducing the channel resistance. This type of FET is known as an *insulated-gate FET* (*IGFET*) or *metal-oxide semiconductor FET* (*MOSFET*) after the form of construction used. MOSFETs can be used in either depletion or ENCHANCEMENT MODE.

field emission, *n*. the EMISSION of electrons in a very large electric field. Any sharp point at a high potential can cause field emission, and this can be a cause of failure or flashover, particularly in large valves.

field frequency, *n*. the rate of repetition of the complete screen scan in a TV system. See RASTER.

field magnet, *n*. a permanent magnet that is used to obtain a MAGNETIC FIELD. The field can be used in a small DC motor or for deflecting an electron beam. An electromagnet is more controllable, so a FIELD COIL is more often used.

field-strength meter, *n*. an instrument used to measure received signal strengths. Field strength is also called *intensity of field*. The meter typically uses tuning circuits, followed by a rectifier to obtain a DC voltage proportional to the amplitude of the carrier. The meter is used in conjunction with an aerial to plot the strength of carrier signal at various places remote from a transmitter. This allows maps of field strengths to be drawn up to assess the effective reception area of a transmitter.

filament, *n*. a thin metal wire heated by passing CURRENT through it, used in valves to provide cathode heating or electron EMISSION. For indirect cathode heating, molybdenum wire is used. For direct emission, tungsten is the most common filament material, though platinum is used in some x-ray tubes and x-ray rectifiers.

filament display, *n*. an ALPHANUMERIC display that is manufactured using tiny metal filaments set into a figure eight pattern. This allows the normal form of SEVEN-SEGMENT DISPLAY decoder to drive the filaments and provide a display that is brighter than can be achieved with LEDs, albeit with an increased power requirement.

film, *n*. a thin coating of any material.

film resistor, *n*. a RESISTOR that is manufactured by coating a film of metal or carbon onto a ceramic cylinder. A spiral is then cut into the film to adjust the resistor to its nominal value. Film resistors have now replaced most of the older resistor types for use in electronics.

filter, *n*. a NETWORK that can select signals of a required frequency range. Any filter will have a PASS BAND, meaning the range of frequencies that pass through it unattenuated, and a STOP BAND of frequencies that are greatly attenuated. The main types are LOW-PASS FILTERS, HIGH-PASS FILTERS, BAND-PASS FILTERS and BAND-STOP FILTERS. Filters may contain only PASSIVE COMPONENTS such as resistors, capacitors and inductors, or use ACTIVE COMPONENTS such as transistors and ICs. Modern active filters are much easier to design than passive filters, though computer-aided design systems make either type reasonably easy to deal with.

Compare ALL-PASS NETWORK.

final anode, *n*. the ANODE in a CATHODE-RAY TUBE design that collects most of the emitted electrons. The final anode will be a conducting layer either on the screen (see ALUMINIZED SCREEN) or immediately surrounding the screen.

first-in/first-out (FIFO) buffer or **register,** *n*. a data-storage device for computers in which the first piece of data placed into the buffer or register is the first to be retrieved.

first-in/last-out (FILO) buffer or **register,** *n*. a data-storage device for computers in which the first piece of data placed into the buffer or register is the last to be retrieved.

fixed return, *n*. a wave echo from a fixed object such as a building or a mountain. The problem posed by fixed returns is that they can make it difficult to detect moving objects. See also RADAR, CANCELLATION CIRCUIT.

flash, *vb.* to apply a voltage PULSE to a COMPONENT. Flashing can be used to burn away tiny sharp points, because of intense field emission, and is often used in the AGEING of thermionic valves.

flashover, *n.* a temporary breakdown of insulation, allowing a spark or discharge.

flat line, *n.* a power TRANSMISSION LINE that is perfectly matched to its load, with no trace of STANDING WAVES.

flatpack, *n.* a thin package that contains an INTEGRATED CIRCUIT. The IC is connected to leads that emerge from the edges of the pack. Compare DIL PACKAGE.

flat tuning, *n.* a tuning position at which a variation of the tuning control produces very little change of signal strength at the DEMODULATOR.

F layer or **Appleton layer,** *n.* the main reflecting layer in the IONOSPHERE, extending from about 150km to 1,000km above the Earth's surface. The layer is very strongly ionized and will reflect waves with wavelengths of between 6mm and 20m.

Fleming's rules, *n.* a method of remembering the directional relationship between current, magnetic field and force. See Fig. 32.

flicker, *n.* the small variations in brightness that are obvious to the eye. Because the eye stores an image for a short time, about a tenth of a second, small variations in brightness are not perceived if they occur faster than about 16 to 24 times per second. For bright pictures, however, a much higher repetition rate must be used if the eye is not to notice flicker, hence the use of a field rate of 50 fields per second for TV.

flicker effect, *n.* the irregular emission of current carriers, causing FLICKER NOISE.

flicker noise, *n.* a type of noise signal caused by tiny variations in CURRENT. This type of noise exists because current carriers (ELECTRONS or HOLES) are not emitted at a perfectly uniform rate, either into a vacuum or into semiconductor material.

flip chip, *n.* an INTEGRATED CIRCUIT chip connected directly to a circuit. The flip chip uses thick bonding pads that can be welded to circuit connections when the chip is inverted.

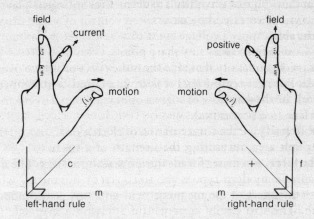

Fig. 32. **Fleming's rules**. The left-hand rule is used to remember the direction of the force on a conductor bearing current in a field of magnetic flux. The right-hand rule indicates which end of a conductor will become positive when the conductor is moved in a field of magnetic flux.

flip-flop, *n*. a bistable device (see BISTABLE CIRCUIT) used in digital circuits. The output of a flip-flop changes state (from 0 to 1 and vice versa) each time an input pulse is applied. Some flip-flops react to the rising or falling edge of a pulse (*edge-clocked devices*), and some to the height of the pulse (*level-clocked devices*). See also D-TYPE FLIP-FLOP, J-K FLIP-FLOP, MASTER–SLAVE FLIP-FLOP, R–S FLIP-FLOP.

floating, *adj*. (of a device or connection) the state of being unconnected to any voltage or signal.

flood gun, *n*. an ELECTRON GUN that produces a wide parallel beam of electrons. This is used in a direct–view STORAGE TUBE.

floppy disk, *n*. a thin, flexible, plastic DISK coated with magnetic material and used as a method of data storage for small computers.

fluorescence, *n*. the emission of light without heating. A fluorescent substance emits light when it is struck by electrons or by high–energy radiation such as ultraviolet radiation.

fluorescent screen, see FLUORESCENCE, PHOSPHOR.

flutter, *n*. a rapid variation in the pitch of a note that should be constant. Flutter is usually a fault in a recording or playback system, often caused by poor speed control of a tape drive or turntable.

Compare wow.

flux, *n.* **1.** a quantity that represents the effect of a FIELD over an area. Formerly called *lines of force*. **2.** a liquid or paste used to promote the easy flow of SOLDER or brazing metal over a metal surface (see SOLDERING).

flux density, *n.* the concentration of electric or MAGNETIC FLUX per unit area, measuring the strength of a FIELD.

fluxmeter, *n.* a meter for measuring MAGNETIC FLUX. The most common modern type is the HALL-EFFECT fluxmeter, which uses the effect of the magnetic field on a tiny semiconductor slab. The slab carries current, and applying a magnetic flux causes a potential difference to be generated across the slab. This potential difference is amplified and used to drive a meter that is calibrated in terms of flux or flux density.

flyback, *n.* the part of a TIMEBASE waveform in which voltage or current returns to its starting state. See Fig. 33.

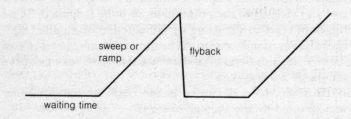

Fig. 33. **Flyback**. The flyback portion of a sawtooth wave. The diagram also shows the waiting time and the sweep or ramp portions of the waveform.

flying-spot scanner, *n.* a device that allows films, either still or cine, to be televised. The scanner consists of a high-brightness CATHODE-RAY TUBE whose moving SPOT (1) is focused onto the film. The light that passes through the film is picked up by a photocell and used to produce the output signal.

After addition of blanking pulses, sync pulses and colour sync, this can be used as a standard TV signal.

flywheel, 1. *n.* a rotating mechanical device that makes use of inertia to store kinetic energy. **2.** *adj.* (of a SYNCHRONIZING PULSE in a TV receiver) making use of a sine-wave OSCILLATOR for generating the line timebase frequency. This oscillator uses a relatively HIGH-Q resonant circuit, so that the oscillation frequency will continue unchanged even if the synchronization is irregular.

FM, see FREQUENCY MODULATION.

focusing, *n.* the effect of making all of the electrons in one beam converge to a point. See also CONVERGENCE.

foil capacitor, *n.* a CAPACITOR that makes use of metal foil as its conducting electrodes. The term usually denotes paper capacitors that consist of thin oiled paper sandwiched between metal foils. The term can also denote some types of electrolytic capacitor in which the plate is of foil, such as the tantalum foil capacitor.

folded dipole, *n.* a DIPOLE AERIAL in which the rod has been folded twice. This leaves the two connections at the centre as before, but reduces the IMPEDANCE of the aerial.

forced-air cooling, *n.* the cooling of power components, (usually transmitting valves) by passing air from a fan over the hot material.

form factor, *n.* **1.** a conversion factor for calculating RECTIFIER output. The form factor for a wave is the ratio of ROOT-MEAN-SQUARE value to the rectified DC value (average value) for a half-cycle. **2.** the ratio of length to diameter for a coil; used in NOMOGRAMS for finding inductance.

forward AGC, *n.* a system of AUTOMATIC GAIN CONTROL that is used with modern transistors. These transistors are operated with a resistive load so that an increase of BIAS will reduce the collector voltage, and the characteristics of the transistors are such that this will reduce the gain. The steady voltage at the demodulator is therefore used to add to the voltage bias. Compare REVERSE AGC.

forward bias, *n.* a BIAS in the direction that causes current to flow easily. The term is used mainly of semiconductor junctions and other types of diodes. Compare REVERSE BIAS.

forward current, *n.* the amount of current flowing in the forward (freely conducting) direction.

forward drop, *n.* the potential difference across a forward biased device such as a semiconductor diode.

forward wave, *n.* **1.** a wave travelling in the intended direction. For example, when a transmitter is connected to an AERIAL system, the forward wave travels from transmitter to aerial. There may be a reflected backward wave from aerial to transmitter that will then result in STANDING WAVES being set up. **2.** the input wave in a TRAVELLING-WAVE TUBE.

Foster–Seeley discriminator, *n.* a form of DISCRIMINATOR (1) circuit that was formerly used in FM receivers of high quality.

Fourier analysis, *n.* a mathematical method of determining the frequency content of a signal. Any NONSINUSOIDAL waveform can be shown to consist of a mixture of frequencies at various amplitudes and phases. Fourier analysis allows the amplitude and phase of each component of a signal to be calculated. Computer programs for this analysis can now be obtained for microcomputers. For further details, see Ref. 6.

four-layer diode, *n.* a semiconductor device with four alternate layers of p-type and n-type material. See THYRISTOR, SILICON-CONTROLLED SWITCH.

four-terminal resistor, *n.* a form of standard RESISTOR for use with POTENTIOMETER measurements. Two thick connectors are provided for passing current through the resistor. Two thin connectors are then used for connecting the resistor to the potentiometer for POTENTIAL DIFFERENCE measurements. This greatly reduces any errors that would be caused by the resistance of contacts.

frame, *n.* a set of two television fields. See RASTER.

frame aerial, *n.* an AERIAL wound in the form of a large loop, used in direction finding and also in very old portable receivers.

Franklin oscillator, *n.* a form of OSCILLATOR that makes use of a two-stage amplifier, with inversion in each stage, and one tuned circuit.

free electron, *n.* an electron that is free to move in a solid, liquid or gas. See CONDUCTION ELECTRONS.

free-field calibration, *n*. the CALIBRATION of a MICROPHONE in terms of output per unit sound-pressure. The calibration has to be carried out so that the presence of the microphone does not disturb the sound-wave pattern (the free field). If this is not possible, then the results have to be adjusted to allow for the field disturbance.

free oscillation, *n*. an OSCILLATION that is not supplied with energy after an original impetus. Free oscillations will die away at a rate that depends on the amount of damping (see DAMPED) in the circuit.

free space, *n*. any space, such as a vacuum, that has unity values of RELATIVE PERMITTIVITY and RELATIVE PERMEABILITY. In practical terms, the air approximates to free-space conditions.

frequency, *n*. the rate at which a waveform action repeats, measured in HERTZ.

frequency analyser, *n*. a measuring device that can measure the amplitude and phase of the frequency components of a signal, including FUNDAMENTAL FREQUENCIES and HARMONICS. See FOURIER ANALYSIS.

frequency band, *n*. a range of FREQUENCIES (usually RF) used for a particular purpose in telecommunications. There are, for example, frequency bands allocated by international agreement (usually violated by at least one country and by innumerable 'pirate' broadcasters) for medium wave broadcasting, television, mobile radio, etc.

frequency changer, *n*. the important mixer stage in a SUPERHETERODYNE receiver. In this stage, the incoming (variable) signal frequency is converted to a fixed intermediate frequency for subsequent amplification.

frequency compensation, *n*. the design of a circuit to allow it to be used for wideband purposes. See COMPENSATED ATTENUATOR.

frequency deviation, *n*. the change of CARRIER FREQUENCY caused by FREQUENCY MODULATION.

frequency discriminator, *n*. a CIRCUIT that produces an output voltage proportional to input frequency over a limited range. Discriminators are used in FM demodulation, and in frequency controllers. Circuits such as the RATIO DETECTOR and the FOSTER-SEELEY DISCRIMINATOR have now been almost completely replaced by pulse-counting ICs, such as the PHASE-LOCKED LOOP.

frequency divider, *n.* a CIRCUIT whose output is a lower frequency than that of the input, equal to the input frequency divided by an integer. Dividers generally make use of high-speed digital COUNTER integrated circuits.

frequency doubler, *n.* a circuit whose output is at twice the frequency of the input. See FREQUENCY MULTIPLIER.

frequency meter, *n.* an instrument used to measure FRE-QUENCY. Nowadays, this consists of a counter and a time standard, which effectively counts the number of cycles of the input in one second. For microwave frequencies, wavelength rather than frequency is measured, using calibrated CAVITY RESONATORS.

frequency modulation (FM), the MODULATION of a wave by the alteration of its FREQUENCY rather than its AMPLITUDE. The amplitude of the modulating wave corresponds to the frequency of the carrier. The maximum change of frequency that is permitted by the specification for the system is called the FREQUENCY DEVIATION. The main advantage of the system is that fluctuations of carrier amplitude caused by fading or interference should not affect the demodulated output at the receiver. See also PHASE MODULATION.

frequency multiplier, *n.* a device whose output is at a FREQUENCY which is an integer multiple of the input frequency. Frequency multiplication is used in transmitters, particularly as a way of allowing a single crystal oscillator to provide several different control frequencies in a number of different bands. The basis of frequency multiplication is an underbiased stage, whose output is rich in harmonics. The required harmonic is selected by making the load a resonant circuit of the desired frequency. The most common multiplication ratios are two (FREQUENCY DOUBLER) and three (frequency tripler), because the amplitude of harmonics at higher ratios is generally insufficient for reliable use.

frequency pulling, *n.* an alteration in the FREQUENCY of an

OSCILLATOR because of the electrical effect of a circuit connected to it. Applies to alteration of frequency caused by loading, because the frequency of oscillation is affected by the dynamic resistance of the oscillator tuned circuit, and the load is connected in parallel with this dynamic resistance, so reducing the overall value. Frequency pulling is a particular problem in BEAT-FREQUENCY OSCILLATORS that are intended to produce low frequency outputs.

frequency range, *n.* the set of frequencies over which a device or circuit is intended to operate.

frequency standard, *n.* **1.** a very stable oscillator whose output is used to calibrate other instruments. Nowadays, low cost rubidium MASERS can be bought for this purpose. **2.** the standard transmissions from the Rugby transmitter that are used to check oscillator frequencies in the UK.

fringe, *n.* an area at a long distance from a transmitter in which reception is only just usable.

front porch, *n.* a part of a TV SYNCHRONIZING PULSE, consisting of a short interval of BLACK LEVEL that immediately precedes the line synchronizing pulse.

frying, *n.* **1.** the sizzling sound that usually indicates ARCING in a high voltage circuit. **2.** noise in an audio circuit caused by poor contacts.

fsd, see FULL-SCALE DEFLECTION.

full adder, *n.* a LOGIC circuit that carries out the complete addition action. For two bits operation, a full adder needs three inputs, consisting of the two bits to be added, plus any carry bit from a previous operation. The output consists of the sum digits and the carry bit for use by subsequent devices. See ADDER, HALF-ADDER.

full-scale deflection (fsd), the deflection of the needle of a meter movement to the last figure on the dial.

full-wave dipole, *n.* a DIPOLE aerial whose total length is equal to a full wavelength of the signal frequency.

full-wave rectifier, *n.* a RECTIFIER circuit that produces a positive half-wave peak in one direction for each half of an AC wave. This is carried out by means of a bridge rectifier circuit. See Fig. 34 on page 132.

Fig. 34. **Full-wave rectifier**. The circuit uses a diode bridge.

function generator, *n*. a type of signal GENERATOR that can produce a set of different waveforms.

fundamental frequency or **basic frequency,** *n*. the lowest frequency of repetition in a wave that can also include HARMONICS. See also FOURIER ANALYSIS.

fuse, *n*. a safety device consisting of a short piece of metal wire made from a material with a low melting point. Excessive CURRENT flowing through the fuse will melt the metal, so interrupting the circuit. The fuse then has to be replaced after the fault that caused the excessive current has been located and repaired. See also CIRCUIT BREAKER.

G

gain or **amplification,** *n*. the ratio of signal output to signal input for an amplifier. The ratio is often quoted in decibels, using 10log (out/in) for power ratios and 20log (out/in) for voltage ratios. The gain of an AERIAL is the ratio of the signal power transmitted or received in the intended direction compared with the signal to or from a simple DIPOLE. Compare ATTENUATION.

gain control, *n*. a POTENTIOMETER (1) or switch for varying signal amplitude.

gallium arsenide, *n*. a compound SEMICONDUCTOR. Unlike silicon or germanium, gallium arsenide is not an element. It is almost impossible to dope by DIFFUSION, and modern methods of DOPING rely on ION IMPLANTATION. The doped material has very low resistivity, but its reversed biased junctions are of very high resistance. At present, gallium arsenide is used mainly for microwave diodes, and for high-speed field-effect transistors that can be used at UHF.

ganged circuits, *n*. a set of CIRCUITS in which VARIABLE CAPACITORS, INDUCTORS or POTENTIOMETERS are mechanically linked and are operated with a single control. The ganging of variable capacitors in a SUPERHETERODYNE receiver, for example, allows the tuning of the oscillator and aerial frequency circuits to be altered together in step.

ganging, *n*. the mechanical connection of adjustable COMPONENTS so that several can be operated by a single control.

gap, *n*. a narrow break in a CIRCUIT. A *magnetic gap* consists of a narrow piece of nonmagnetic material placed in a magnetic circuit. This is put in to prevent SATURATION of the magnetic material. A SPARK GAP is often included in high-voltage circuits. This consists of two metal conductors close together, one at high voltage and the other earthed. The principle is that a voltage surge will cause energy to be lost in the form of a spark rather than in damaging components.

gas breakdown, see AVALANCHE.

gas discharge, *n*. the flow of current in an ionized gas (see IONIZATION). Gases do not conduct current unless ionized, and a high electric field must be used to start ionization. The voltage that is required to start ionization will be higher in the absence of light, unless the gas in the tube is slightly radioactive. One former use of gas-discharge tubes was as voltage reference standards, since the voltage drop across a conducting gas is fairly constant. During the action of a gas-filled tube, the gas can be seen to glow, and this leads to applications of the effect as display devices. See DISCHARGE.

gas-filled tube, *n*. any type of valve that contains low-pressure gas rather than a vacuum. GEIGER-MÜLLER TUBES are gas-filled, as were the old thyratrons and ignitrons that were used as electronic relays. Gas-filled tubes were also used as voltage-reference devices and for display.

gate, *n*. **1.** the controlling electrode of a FIELD-EFFECT TRANSISTOR. **2.** a CIRCUIT that uses one WAVEFORM to control the passage of another. In analogue circuits, a gate will pass an input signal for a time that is determined by a gating signal, usually a square wave. Digital circuits use gates to carry out logic actions (see AND GATE, OR GATE, EXCLUSIVE-OR GATE, NOT GATE.

gate array, *n*. a form of INTEGRATED CIRCUIT that consists of many separate gates. If these gates are not connected to each other, the array is an UNCOMMITTED LOGIC ARRAY. See EPLD.

gate expander, *n*. a CIRCUIT that is connected to the INPUT of a logic gate so as to allow further inputs to be connected. See FAN-IN, FAN-OUT.

Geiger-Müller tube, *n*. a form of GAS-FILLED TUBE used to detect ionizing radiation. The tube contains a low-pressure gas, and a trace of de-ionizing material such as bromine. Two electrodes in the tube are kept at a potential difference that is lower than is needed to start a discharge. When an ionizing particle enters the tube, gas is ionized, but the effect of the de-ionizing material is to cause recombination of these ions when the particle passes out of the tube. The tube therefore passes current only for a brief interval, one pulse for each particle. See also DEAD TIME.

generator, *n*. **1.** a DEVICE that can supply electrical power, such as dynamos and alternators, both of which convert mechanical energy into electrical energy. **2.** any signal source that can be represented as a voltage or current generator in an equivalent circuit.

germanium, *n*. an element that was the first to be used for manufacturing transistors. Its use has now been almost completely superseded by that of SILICON.

getter, *n*. a material for removing the last traces of gas from a vacuum tube. A getter consists of a thin film of a metal such as barium. This is a reactive metal that will absorb any traces of gas that may be produced as the tube is used. The use of getters is confined to the smaller receiving valves and to CATHODE-RAY TUBES, because transmitting valves run at a temperature that would vaporize the getter. See also OUTGASSING.

ghost, see ECHO.

giga-, *prefix.* denoting a multiple equal to 10^9.

glass electrode, *n.* a device for measuring the acidity (pH) of solutions, consisting of a wire connection to a conducting liquid inside a thin glass bulb. The voltage from a glass electrode needs to be amplified before it can be measured.

glow lamp, *n.* a GAS-FILLED TUBE used as an indicator or voltage regulator.

Gm, see MUTUAL CONDUCTANCE.

gold-bonding, *n.* a method of making a JUNCTION between N-TYPE germanium and a gold wire. The method was formerly the only method available for the manufacture of high-speed diodes.

gramophone, *n.* a sound reproducing system that uses a rotating plastic disc with a groove whose walls are mechanically engraved with the pattern of a sound wave. See also REPRODUCTION OF SOUND, COMPACT DISC.

graph recorder, *n.* a form of CHART RECORDER.

graphic symbol, *n.* a symbol used to represent a component in CIRCUIT DIAGRAMS.

grass, see GROUND CLUTTER.

grid, *n.* an ELECTRODE that controls ELECTRON flow in a vacuum tube. The type used in CATHODE-RAY TUBES consists of a small aperture in a top-hat shaped electrode. In a transmitting valve, the grid is a winding of molybdenum wire surrounding the hot FILAMENT.

grid bias, *n.* the voltage applied between CATHODE and GRID of a vacuum tube to control electron flow. The BIAS is normally applied with the grid negative, and at a sufficiently large negative potential the electron stream will be cut off.

grid dip, *n.* a form of passive TELEMETRY in which inductive COUPLING is used to transmit information over distances of up to 50cm. The name arises from a now obsolete circuit used to detect the frequency of a passive resonant circuit by its effect on the grid current of a thermionic valve oscillator tuned to the same frequency. Grid–dip telemetry is extensively used for biomedical work in which measurements have to be made by sensors implanted within a patient, where no physical connections are possible.

grid emission, *n.* the emission of electrons from an overheated GRID, usually in a transmitting valve used near its maximum ratings. The electron from the grid will be accelerated to the anode, and will not be controlled by the grid bias. This can result in more overheating, causing failure of the valve. Grids are commonly coated with graphite to reduce the emission of electrons and to help dissipation of heat by radiation.

grid modulation, *n.* a method of achieving AMPLITUDE MODULATION in valve-based transmitting equipment. The final power amplifier valve has its BIAS applied through a transformer winding to which is applied the modulating frequency. The advantage of this form of modulation is that the power that is required is relatively low. The disadvantage is that the power output stage has to be reasonably linear in operation, which is not the case with the common CLASS C design.

ground, see EARTH.

ground absorption, *n.* the loss of radiated signal power to EARTH. If the ground wave is absorbed rather than reflected, the range of the transmitter will be fairly short.

ground clutter, *n.* RADAR reflections from irregular ground. These cause a fuzzy screen display that looks like grass.

grounded-base connection, see COMMON–BASE CONNECTION.

grounded-collector connection, see EMITTER FOLLOWER.

grounded-emitter connection, see COMMON–EMITTER CONNECTION.

ground plane, see EARTH PLANE.

ground wave, *n.* a wave that has been reflected from the ground. If this happens to a radar echo, the distance measurements for the signal will be incorrect. Compare SKY WAVE.

ground return, *n.* ground echoes that cause GROUND CLUTTER.

group velocity, *n.* the velocity of a group of electromagnetic waves in a medium other than a vacuum. This velocity is always less than the velocity of the waves in a vacuum. Individual waves within the group *appear* to travel with a PHASE VELOCITY that is greater than the velocity of the waves in a vacuum.

grown junction, *n.* an old method of producing a semi-conductor JUNCTION by adding DOPING impurities to the molten material from which a crystal is being pulled.

guard band, *n.* **1.** an unused FREQUENCY BAND. The purpose of this is to avoid the chance of crosstalk between two adjacent bands. **2.** an earthed metal strip that avoids the spread of an electric field, used in standard capacitors.

Gunn diode, *n.* a microwave DIODE that is used as an oscillator in microwave applications, and which has replaced KLYSTRONS for many applications. The Gunn diode is made from GALLIUM ARSENIDE, and emits microwave radiation when a large electric field is placed across the material.

Gunn effect, *n.* the generation of MICROWAVE OSCILLATIONS from a GALLIUM ARSENIDE diode.

gyrator, *n.* a MICROWAVE circuit COMPONENT. Its action is to pass signals in one direction, but reverse the phase of signals travelling in the other direction.

H

halation, *n.* a fuzzy glow around the SPOT on a CATHODE-RAY TUBE. The effect is noticeable on oscilloscope and radar tubes and is caused by internal reflections of light within the thick glass at the front of the screen.

half-adder, *n.* a simple adding circuit for two binary bits. Only two inputs are needed, because no carry input or output is provided. The half-adder can be constructed from any standard GATE type, such as NAND or NOR. See Fig. 35 on page 138. See also ADDER, FULL ADDER.

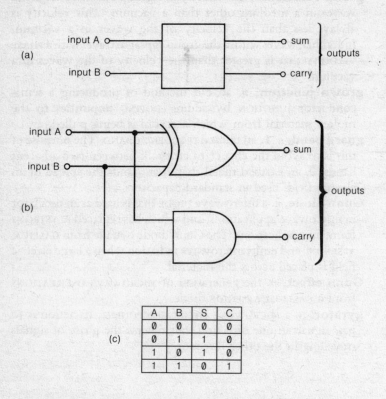

A	B	S	C
0	0	0	0
0	1	1	0
1	0	1	0
1	1	0	1

Fig. 35. **Half-adder**. (a) The two-bit half-adder symbol. (b) Practical implementation. (c) and Truth table.

half-duplex, *n*. a line communication system that allows signals to pass in either direction, but not at the same time. Compare DUPLEX, SIMPLEX.

half-power point or **–3dB point,** *n*. a graph point used in determining the Q FACTOR of a RESONANT CIRCUIT. The frequency limits at which the output power is equal to half of the maximum power output are measured.

half-wave dipole, *n*. a DIPOLE AERIAL whose length is half of the radiated wavelength.

half-wave rectifier, *n*. a RECTIFIER that passes one half of an

AC voltage and blocks the other half (which has the opposite polarity), for example, a single diode.

Hall effect, *n*. a VOLTAGE that is generated by the effect of a magnetic field on a slab of material that is carrying current. SEMICONDUCTORS give particularly large Hall effect voltages, and the effect is used to measure magnetic fields (see FLUXMETER).

Hall probe, *n*. the probe of a HALL EFFECT fluxmeter, containing the semiconductor slab in which the Hall effect occurs.

ham, *n*. a slang term for amateur radio enthusiast.

Hamming code, *n*. a very complicated error correcting code that is used for data transmission. Hamming code is used to correct TELETEXT data signals.

Hanover bars, *n*. a fault condition of the PAL type colour TV system in which the picture appears broken into coloured horizontal bars.

hard disk, *n*. a magnetic data-storage device for computers, in which a rigid disk coated with a ferromagnetic material is spun at high speed. The read-write head 'floats' above the disk on an air cushion. Extremely fast access times can be achieved by this system, and its cost originally restricted its use to MAINFRAME computer systems, though low-cost versions such as the WINCHESTER DISK are now available.

hard valve, *n*. an electronic valve that uses a vacuum, as distinct from a GAS–FILLED TUBE.

hardware, *n*. the electronics components of a computer system, as distinct from program instructions.

Compare SOFTWARE.

hardwire, *vb*. to assemble a CIRCUIT by wiring from component to component rather than by using a printed circuit.

harmonic, *n*. a part of a signal whose frequency is an integer multiple of the FUNDAMENTAL FREQUENCY of the signal. Any periodic waveform other than a sine wave will contain harmonics.

Compare SUBHARMONIC.

harmonic generator, *n*. a CIRCUIT that deliberately generates HARMONICS. This can use reverse-biased transistors, diodes or other NONLINEAR elements. The aim is to steepen the

Fig. 36. **Hartley oscillator**. The Fig. shows one form of the Hartley oscillator circuit, using a tapped inductor for feedback.

sides of any sine wave and so result in the generation of harmonics.

Hartley oscillator or **tapped–coil oscillator,** *n*. an oscillator circuit that uses a tapped inductor to obtain a feedback signal. See Fig. 36. See also COLPITTS OSCILLATOR.

H–attenuator, *n*. an ATTENUATOR of symmetrical construction intended for attenuating two signals by an equal amount. These signals may be the inputs or outputs of a BALANCED AMPLIFIER. See Fig. 37.

Fig. 37. **H-attenuator**. An example of an H-attenuator, using resistors. The design is symmetrical and is intended for balanced signals.

head, *n.* a reading or writing recording device. See READ/WRITE HEAD, RECORDING OF SOUND, SOUND REPRODUCTION.

heat detector, *n.* any device that senses temperature change. Examples include THERMOCOUPLES, THERMISTORS, and PYRO-ELECTRIC generating materials.

heater, *n.* **1.** a valve filament or other heating element. **2.** the molybdenum spiral that is placed inside the CATHODE of an indirectly heated valve, and insulated from it. **3.** another name for (a) a WIRE-WOUND RESISTOR in a crystal oven, (b) a THERMOSTAT accelerating heater.

heating effect, *n.* the effect of CURRENT *I* driven by a voltage *V* passing through a RESISTANCE *R*. The heat dissipation rate *P* in watts may be found from $P = IV$ or $P = I^2R$.

heating time, *n.* the time needed for a hot cathode device to reach operating temperature.

heat sink, *n.* a massive metal slab to which power transistors can be bolted. The purpose of a heat sink is to spread the conducted heat from the collector of a transistor over a large mass and a large area, and so ultimately to the air. The transistor will still have to be operated in such a way that the rate of power dissipation does not exceed the rate of heat dissipation.

Heaviside layer, see E LAYER.

height control, *n.* the TELEVISION RECEIVER control for amplitude of frame scan. This has the effect of altering the picture height. Modern receivers either dispense with this control or use a preset POTENTIOMETER.

helical aerial, *n.* an AERIAL that consists of a wire in a corkscrew shape. The radiated wave is elliptically POLARIZED (1).

helical potentiometer (helipot), *n.* a POTENTIOMETER in which the element is in helical form. This means that several turns of the actuating shaft are needed to wind the contact from one end of the element to the other. Such a potentiometer, using anything from 3 to 50 turns from one stop to the other, has very high resolution (see RESOLUTION OF POTENTIOMETER), and is used in measuring instruments.

helipot, see HELICAL POTENTIOMETER.

Helmholtz coils, *n.* a pair of identical coils placed on the same

141

axis and separated by a distance equal to coil radius. The field in the space between the coils is fairly uniform.

henry, *n*. the unit of INDUCTANCE, self or mutual. Symbol: H. The henry is the unit equivalent to volt-seconds per ampere. Named after Joseph Henry (1797–1878), US physicist.

hertz (Hz), *n*. the unit of FREQUENCY, equal to one complete cycle per second. Symbol: Hz. Named after Heinrich Hertz (1857–94), German physicist.

heterodyne, 1. *adj*. (of a circuit) producing a BEAT FREQUENCY by mixing an incoming frequency with a locally-generated oscillation that is at a slightly different frequency. **2.** *vb*. to mix two frequencies together to produce a beat frequency, as in a SUPERHETERODYNE RECEIVER or a HETERODYNE WAVEMETER.

heterodyne wavemeter, *n*. a form of FREQUENCY METER that operates with a calibrated oscillator. The oscillator frequency is varied until beats (see BEAT FREQUENCIES) of a particular frequency (often zero) are detected. The input frequency is then read from the calibrated scale.

heterojunction, *n*. a JUNCTION (2) between different semiconductor materials, or between a semiconductor and a metal.

hexadecimal scale, *n*. the number scale that uses 16 digits. The letters A to F are used to represent the decimal numbers 10 to 15 in this scale. For example, the hexadecimal number A5 is the decimal number 165.

HF, see HIGH FREQUENCY.

hi-fi, *abbrev. for* high-fidelity sound. Hi-fi covers all aspects of RECORDING OF SOUND and SOUND REPRODUCTION with the aim of securing the most realistic possible reproduction. The term is often used indiscriminately to denote stereo audio systems that are of noticeably low fidelity.

high frequency (HF), *n*. **1.** the FREQUENCY BAND that covers the frequencies between 3 and 30 megahertz approximately. **2.** any frequency higher than mid-range audio frequency.

high-logic level, *n*. the actual voltage level that is taken to represent the logic 1. For most modern TTL LOGIC CIRCUITS, this means any voltage between +3.5 and +5.0 volts.

high-pass filter, *n.* a FILTER whose PASS BAND starts at a high frequency and continues indefinitely.

high-Q, *adj.* (of an inductor or tuned circuit) having a large ratio (100 or more) of inductive IMPEDANCE to resistance at the RESONANT FREQUENCY.

high tension (HT), *n.* an obsolete term for high VOLTAGE, usually taken to mean voltages in the range of 100 to 500V. See also EHT.

high-voltage test, *n.* a method of testing INSULATION. The test consists of applying higher than normal voltages across the insulation, often in the form of pulses. The quality of the insulation is measured by the current that passes during each pulse.

hiss, *n.* the particularly obtrusive form of NOISE from recorded tape, caused by random magnetization of particles on the tape. Tape hiss is particularly noticeable on tapes of narrow width operated at low speeds. This makes some form of COMPANDER system, such as DOLBY or DBX, essential for cassette systems if reasonably good reproduction is needed.

holding current, *n.* the minimum CURRENT needed to maintain conduction of a THYRISTOR. The current that flows between the anode and cathode of a thyristor serves also to keep the thyristor switched on. If this current falls below a minimum holding level, the thyristor will switch off. Too low a voltage in the forward direction will also allow the thyristor to switch off.

hole, *n.* the space that is left in the atomic arrangement of a crystal when an ELECTRON is removed. This space is mobile and behaves as if it carried positive charge.

hole conduction, *n.* the CONDUCTION in a metal or a semiconductor caused by HOLE movement in the direction of a positive field.

hole current, *n.* the amount of CURRENT that is due to HOLE movement. In several metals, a substantial amount of the current that can flow is conducted by hole movement. In p-type semiconductors, almost all of the current is conducted by hole movement.

hole trap, *n.* a fault in a semiconductor CRYSTAL that can stop the movement of HOLES by allowing recombination with an electron.

homing beacon, see BEACON.

homopolar generator, *n*. a GENERATOR that uses a rotating metal disc rather than a coil. The homopolar generator delivers low-voltage DC without the use of any form of COMMUTATOR.

honeycomb coil, *n*. an old-fashioned type of coil construction that reduces STRAY CAPACITANCE between the turns of the coil.

hook-up or **lash-up,** *n*. a temporary CIRCUIT for assessment or measurement.

horizontal blanking, *n*. a SIGNAL applied to the grid of a receiver or camera CATHODE-RAY TUBE to cut off the beam and so avoid signals being generated or displayed during the LINE FLYBACK period.

horizontal hold, *n*. the control over SYNCHRONIZATION of the HORIZONTAL TIMEBASE of a TELEVISION RECEIVER.

horizontal polarization, *n*. a property exhibited by an electromagnetic wave in which the electric field vector is horizontal. A wave transmitted from a horizontal aerial will be horizontally polarized. The direction of polarization of a wave is by convention taken to be the direction of the electric-field component of the wave.

horizontal sweep, *n*. the movement of an ELECTRON BEAM horizontally across the face of a CATHODE-RAY TUBE. This is the result of applying a ramp waveform of voltage to horizontal deflection plates in an INSTRUMENT TUBE or a ramp waveform of current to the horizontal deflection coils of a PICTURE TUBE.

horizontal timebase, *n*. the circuit that generates the horizontal TIMEBASE waveform.

horn aerial, *n*. a MICROWAVE aerial consisting of a horn that starts with the waveguide and flares out in each direction.

horn loudspeaker or **horn-loaded loudspeaker,** *n*. the most efficient form of LOUDSPEAKER, used as a comparison standard. The horn loudspeaker consists of a DRIVER unit that can be a conventional electromagnetic unit with a small cone. The speaker walls then follow the pattern of an exponential curve, increasing in area. This loudspeaker is a relatively efficient converter of electrical energy into sound energy (4%

typically), but requires a lot of space. The material that is used for the walls of the horn must not resonate within the audible frequency range.

horseshoe magnet, *n.* a MAGNET whose shape is like that of a horseshoe. This means that the poles of the magnet are close, causing an intense field across the air gap.

hot–carrier diode, see SCHOTTKY DIODE.

hot cathode, *n.* a CATHODE that emits electrons into a vacuum when heated. See also COLD–CATHODE EMITTER.

hot dip or **tinning bath,** *n.* a method of coating metals with other metals by dipping them into a bath of molten metal. The method is used to coat PRINTED CIRCUIT BOARDS with solder.

hot electron, *n.* a high energy electron.

hot spot, *n.* a part of an ELECTRODE that is overheated. Hot spots become particularly troublesome in vacuum devices if they start to emit electrons as a result of their high temperature. A hot spot in a semiconductor can cause diffusion of impurity, so altering the characteristic of the material.

hot–wire meter, *n.* a current-measuring instrument that operates on the hot-wire principle. In a typical hot-wire meter, a wire is held between supports, and a tensioning spring is attached to the centre of the wire. The attachment to the needle movement is also made at the centre. When the wire is heated by passing current it will expand. The resulting sag at the centre of the wire is mechanically amplified by levers and used to drive the needle. Hot-wire instruments, though not very accurate, are useful for indicating true ROOT–MEAN–SQUARE values of high-frequency currents.

howl, *n.* an unwanted audio OSCILLATION. Howl is caused by unwanted FEEDBACK, and this can be in audio–amplifier stages, in radio-frequency stages, or as a result of acoustic feedback (from a loudspeaker to a microphone or gramophone pick-up, for example).

h–parameter, *abbrev. for* hybrid PARAMETER. Hybrid parameters are sets of CHARACTERISTIC figures that have different units. When graphs are drawn of component or circuit characteristics, the slope of each graph will yield a parameter figure that will have units such as resistance, conductance, gain, etc. Hybrid parameters form sets whose units are not consistent, i.e. not all resistances, nor all ratios, but a mixture of different types.

H-plane, *n.* the direction of the magnetic field portion of a MICROWAVE signal.

See WAVEGUIDE.

HT, see HIGH TENSION.

hue, *n.* the spectral colour of a portion of a picture. In COLOUR TELEVISION applications, a given colour has two measurable quantities, hue and *saturation*. Hue refers to the colour itself, saturation to the ratio of pure colour to white.

hum, *n.* a low frequency signal, usually picked up from AC mains supplies (i.e. *mains hum*). The picking up of hum is a problem for designers of high-gain audio equipment. It cannot be eliminated by using simple FILTERS, because the action of a RECTIFIER generates HARMONICS of the hum frequency, and these harmonics radiate.

hum modulation, *n.* the MODULATION of signal AMPLITUDE by low-frequency hum.

hunting, *n.* an OSCILLATION in a control SYSTEM, i.e., any system in which electronic circuits control mechanical or other non-electronic actions and in which a FEEDBACK CONTROL LOOP is used. 'Hunting' is the consequence of poor design in which a NEGATIVE FEEDBACK loop with insufficient damping (see DAMPED) has been applied to an unsuitable system. The result is that the feedback overcorrects, so that the system never becomes stable.

hybrid IC, *n.* a form of INTEGRATED CIRCUIT that mixes COMPONENTS on the chip with components separately connected. The added components are welded to bonding pads, and are components that cannot easily be manufactured in IC form, such as capacitors, inductors and quartz crystals. Hybrid ICs are used mainly in military applications.

hybrid junction or **Magic-T junction** or **rat-race junction,** *n.* a method of connecting WAVEGUIDES so as to change signal direction and avoid reflected signals.

hybrid-pi equivalent, *n.* an old form of EQUIVALENT CIRCUIT for a TRANSISTOR. This has seldom been used since silicon transistors became predominant, because simpler equivalents can now be used.

hysteresis, *n.* an effect in which the direction of change of a quantity must be considered as well as size of change. See HYSTERESIS LOOP.

hysteresis distortion, *n.* a form of signal distortion that is caused by HYSTERESIS.

hysteresis loop, *n.* the shape of a graph of any quantity that exhibits hysteresis. The best-known example is MAGNETIC HYSTERESIS. Such a graph has a loop shape, because the path taken as one plotted quantity is increased is not the same as the path taken when the quantity is decreased. Only the ends of the loop are common to the two paths. The area of the loop usually indicates the amount of energy that is required during each cycle.

hysteresis loss, *n.* the loss of energy that is the result of tracing out a graph that contains a HYSTERESIS LOOP. The amount of energy lost is represented by the area of the hysteresis loop.

Hz, see HERTZ.

I

IC, see INTEGRATED CIRCUIT.

ideal bunching, *n.* the gathering of moving electrons into tightly packed groups, with no electrons between the groups. See BUNCHER, KLYSTRON.

ideal crystal, see PERFECT CRYSTAL.

ideal transformer, see PERFECT TRANSFORMER.

ident signal, *n.* a phase-identifying signal in the PAL colour TV standard. The ident signal enables the receiver to recognize the correct phase of the **V** component of the colour signal, that is inverted in alternate lines.

idle component, see REACTIVE CURRENT.

IEE, *abbrev. for* Institution of Electrical Engineers, the senior electrical-engineering institution in the UK.

IEEE, *abbrev. for* Institute of Electrical and Electronic Engineers, the US institute for professional engineers in all branches of electrical technology.

IF, see INTERMEDIATE FREQUENCY.

IFF, *abbrev. for* identification friend or foe, a form of RADAR in which a coded radar signal will be decoded and correctly returned by a friendly aircraft. See INTERROGATING SIGNAL, TRANSPONDER, SECONDARY RADAR.

IF strip, *n.* the part of a SUPERHETERODYNE RECEIVER that operates at the INTERMEDIATE FREQUENCY. This consists of all the stages from the MIXER to the demodulator, along with the AGC connections.

IGFET, see FIELD-EFFECT TRANSISTOR.

ignitron, *n.* an old form of mercury-vapour controlled RECTIFIER for very high voltages and large currents.

I²L, see INTEGRATED-INJECTION LOGIC.

image converter or **image intensifier,** *n.* a device that achieves light amplification or frequency changing by the use of a PHOTOCATHODE and a PHOSPHOR operated with a large potential difference between them. An image which may be of ordinary light, or ultraviolet or infrared light, causes electrons to be emitted. These electrons are accelerated by the electrodes, and their relative positions maintained until they strike the phosphor. The electrons that strike the phosphor form a bright image. This image will be a (visible) light image, a copy of the original image which may be too dim to see, or may be composed of invisible wavelengths. Image converters and intensifiers are used with x-ray systems, allowing x-ray dosage to be greatly reduced, and in infrared night-sights.

image frequency, *n.* the frequency of a signal into a SUPERHETERODYNE RECEIVER that will provide the same INTERMEDIATE FREQUENCY as the correct frequency to which the receiver is tuned. For example, if the receiver is tuned to 98MHz, using a 10.7MHz IF, then the oscillator frequency will be 108.7MHz. An input frequency of 119.4MHz, however, will also produce an IF of 10.7MHz (by subtracting the oscillator frequency), and this is the 'image frequency'. If the IF is suitably chosen, the image frequency should be spaced sufficiently far from the desired frequency to be rejected by the RF tuning circuits. When a low frequency IF is needed, the DOUBLE-SUPERHET RECEIVER principle will avoid image frequency problems.

image impedance, *n.* the value of IMPEDANCE measured at the terminals of a FILTER network, i.e. the values of input impedance (with output open circuit) and output impedance (with input open circuit).

image orthicon, *n.* a form of TV CAMERA TUBE that was used until the start of colour TV broadcasting, when it was largely replaced by the VIDICON type of tube.

IMPATT diode, *n.* a form of junction DIODE that oscillates when reverse-biased into AVALANCHE conditions. The oscillations are at MICROWAVE frequencies, and can be tuned by placing the diode in a RESONANT CAVITY.

impedance, *n.* the complex sum of AC RESISTANCE and REACTANCE. Symbol: Z; unit: ohm. If an AC signal is applied to a circuit containing reactive components, the phase of the output current will not necessarily be the same as the phase of the output voltage. The relationship between V (complex voltage) and I (complex current) cannot therefore be described by a scalar quantity such as resistance, as is the case for DC circuits. A 'two-part' quantity such as a vector or COMPLEX NUMBER is needed, and this quantity is termed *complex impedance*. See Fig. 38 (p.150). See Ref. 2 for more details.

impedance matching, *n.* a method of ensuring that the IMPEDANCES of two circuits that are to be connected are equal. Impedance matching is particularly important for RF power circuits and TRANSMISSION LINES. The most efficient transfer of power from an AMPLIFIER to a LOAD occurs when the output impedance of the amplifier equals the input impedance of the load. In a transmission line, matching impedances prevents reflections (leading to losses) that would otherwise occur at the point where unequal impedances were connected. FILTER sections that are to be connected together will operate correctly only if the impedances are matched.

impregnated cable, *n.* a cable that uses paper or cloth insulation impregnated with oil.

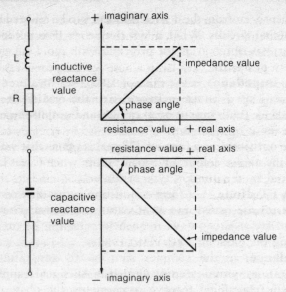

Fig. 38. **Impedance**. See main entry.

impulse, *n.* **1.** a sudden rise and fall of voltage or current. Impulses are generated by switching, particularly in inductive circuits, and also by spark discharges. **2.** in signal analysis, a theoretical concept denoting a pulse of infinite height and zero width.

impulse generator, *n.* a GENERATOR that provides an impulse voltage or current. Impulse generators are used for testing insulation, and often use electrostatic generators like the Van-de-Graaf generator.

impulse noise, *n.* a form of radio frequency NOISE that arises from SPARKS. The spark ignition system of petrol engines is one common source of impulse noise. Another source is sparking contacts in thermostats (refrigerators, central heating systems). Impulse noise is particularly troublesome to VHF transmissions, particularly FM and TV transmissions that have a broad bandwidth.

impurity, *n.* the atoms contained in a semiconductor CRYSTAL that are not of the semiconductor element or compound.

Impurity may exist because it cannot be removed, or because it has been deliberately added, in which case it is referred to as a DOPING impurity.

incandescent lamp, *n.* a lamp whose light is generated by a hot object, usually a metal filament.

incremental resistance or **slope resistance** or **differential resistance,** *n.* the slope of the graph of voltage plotted against current for a component or circuit. This corresponds to the EQUIVALENT RESISTANCE for a small signal applied with the bias set to the same voltage and current levels.

indicating instrument, *n.* an instrument that indicates that a current or voltage exists, but does not measure the value.

indicator tube, *n.* a form of miniature CATHODE-RAY TUBE. Typically, indicator tubes are built into equipment so that WAVEFORMS can be checked without the need to connect up a separate OSCILLOSCOPE.

indirect wave, *n.* a radio wave that reaches a RECEIVER by reflection from, for example, the IONOSPHERE.

induce, *vb.* to produce an electrical effect at a distance. An electrostatic CHARGE can be induced in any object by bringing up another charge. A MAGNETIC FLUX can be induced in a magnetic material by bringing up a magnet or a coil that is carrying current.

induced current, *n.* the CURRENT that flows in a CONDUCTOR because the magnetic field around the conductor is cutting through lines of magnetic flux.

induced noise, *n.* the NOISE that is induced from another circuit. For example, HUM in an audio circuit may be induced from a mains transformer by way of an EARTH LOOP.

inductance, *n.* the quantity that relates MAGNETIC FLUX to the CURRENT that causes it. Symbol: L; unit: henry. Inductance of two types exists, SELF-INDUCTANCE as applied to a single inductor such as a coil, and MUTUAL INDUCTANCE.

induction, *n.* the process of inducing MAGNETISM or CHARGE.

induction compass, *n.* a miniature AC GENERATOR that acts as a magnetic compass. A coil rotates, and the peak output is obtained when the axis of the coil (at right angles to the axis of rotation) faces along the magnetic north-south axis.

induction flowmeter, *n.* a method of measuring the flow rate for a conducting liquid. The flow of the liquid is at right angles to a MAGNETIC FIELD, and a small voltage is generated or induced across the liquid which can be measured. The importance of the method is that there need be no interference with the flow of the liquid, and the method is equally applicable to very hot or very cold liquids, or to ionized gases (see IONIZATION). The principle is also used as a method of generating power, the magnetohydrodynamic generator.

induction furnace or **induction heater,** *n.* a method of melting metals by making the metal a part of the secondary winding of a TRANSFORMER. This is used for large-scale heating; for small samples an EDDY CURRENT HEATER is more useful.

induction heater, see INDUCTION FURNACE, EDDY CURRENT HEATER.

induction instrument, *n.* a form of MOVING-IRON METER. The STATOR coil is supplied with the alternating current to be measured. The EDDY CURRENTS that are induced in a movable conductor cause force effects that move the conductor, and a needle, against the restoring force of a spring.

induction microphone, see RIBBON MICROPHONE.

induction motor, *n.* a type of MOTOR that depends on INDUCTION effects. The FIELD COILS are fed with AC, and induce currents in the ROTOR coils (these may be metal bars). The forces between the two fields cause the rotor to rotate. Many types of induction motors are not self-starting, and have to be spun to operating speed by an auxiliary motor.

inductive load, *n.* a LOAD in which the phase of voltage leads the phase of current.

inductor, *n.* a COIL, loop or wire that is used for its inductance value.

infrared, *n.* the range of radiated waves with WAVELENGTHS of about 700nm to 1mm. These are the wavelengths that are longer than that of the red colour in the visible spectrum, hence the name. The main effect of these waves on any object that they strike is heating, and they are emitted mainly by hot objects.

infrasonic, see SUBSONIC.

inhibit, *vb.* to suppress an OUTPUT, or prevent an INPUT from having any effect.

inhibit pulse, *n.* a PULSE applied to a magnetic CORE to prevent writing. See also COINCIDENT HALF–CURRENT SWITCHING.

injection, *n.* **1.** the applying of a SIGNAL, particularly a test signal, to a CIRCUIT. **2.** the supply of a signal from an OSCILLATOR into a MIXER. **3.** the introduction of CARRIERS into a SEMICONDUCTOR.

in-phase component, *n.* **1.** the portion of a voltage SIGNAL that is in phase with current (formerly called *active current*). **2.** the portion of a current signal that is in phase with voltage (formerly called *active voltage*), i.e., having a PHASE ANGLE of zero between the voltage wave and the current wave. Where a phase difference between voltage and current exists, either voltage or current can be considered to consist of an in-phase component and an out-of-phase component.

input, *n.* **1.** a SIGNAL taken into a component or circuit. Compare OUTPUT **2.** the connections to which the signal is applied.

input impedance, *n.* the complex quantity (see COMPLEX NUMBER, IMPEDANCE) relating signal voltage amplitude and phase to signal current amplitude and phase at an INPUT.

input/output, *n.* the parts of a computer circuit that deal with the INPUT (1)or OUTPUT of signals.

insertion gain, *n.* the GAIN of an amplifier when it is placed between a source of SIGNALS and a LOAD. The figure is usually expressed in decibels.

insertion loss, *n.* the loss of SIGNAL power due to a NETWORK placed between a source of signal and a LOAD. The figure is usually expressed in decibels.

instantaneous current, *n.* the value of CURRENT in an AC circuit at some instant of a signal cycle.

instantaneous frequency, *n.* the FREQUENCY of a SIGNAL at any instant. See FREQUENCY MODULATION.

instantaneous power, *n.* the power transferred or dissipated in a CIRCUIT or a COMPONENT at an instant.

instrumentation, *n.* the equipping of a system with instruments that measure and monitor the state of the system.

instrument rating, *n.* the limit of current or voltage that can be applied to a measuring instrument without causing damage. If no rating is known, a figure of 1.5 times FULL-SCALE DEFLECTION is often assumed.

instrument sensitivity, *n.* the ratio of the number of dial scale divisions to the unit that is being measured. Examples are divisions per volt, per milliamp, per watt, etc.

instrument transformer, *n.* a form of CURRENT TRANSFORMER used for measuring large ALTERNATING CURRENTS.

instrument tube, *n.* a form of CATHODE-RAY TUBE intended as a measuring device rather than for picture display. Instrument tubes need to be operated with beam deflection times that may vary from seconds to fractions of a microsecond. Their size need not be large, but the sensitivity in terms of millimetres of deflection per volt of deflection waveform must be high. Electrostatic deflection is used, and the leads to the deflection plates are often taken through the side of the tube wall to avoid excessive stray capacitance. The deflection usually takes place when the beam is comparatively slow-moving, and the beam is then post-deflection accelerated to its final velocity (see POST-DEFLECTION ACCELERATION). The face of the tube will be flat so that measurements of distance between points on the face can be easily made.

insulate, *vb.* to prevent flow of CURRENT to or from a CONDUCTOR.

insulated gate FET(IGFET), see FIELD-EFFECT TRANSISTOR.

insulated system, *n.* an electrical supply system with no EARTH. The system is used mainly when double insulation is possible, with no metal parts accessible to the user.

insulating resistance, *n.* the value of RESISTANCE between points that are insulated. The value can be used to calculate leakage current value, but it is important to remember that insulating resistance is nonlinear (i.e. can change with applied voltage), and can be greatly affected by the presence of moisture.

insulation, *n.* material with very high RESISTIVITY used for making INSULATORS.

insulator, *n.* any material used to separate CONDUCTORS and prevent CURRENT flow between them. See INSULATION.

integrated circuit (IC), *n.* a CIRCUIT that is constructed entirely on a SILICON CHIP. The silicon is used to form TRANSISTORS (usually FET types), RESISTORS, and, less commonly, CAPACITORS. This is made possible by using doped silicon as a conductor and silicon oxide as an insulator. The main advantages in the use of ICs are reliability and cheapness. A conventional circuit makes use of a number of components that have to be electrically connected. In such conventional circuits, the reliability greatly decreases as the number of components is increased, partly because each component contributes another potential source of failure, and partly because each interconnection is unreliable.

The IC is manufactured as a single COMPONENT, which keeps down the cost, and has the reliability of a single semiconductor component, despite the fact that it may carry out the actions of a circuit with thousands of components and interconnections.

integrated–injection logic or **I²,** *n.* a form of INTEGRATED CIRCUIT construction using BIPOLAR TRANSISTORS.

Fig. 39. **Integrator**. An integrator in symbol form, and the effect of an integrator on various circuit waveforms.

integrator, *n.* a CIRCUIT that smooths out a PULSE into a half-wave of longer duration and lower amplitude. The application of repeated pulses to an integrator will have the effect of creating a steadily increasing voltage level. The term arises from the mathematical operation of integration. The output wave from an integrator is represented by an expression that is the time integral of the expression for the input signal. See Fig. 39.

intelligibility, *n.* a measure of the utility of a communication system derived from the percentage of correctly received meaningless words in a sample transmission.

intensity, *n.* **1.** an alternative term for strength of an electric or magnetic field (see FIELD–STRENGTH METER). **2.** the brightness of the SPOT (1) on a CATHODE–RAY TUBE.

intensity modulation, *n.* the variation of brightness of the light SPOT (1) on the face of a CATHODE–RAY TUBE. Intensity modulation is essential to TV reception, and is an option in most oscilloscopes.

intercarrier sound, *n.* a system of sound IF used in COLOUR TELEVISION receivers. The sound signal is frequency-modulated and transmitted on a frequency that is 6MHz higher than the video signal carrier. The RF and IF stages of a receiver deal with the whole band of frequencies. At the video DEMODULATOR, the nonlinear action of the diode mixes the sound and vision carriers (at their IF frequencies) to produce a 6MHz intercarrier frequency. This signal is still frequency-modulated with the sound signal, and is filtered off to be further amplified and then frequency-demodulated.

interchangeability, *n.* the ability to replace COMPONENTS in a CIRCUIT without detriment to the action of the circuit.

interconnection, *n.* the making of CURRENT paths between circuits or devices, e.g. between different circuit boards in a SYSTEM.

interelectrode capacitance, *n.* the CAPACITANCE between the separate electrodes of a device. Capacitance of this type, such as the capacitance between the BASE and COLLECTOR of a transistor, may adversely affect operation. For example, the capacitance will affect the phase of high-frequency signals, and will also have to be charged and discharged when pulse signals are being used.

interface, *n.* a CIRCUIT that allows SIGNALS to be passed between two otherwise incompatible systems.

interference, *n.* any form of unwanted signal, which may be NOISE, natural or man-made, or a transmitted signal on the same frequency or on an adjacent frequency.

interlace, *n.* the deliberate interweaving of lines on a TV RASTER.

interlock, *n.* a form of safety SWITCH that allows power to be applied only when doors of cabinets are shut, and all live points covered. In ROBOTICS, interlocks are used to ensure that a robot cannot move if a human is in the operating area.

intermediate frequency (IF), *n.* the FREQUENCY used for the main amplifying stages in a SUPERHETERODYNE RECEIVER. The term arose because the frequency is intermediate between audio (or video) frequency and the incoming carrier frequency.

intermodulation, *n.* the unwanted MODULATION of one frequency by another, caused by a NONLINEAR stage.

internal resistance, *n.* the RESISTANCE of the internal circuits of a BATTERY or GENERATOR. Any source of signal (or DC) can be represented as a voltage supply in series with an internal resistance. The size of the internal resistance is found by measuring the change of output voltage per change of supplied current.

interrogating signal, *n.* a PULSE signal that triggers a coded reply from a matching device, the TRANSPONDER. The system is used to identify friendly aircraft, or aircraft that belong to one group. See also IFF, SECONDARY RADAR.

interrupt, *n.* a PULSE signal applied to a microprocessor at an interrupt INPUT. This signal will cause normal processing to be suspended while a special software routine, the interrupt service routine, is run.

interrupter, *n.* a DEVICE that switches a CURRENT on and off at set intervals.

interstage coupling, *n.* a method of passing SIGNAL from one part of a circuit to another, or one stage to another.

intrinsic, *adj.* **1.** of or relating to a specific quality of a material. **2.** (of a SEMICONDUCTOR) consisting of pure undoped material.

intrinsic stand-off ratio, *n.* the ratio of triggering voltage to applied voltage in a UNIJUNCTION.

inverse gain, *n.* the GAIN figure for a TRANSISTOR operated with COLLECTOR and EMITTER (1) reversed.

inversion, *n.* the action of an inverting AMPLIFIER on a SIGNAL. High and low voltages in the parts of the signal are interchanged, producing a WAVEFORM that is the mirror image of the INPUT.

inverter, *n.* **1.** an ANALOGUE or DIGITAL CIRCUIT or device that inverts a signal. The digital inverter is also called *NOT gate*. The digital inverter converts a 0 to a 1, and a 1 to a 0. **2.** a circuit that converts DC into AC (a power oscillator). Also called *power converter*.

inverting amplifier, *n.* an AMPLIFIER whose OUTPUT is inverted (see INVERSION) with respect to the INPUT. Any single-stage transistor amplifier with input to the base and output from the collector load will be inverting.

ion, *n.* the particle with CHARGE that is the result of an electron being added to or taken from a neutral atom. For a few materials, two electrons can sometimes be added or removed. See POSITIVE ION, NEGATIVE ION.

ion burn or **ion spot,** *n.* a form of damage to the PHOSPHOR screen of a CATHODE-RAY TUBE. The damage is caused by NEGATIVE ION bombardment, and results in the phosphor becoming deactivated, so that it no longer emits light when struck by electrons. The negative ions result from remaining gas atoms that have been struck by electrons. See also ION TRAP, SCREEN BURN.

ionic conduction, *n.* a form of CONDUCTION by the movement of positive or negative ions.

ion implantation, *n.* a method of DOPING a semiconductor by bombarding the surface with IONS of the doping material. The technique can be more closely controlled than other doping methods, and is particularly useful for making GALLIUM ARSENIDE FETs.

ionization, *n.* the formation of IONS from neutral atoms. High energy particles or radiation are needed to form ions in a gas at normal temperature. In the absence of such particles or radiation, a gas can be ionized by strong electric fields (particularly when the gas is at low pressure) or by very high temperatures of the order of several thousand kelvin. A completely ionized gas is called a *plasma*.

ionization chamber, *n.* a space in which the production of IONS can be detected. An ionization chamber contains gas, which may be air (a mixture of the gases nitrogen and oxygen), and two ELECTRODES with a POTENTIAL DIFFERENCE between them. If ions are produced in the gas, the movement of the ions between the electrodes produces a brief current that can be detected. This is the basis of most methods of measuring radiation from outer space or from radioactive materials. See also GEIGER–MÜLLER TUBE.

ionization current, *n.* the current that flows in an IONIZATION CHAMBER as the result of ionization of the gas.

ionization gauge, *n.* a method of measuring low gas pressures. A stream of electrons is used to ionize the gas within the gauge, and the IONS that are produced are attracted to a positive electrode. The ion current is related to the pressure over a wide range of low pressures.

ionizing radiation, *n.* the particles or waves that will cause IONIZATION of any gas through which they travel.

ionosphere, *n.* the outer layers of the atmosphere. These consist of air at low pressure that is ionized by the bombardment of particles from the sun. The IONIZATION is most intense when the sun shines directly on the layer, and the lower regions revert to a normal less–ionized state when the sun is shielded from them by the Earth. Several distinct layers have been identified. These shift in size and position according to the time of day, the season, and the state of the sun. The ionosphere layers will reflect radio waves whose wavelength is more than 20m or less than 6mm. The layers were known at one time as the Appleton or Heaviside–Kennelly layers. See also C LAYER, D LAYER, E LAYER, F LAYER.

ionospheric focusing, *n.* the increasing of signal strength at a RECEIVER because of the effect of the curvature of the IONOSPHERE layers. The curved layers act as a concave mirror for radio signals.

ion spot, see ION BURN.

ion trap, *n*. a method of preventing ION BURN in a CATHODE-RAY TUBE. The electron gun of a cathode-ray tube is tilted sideways, so that any particle emerging straight along the axis of the gun will strike the neck of the tube. The ELECTRON BEAM is deflected back onto its correct path by a small magnet, but the heavier ions are not measurably affected and strike the tube neck. Ion traps are used on monochrome TV tubes; neither oscilloscope nor colour TV tubes are affected greatly by ion problems.

I²R loss, see JOULE LOSS.

iron loss, *n*. the loss of energy because of HYSTERESIS in a magnetic core in an inductor. See also EDDY CURRENT, CORE.

irradiation, *n*. the act or process of exposure of a material to IONIZING RADIATION or neutral particles.

ISO, *abbrev. for* International Standards Organization.

isolate, *vb*. to disconnect from a supply, or to make only an indirect connection.

isolating transformer, *n*. a double-wound TRANSFORMER that is used to supply power to a system. Because of the insulation between the windings, there is no direct connection between the system and the mains supply. Isolating transformers are extensively used in servicing workshops to ensure that no equipment can be dangerous because of a direct connection to the mains.

isolating diode, *n*. a DIODE that is used to allow PULSES to pass in one direction only.

isolator, *n*. a MICROWAVE device made from ferrite that allows a wave to travel along the waveguide in one direction, but absorbs any reverse wave.

isotropic, *adj*. (of a material) having measured quantities unaffected by direction. Many quantities, particularly magnetic quantities, are affected by the direction of metal CRYSTALS, and thus are ANISOTROPIC, having different values when measured along different crystal axes.

iterative impedance, *n*. the value of IMPEDANCE measured in a NETWORK, where the impedance can be connected at one end of a network, thus making the network impedance at the other end identical. If a network has the same value of iterative impedance at both ends, then that value is equal to the CHARACTERISTIC IMPEDANCE. See also IMAGE IMPEDANCE.

J

jack plug, *n.* a type of plug originally used for telephone connectors. Jack plugs of several sizes are used in audio circuits, and stereo versions are available.

jamming, *n.* the deliberate interference with TRANSMISSIONS using signals on the same or a very close frequency.

JEDEC, *abbrev. for* Joint Electron Device Engineering Council, the standardizing body in the US that allocates transistor and other active device reference numbers.

JETEC, *abbrev. for* Joint Electron Tube Engineering Council, the standardizing body in the US that controls development of valves and electron-beam devices.

JFET, *abbrev. for* junction FIELD–EFFECT TRANSISTOR.

jitter, *n.* an instability of DC or SIGNAL level resulting in small variations in amplitude or phase, particularly of a PULSE signal. Phase jitter on a pulse appears on an oscilloscope display as an irregular oscillation in the horizontal direction.

J-K flip-flop, *n.* a FLIP-FLOP with two data inputs (labelled J and K). Its operation is summarized in the truth table (state table) shown in Fig. 40b on page 162. If J and K are complements, Q takes the value of J at the next clock edge. If J and K are both low (0) the output does not change. If J and K are both high (1), the output Q will 'toggle' or change state after each clock edge. $\bar{Q}$ (NOT Q) is always the complement of Q.

Johnson noise, see THERMAL NOISE.

Josephson effect, *n.* the current flow in an insulating gap, the *Josephson junction*, between superconductors (see SUPER-CONDUCTIVITY) at very low temperatures.

joule, *n.* unit of energy, equal to the watt–second. The kilowatt-hour unit is equivalent to 3.6 megajoules.

(a)

(b)

Fig. 40. **J-K flip-flop.** (a) The J-K flip-flop symbol. (b) State table. The state table shows the state of the Q output before (Qt) and after (Qt + 1) the clock pulse, and how this change is affected by the J and K values.

joule effect, *n*. the heating effect of a CURRENT through a RESISTOR.

joule loss or **I²R loss,** *n*. the loss of electrical energy as heat when current flows through a resistor or any material with resistance.

jumper, *n*. a connection, often temporary, between two points. A jumper connection is made by wires or plugs, and is not part of a printed circuit.

junction, *n*. **1.** a contact between two materials. **2.** the connection between differently doped pieces of semi-conductor. **3.** the contact between two metals in a thermo-couple. **4.** a point where wires are joined.

junction box, *n.* a box that contains circuit JUNCTIONS.

junction coupling, *n.* a method of tapping a coaxial line into a cavity so as to pick up or inject MICROWAVE signals.

junction potential, *n.* the ELECTRIC POTENTIAL between two materials that are in contact.

junction transistor, *n.* a BIPOLAR TRANSISTOR that makes use of two close-spaced junctions.

K

Karnaugh map, *n.* a tabular method of designing a given logical function, that allows the most simple implementation to be quickly picked out. The implementation of many logic functions using NOT, AND and OR gates is not unique; for example, there are at least two ways to carry out XOR. Unfortunately, Karnaugh mapping cannot be carried out for logical functions requiring more than four inputs except by computer-aided techniques.

K-band, *n.* the MICROWAVE band covering approximately wavelengths of 8 to 27mm.

keep-alive electrode, *n.* a small discharge ELECTRODE in a gas-filled device that keeps enough IONS present to allow the main discharge to start quickly. See also TRANSMIT-RECEIVE SWITCH.

keeper, *n.* a piece of FERROMAGNETIC material placed across the poles of a permanent magnet. The purpose of the keeper is to complete the MAGNETIC CIRCUIT and so avoid the progressive demagnetization which occurs if a magnetic circuit is left open.

kelvin, *n.* the unit of temperature based on the ABSOLUTE SCALE. Symbol: K. The size of the kelvin is identical to the size of the Celsius degree, but the zero of the Kelvin scale is ABSOLUTE ZERO. Named after Lord Kelvin (1824–1907), UK physicist.

Kelvin scale, see ABSOLUTE SCALE.

Kennelly-Heaviside layer, see E LAYER.

Kerr cell, *n.* a method of controlling light by means of ELECTRIC FIELDS. Liquid in a Kerr cell will rotate the plane of polarization in POLARIZED light according to the size of the electric field applied across the liquid.

keystone distortion, *n.* a form of picture-shape DISTORTION. In optical projection, keystone distortion is caused by projecting a picture onto a screen that is not on the same axis. In early TV cameras, the effect was caused by the geometry of early camera tubes that used an off-centre beam. Keystone distortion can also be caused if the amplitude of the HORIZONTAL TIMEBASE is affected by the amplitude of the VERTICAL TIMEBASE. See Fig. 41.

Fig. 41. **Keystone distortion.** (a) A rectangular shape. (b) The effect on (a) of keystone distortion.

kilo-, *prefix.* denoting 10^3 (1,000). Symbol: k.

kilowatt-hour, *n.* an energy unit used for domestic electricity meters and equal to 3.6MJ.

Kirchoff's laws, *n.* the two laws describing the flow of CURRENTS and summation of VOLTAGES in steady state circuits. The first law states that the algebraic sum of currents at a point in a circuit must be zero. This is true only if no changing magnetic fields are present. The second law states that in any closed circuit, the algebraic sum of the ELECTROMOTIVE FORCES and of POTENTIAL DIFFERENCES must also be zero.

See also SUPERPOSITION THEOREM.

klystron, *n.* an ELECTRON-BEAM tube, formerly widely used in MICROWAVE transmitters and receivers. For low-power applications, such as local oscillators in microwave receivers, reflex klystrons have been replaced by GUNN DIODES, but the tubes are still used for higher power applications. The basis of the klystron is an electron beam that passes through a cavity in which the electrons can be affected by resonant microwaves. Following this cavity, the BUNCHER, the electrons move through the DRIFT SPACE, in which no accelerating fields are applied. The movements of the electrons that were started by the fields in the buncher make the electrons gather into groups or bunches as they pass through the drift space. When the bunched electrons pass into another cavity, the catcher, they can give up their energy to the cavity. This energy will be considerably greater than the energy that was used in the buncher.

For very high power gains, klystrons with several cavities can be used, with each cavity bunching the electrons tighter. The tendency for debunching, caused by electrostatic repulsion of electrons, can be counteracted by magnetic focusing. The REFLEX KLYSTRON is an oscillator that operated by reflecting the bunched electrons back to the buncher.

knife switch, *n.* a form of SWITCH used now only for high voltage and high current supplies. The switch contacts are metal blades, that make a wiping contact with springy holders as the switch is closed.

L

labyrinth, *n.* a type of LOUDSPEAKER enclosure. The sound wave from the rear of the loudspeaker cone is dispersed in a long heavily DAMPED path.

ladder, *n.* a network that is made by connecting alternate T-SECTIONS and PI sections of FILTERS.

lag, *n.* **1.** a signal or phase delay. **2.** an image that is transmitted from a CAMERA TUBE for several frames after it has been removed from the face of the tube.

lagging current or **leading voltage,** *n.* a CURRENT that lags in PHASE behind voltage.

lagging load, *n.* a LOAD in which the current PHASE lags behind the voltage phase such as an inductive load. See also LEADING LOAD.

laminated core, *n.* a TRANSFORMER core that is made by clamping together a set of thin metal laminations. The high resistance between laminations inhibits the flow of EDDY CURRENTS.

laser, *n. acronym for* Light Amplification by Stimulated Emission of Radiation, a generator of monochromatic coherent light (see COHERENT OSCILLATOR). Normal sources emit PHOTONS of light in 'pockets' with the PHASE changing in each group. This lack of phase stability is called *noncoherence*. It is impossible, for example, to set up any light interference experiment in which light of one source can interfere with light from a second source. This is because the phases of the waves are continually changing, cancelling out any interference effects.

The laser generates light by allowing one group of waves to stimulate the emission of the next in a form of RESONANT CAVITY. This ensures that every photon in a laser beam is synchronized, and in phase. Laser light is termed *coherent light*. The synchronization can extend over a very large number of groups, so much so that waves that are separated by as much as a metre of space can still be in phase. Gas lasers use gas discharges as the source of light, and diode lasers use the LIGHT-EMITTING DIODE principle. The main applications for lasers in electronics are in optical transmission, using glass fibres. See also MASER.

latch, *n.* the storage action of a FLIP-FLOP circuit. The output of a flip-flop is said to be latched if it remains constant despite any changes in the input.

lattice filter, *n.* a form of FILTER in which the impedances are arranged in a BRIDGE network.

L band, *n.* the MICROWAVE band covering about 19 to 77cm wavelength.

LCD, see LIQUID CRYSTAL DISPLAY.

L-C network, *n.* a RESONANT CIRCUIT that contains capacitance and inductance. The tuned frequency is inversely proportional to the square root of the product of capacitance and inductance values.

lead, *n*. **1.** an electrical wire. **2.** the advance in phase of one wave as compared to another.

lead–acid cell, *n*. a form of secondary rechargeable cell, or ACCUMULATOR (2), that uses lead plates in sulphuric acid. The lead plates are treated so that one acts as a CATHODE (spongy lead) and the other as an ANODE (packed with lead(IV) oxide).

leader, *n*. the first piece of a recording tape that carries no coating. This part is used only for threading and cannot be recorded on.

lead–in, *n*. a connector through which an AERIAL lead enters a building or a receiver.

leading current, *n*. a CURRENT whose PHASE is earlier than the phase of VOLTAGE. The effect is also called *lagging voltage*.

leading edge, *n*. a voltage change that is the start of a PULSE.

leading load, *n*. a LOAD in which the PHASE of CURRENT is earlier than the phase of VOLTAGE, such as a capacitive load. See also LAGGING LOAD.

leakage current, *n*. the unwanted CURRENT caused by BREAK-DOWN of insulation.

leakage flux, *n*. the MAGNETIC FLUX that is generated by the primary winding of a TRANSFORMER, but not coupled to or used by the secondary. Leakage flux is one source of loss in a transformer. See also HYSTERESIS, EDDY CURRENT.

leakage reactance, *n*. the amount of REACTANCE in a TRANSFORMER that would correspond to the quantity of leakage flux.

Lecher line, *n*. a method of measuring WAVELENGTH. A wave is coupled to a pair of parallel lines, and ANTINODES are found by using a small DIPOLE placed across the lines and connected to a lamp or a diode/meter arrangement. The distance between consecutive antinodes is equal to half a wavelength. A form of Lecher line can also be used for matching lines of different IMPEDANCES. See Fig. 42 on page 168.

LED, see LIGHT–EMITTING DIODE.

left–hand rule, see FLEMING'S RULE.

lengthened dipole, *n*. a form of DIPOLE AERIAL in which the

(a)

half-wavelength

(b)

Fig. 42. **Lecher lines**. (a) The two adjacent positions in which the lamp glows at maximum brightness (or the two positions where it is completely extinguished) are half a wavelength apart. (b) The detector is a low-voltage torch-bulb with two wires soldered to it.

rods have been moved apart to make the overall length greater than normal.

Lenz's law, *n*. a law of electromagnetic induction. The induced current is in a direction such that it produces a MAGNETIC FLUX tending to oppose the original change of flux that causes it. For example, if the applied POTENTIAL DIFFERENCE across an inductor is increased, the increase of current through the inductor causes an increase of flux, and the voltage induced by this change of flux will be in a direction opposite to the applied potential difference, so opposing the change. The practical effect is to reduce the rate at which such a change can be made.

LF, see LOW FREQUENCY.

life test, *n*. a timed use of COMPONENTS in a circuit to determine the time before failure. For very reliable components such as semiconductors, an ACCELERATED LIFE TEST may have to be used.

lifetime, *n*. the average time for which a current CARRIER exists in a SEMICONDUCTOR. This is the average time between electron–hole separation and recombination.

light-emitting diode (LED), *n*. a DIODE that emits light while CURRENT passes. The diode materials are compounds such as gallium arsenide or antimony phosphide. The material around the junction must be transparent so that the light can escape. LEDs are used as voltage indicators in electronic equipment. They are also used in ALPHANUMERIC displays for mains-operated equipment. The amount of current that is needed rules out the use of LEDs for most battery-operated applications, though they were at one time used for calculators and watches. For these low-energy applications, LIQUID-CRYSTAL DISPLAYS are now preferred.

light guide, *n*. an application of FIBRE OPTICS in which the glass fibre allows a light at one place to be seen elsewhere. For example, in a meter a fixed light source can be placed at one end of a fibre. The other end of the fibre can then be used to illuminate the scale needle, moving with the needle.

lightning conductor, *n*. a pointed spike facing upwards on the top of a building. Under conditions of high CHARGE, the air around the point ionizes and allows a quiet controlled discharge to take place, averting a lightning strike.

light pen, *n*. a miniature PHOTOCELL mounted at the end of a pen-holder. This is used along with a computer program to 'write' on the computer monitor screen, or select items by holding the pen at the correct place on the screen.

limb, *n*. a part of a transformer core on which a winding is centred.

limiter, *n*. a CIRCUIT that prevents the AMPLITUDE of a signal from exceeding a preset level. See also CLIPPER, CLAMPING DIODE.

line, *n*. **1.** see TRANSMISSION LINE. **2.** a horizontal scan of a TV screen.

linear, *adj*. of, in, along, or relating to a straight line. The term is generally applied to a relationship that produces a straight line on a graph. A linear SYSTEM is one in which the input signal V_{in} is related to the output signal V_{out} by an equation of the form

$$V_{out} = A \times V_{in} + B$$

where A and B are constants. Compare NONLINEAR.

linear amplifier, *n*. an AMPLIFIER with low DISTORTION. The graph of output plotted against input for such an amplifier is mainly a straight line. For the region of the graph that is a straight line, the distortion will be minimal.

linear circuit, *n.* a CIRCUIT for which the output/input graph is a straight line.

linear detector, *n.* a DEMODULATOR for which the demodulated output is linearly proportional to the amount of modulation of the carrier.

linear network, *n.* a NETWORK in which the graph of voltage plotted against current is always a straight line.

linear scan, *n.* a SCAN across the face of a CATHODE-RAY TUBE at a constant speed. This is not necessarily produced by a LINEAR TIMEBASE, because the shape of the tube face and the characteristics of the deflection system can cause nonlinearity.

linear timebase, *n.* a timebase whose waveform is a straight line SAWTOOTH.

line flyback, *n.* the part of a TV line TIMEBASE waveform in which the voltage or current returns to its starting value. See also RASTER.

line communication, *n.* the sending of SIGNALS by wire as distinct from using radiated waves.

line frequency, *n.* the FREQUENCY of line (horizontal) scan in TV. In the US the term is also used to mean the mains supply frequency of 60Hz.

line of flux, *n.* a line in a DIAGRAM that shows the direction of magnetic FLUX DENSITY. See also LINE OF FORCE.

line of force, *n.* a term that is sometimes used to denote ELECTRIC FIELD direction, with LINE OF FLUX used to denote MAGNETIC FIELD direction. The two are more often used interchangeably.

line reflection, *n.* the reflection of a signal from the far end of a TRANSMISSION LINE. This will cause a STANDING-WAVE pattern if a steady signal is being sent continually down the line.

line-sequential television, *n.* an early type of COLOUR TELEVISION SYSTEM in which the colour signals for each line are sent in line sequence. The system is still used for specialized purposes, particularly narrow bandwidth transmissions.

line voltage, *n.* the VOLTAGE between the wires of a TRANSMISSION LINE. In the US, line voltage is the AC supply voltage of 115 volts.

link, *n.* **1.** a system of TRANSMITTERS and RECEIVERS that connects two points by means of radio signals. **2.** a mechanical connection between SWITCHES that results in GANGING the switches. **3.** a wire connection between points on a circuit board.

lin-log response, *n.* a specialized AMPLIFIER circuit characteristic. The circuit gives a linear response for small signals, but logarithmic for larger signals. This enables a very large signal amplitude range to be used without overloading, a feature that is particularly important for radar receivers.

lip microphone, *n.* a form of MICROPHONE case construction for outdoor use, designed to be used very close to the lips, often as part of a headphone/microphone assembly. The advantage is that wind noise and other external noises are greatly reduced because the sensitivity does not need to be high.

lip-sync, *n.* a very close synchronization of sound and picture. This is a problem in film, where the sound is separately recorded, rather than of TV. If true lip-sync is achieved in a film, the lip movement of speakers corresponds with the sounds.

liquid crystal, *n.* a liquid whose (long) molecules can be aligned like the atoms of a CRYSTAL under the influence of an electric field. The alignment of these molecules causes light transmitted to the crystal to be POLARIZED. Many types of liquid-crystal materials are based on cholesterol, a fatty-acid.

liquid-crystal display (LCD), *n.* a form of ALPHANUMERIC display that uses a POLARIZED filter fitted over a liquid crystal CELL or set of cells, and a reflector. With no FIELD applied to any cell, light passes through the filter and is reflected back from the rear of each cell. When an electric field is applied to a cell, the change in polarization of the cell makes it opaque, and with no reflected light the cell looks black from the outside. The cells are usually arranged in the form of a SEVEN-SEGMENT DISPLAY, but can take the form of words, diagrams or any other shape that is required.

Lissajou figure, *n.* a pattern that is traced out by two objects vibrating in directions at right angles to each other. The term is used in electronics to describe a technique that can be used for

171

very precise frequency comparison. One FREQUENCY, a standard, is applied to one pair of deflection plates (or amplifier) of an OSCILLOSCOPE. An unknown frequency is then applied to the other plates. If the signals are identical in amplitude and frequency, the resulting shape will be a straight line (frequencies in phase), a circle (90 degree phase difference), or an ellipse if the phases are of a different value. If the frequencies are not equal, the ellipse will rotate. For frequencies that are harmonically related (twice, three times, etc.), the display shows patterns in which a count of the peaks gives the ratio of frequencies. The slightest change of phase will cause a rotation of the pattern.

live, *adj*. (of an electrical device) at high voltage or with signal present.

load, *n*. a COMPONENT or DEVICE that dissipates power from a CIRCUIT. The output of most electronic circuits is delivered to a load such as a heater, motor, aerial, loudspeaker, etc. All such loads require power to be converted, so the circuits that supply loads need to be capable of delivering the required power.

load impedance, *n*. the IMPEDANCE of a LOAD as it appears to the OUTPUT circuit. Few loads are purely resistive, and many loads have MOTIONAL IMPEDANCE that will cause their apparent impedance value to vary with frequency or with time.

loading coils, *n*. the INDUCTORS that are added to a CIRCUIT. For a TRANSMISSION LINE, loading coils are connected at intervals to correct the value of CHARACTERISTIC IMPEDANCE. For the oscillator of a SUPERHETERODYNE RECEIVER, loading coils are added in order to change the frequency band to a lower band, typically from medium wave to long wave.

load line, *n*. a line drawn on a graph to represent the behaviour of a LOAD. The usual load line is drawn on a graph of output current against output voltage. The line then represents the conductance of the load, and allows the signal output voltage to be read off against signal current values. See Fig. 43.

load matching, *n*. the adjusting of a LOAD impedance to maximize the transfer of power.

lobe, *n*. the elliptical shape that is the contour line of constant field strength from a transmitting AERIAL. The term is also

Fig. 43. **Load line**. A load line drawn on a current-voltage CHARACTERISTIC. The slope of the load line is proportional to the resistance of the load, and points on the load line are the values of collector current and voltage (in this example) that can be obtained with this particular load value.

applied to a receiving aerial to show the contour line of equal values of sensitivity. The radiation pattern of an aerial shows lobes of different field values. See Fig. 44.

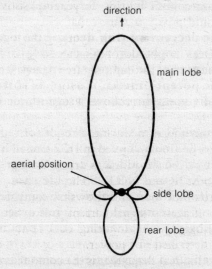

Fig. 44. **Lobe**. See main entry.

lobe switching, *n.* an electronic method of altering the direction of peak sensitivity of an AERIAL by using several driven elements and varying the phase of signals to each.

local oscillator, *n.* the oscillator within a SUPERHETERODYNE RECEIVER. The signal from the local oscillator beats with the incoming signal to form the INTERMEDIATE FREQUENCY.

lock-in, *vb.* to synchronize the FREQUENCY of an OSCILLATOR. One oscillator is said to be locked-in to another if it oscillates with the same frequency and (usually) with the same phase.

locking-on, *n.* **1.** the establishing of automatic control over a varying quantity such as range, direction, frequency, etc. **2.** an AUTOMATIC FREQUENCY CONTROL circuit that will lock-on when the (manual) tuning is almost correct, and will from then on maintain that tuning automatically. **3.** the action of mechanical tracking systems, such as RADAR aerials, that lock onto a target and from then on follow it as long as it is within range.

locking relay, *n.* a RELAY that can be mechanically or electrically locked in one position. The relay may be latched, meaning that the current to the coil can be supplied through relay contacts. Once the relay has been operated by another circuit (using a push button, for example), it will remain energized until power is removed.

logarithmic decrement (log.dec.), *n.* the logarithm of the ratio of the peak amplitudes of two successive OSCILLATIONS of a system, a measure of the damping (see DAMPED) of oscillation.

logarithmic potentiometer, *n.* a form of POTENTIOMETER in which the division ratio follows a logarithmic rather than a linear law.

logic, *n.* a method of deducing a result (OUTPUT) from data (INPUT). George Boole showed in 1832 that all human logical processes could be described in terms of four simple steps, AND, OR, XOR and NOT. See LOGIC GATE.

logic circuit, *n.* a DIGITAL circuit that compares INPUTS and gives an OUTPUT according to a logic rule or set of rules. The elementary logic actions are carried out by LOGIC GATES, whose actions are described in TRUTH TABLES or STATE tables.

logic diagram, *n.* a DIAGRAM for a LOGIC CIRCUIT that shows LOGIC GATES, in symbol form. This is not the same as an electronics circuit diagram, because it ignores power supplies, the internal circuitry of gates, and any connections that are not logic signal connections. The positions of gates in the diagram may not correspond to their physical position on a circuit diagram.

logic element, *n*. a single LOGIC GATE or FLIP–FLOP.

logic gate, *n*. a CIRCUIT that carries out a single LOGIC action. The OUTPUT of a logic gate is determined completely by the combination of INPUTS to that gate at that instant. The fundamental actions are AND, OR, XOR and NOT, but the main logic gates that are manufactured in integrated circuit form are NAND GATE and NOR GATE. This is because any other gate action can be obtained by appropriate connections of NAND gates, or by (different) connections of NOR gates. Fig. 45 on page 176 shows the truth tables for the NAND and NOR gates, and illustrates how some other gate actions can be obtained by the use of NAND gates.

logic level, *n*. the VOLTAGE range that is represented by a BINARY NUMBER, 0 or 1.

logic one, *n*. the VOLTAGE that corresponds to the BINARY NUMBER 1. For TTL logic circuits, this can be any voltage between 3.5V and 5.0V.

logic probe, *n*. an instrument for reading LOGIC LEVELS. A flying lead is earthed, and the probe tip is placed on some connection in the logic circuit. The probe will then indicate whether the logic voltage is 0, 1, or an oscillating voltage.

logic symbol, *n*. a shape on a DIAGRAM that represents a fundamental LOGIC action. The shapes that originated in the US have been used by manufacturers of ICs and most users for a considerable time. See Fig. 46 on page 177. Several attempts have been made to establish different shapes as a British Standard, and these shapes are used for teaching and in public examinations, but are seldom encountered elsewhere.

logic zero, *n*. the binary 0 level of voltage. This is usually any voltage in the range 0 to +0.8V. See LOGIC LEVEL.

long-line pull, *n*. a change of oscillator FREQUENCY when its output is fed to a long TRANSMISSION LINE.

long-persistence screen, *n*. a form of PHOSPHOR screen once

(a)

AND gate constructed
from NAND gates

OR gate constructed
from NAND gates

(b)

Fig. 45. **Logic gate**. The Fig. shows the symbols and truth tables (a) and how the action of other gates (b) can be obtained by using just one gate type, in this case the NAND gate.

Fig. 46. **Logic symbol**. The symbols for gate actions. Two sets of symbols are shown, the usual international symbol on the left hand side of each pair, and the BS symbol (used in some examinations in the UK) on the right.

used for RADAR displays. A long-persistence screen gives a bright glow when the ELECTRON BEAM strikes a SPOT, and the glow continues at lower brightness, often in another colour, for a considerable time afterwards. This allows changes in the position of a radar target to be seen as a trail, gradually fading at the end. The tube must be viewed in darkness, and the operator has no control over persistence, so that the tube cannot easily be 'erased'.

At one time, the direct-view STORAGE TUBE was seen as a replacement for the long-persistence tube, but these were replaced in turn by computer-operated systems in which the retention of information is in a computer memory, and the displays are TV type displays. This allows the displays to be viewed in more normal illumination, the persistence time to be controlled, and the screen cleared if the trails become confusing.

long-tailed pair, see DIFFERENTIAL AMPLIFIER.

long wave, *n*. the range of WAVELENGTHS that is measured in kilometres rather than in metres.

loop, *n*. a connection of the output of a circuit or SYSTEM to its input, so causing FEEDBACK.

loop aerial, *n*. an AERIAL in the form of a flat COIL. See also FRAME AERIAL.

loop direction-finding, see DIRECTION-FINDING.

loose coupling or **undercoupling,** *n*. a form of tuned COUPLING in which the COUPLING COEFFICIENT has a low value, so that only a small fraction of the signal in one circuit is transferred to the other. A loose coupling has the advantages that the BANDWIDTH can be small and that the connection of a load to the output does not greatly affect either the tuning or the amount of signal transferred. Compare TIGHT COUPLING. See also OVERCOUPLING, CRITICAL COUPLING.

Lorentz force, *n*. the force on an ELECTRON or ION that is moving in a MAGNETIC FIELD.

loss, *n*. a dissipation of power.

loss angle, *n*. a measurement of LOSS from a CAPACITOR. A perfect capacitor would have a phase angle of 90 degrees, current leading voltage. In practice, the angle is very slightly less (as little as a thousandth of a degree) because of the loss of energy caused by slight electric HYSTERESIS. The difference is the 'loss angle'.

lossless line, *n*. an imaginary TRANSMISSION LINE with no loss. A real line can be imagined as a length of theoretically perfect lossless line with a series resistor in which all of the loss of signal takes place.

lossy, *adj*. (of a material) dissipating energy, a term applied to, for example, an insulator that has current leakage.

lossy line, *n*. a TRANSMISSION LINE that dissipates signal.

loudspeaker, *n*. a TRANSDUCER that converts electrical signal energy into sound (acoustic) energy. Sometimes shortened to *speaker*. See also DRIVER, VOICE COIL, SPIDER, ELECTROSTATIC LOUDSPEAKER.

lower sideband, *n*. the FREQUENCY RANGE that is obtained by subtracting each modulating frequency from the CARRIER FREQUENCY.

low frequency (LF) or **long-wave band,** *n*. the band that covers the frequencies 30kHz to 300kHz.

low-frequency compensation, *n*. the AMPLITUDE and phase correction of a low-frequency signal (see PHASE-CORRECTION CIRCUIT). A signal containing low frequencies will have these frequencies attenuated and phase shifted by the coupling time constants of an amplifier. The low-frequency compensating circuits are designed to restore normal amplitude and phase.

low-level modulation, *n*. the MODULATION of a CARRIER while it is at a low AMPLITUDE. The modulated carrier is then amplified. Amplitude modulation is usually carried out at high level and frequency modulation at low level (on the oscillator). The use of low-level modulation means that subsequent radio frequency amplification must use fairly LINEAR stages.

low logic level, *n*. the level 0 voltage, usually in the range of 0 to 0.8V.

low-pass filter, *n*. a FILTER whose PASS BAND extends from DC up to the cutoff frequency of the filter.

LSI, *abbrev. for* large scale integration, of the order of ten thousand active DEVICES per CHIP. See also MSI, VLSI.

luminance, *n*. the part of a VIDEO signal that carries light/shade information, the monochrome signal. See also COLOUR TELEVISION.

luminance amplifier, *n*. the AMPLIFIER in a COLOUR RECEIVER receiver that deals with the LUMINANCE signal.

luminescence, *n*. the illumination of a material because of bombardment with electrons or other radiation.

lumped parameter, *n*. a 'spread-out' value that is treated as a single COMPONENT. A TRANSMISSION LINE, for example, will have a value of inductance per metre and capacitance per metre. A length of line can therefore be simulated by using inductors and capacitors of the appropriate values, which are the lumped parameters.

M

machine code, *n*. a PROGRAM in BINARY CODE for a MICROPROCESSOR.

magamp, see MAGNETIC AMPLIFIER.

magic-T, see HYBRID JUNCTION.

magnet, see PERMANENT MAGNET, ELECTROMAGNET.

magnetic amplifier (magamp), *n*. a form of AC power AMPLIFIER with very high power GAIN. A control winding on a MAGNETIC CORE (1) is used to control the magnetic characteristics of the core, and so vary the REACTANCE of another winding. The power supply to the magnetic amplifier is AC, and the signals are DC or slowly changing signals.

magnetic circuit, *n*. a closed path in a magnetic material. The magnetic circuit 'conducts' MAGNETIC FLUX in the same way that a metal circuit conducts current.

magnetic core, *n*. **1.** a piece of magnetic material on which an inductor can be wound. **2.** in computing, the miniature magnetic rings that were formerly used for constructing core-store memory in large computers. The principle is that a binary 1 is stored in the form of one direction of magnetic flux, and a binary 0 as the opposite direction. The cores are read and written by passing current through wires that thread through each core. Modern computers, however, almost always use SEMICONDUCTOR memory.

See also COINCIDENT HALF–CURRENT SWITCHING.

magnetic damping, *n*. a method of damping (see DAMPED) mechanical OSCILLATIONS by using induced currents. The oscillating object is attached to a piece of metal that moves between the poles of a magnet. The EDDY CURRENTS induced in the metal set up forces that oppose the motion (LENZ'S LAW), thus damping the motion. The advantage of magnetic damping is that the damping force is proportional to speed. This means that the maximum damping is achieved when the movement is a maximum, and there is practically no damping when the object is almost at rest.

magnetic deflection, *n.* the DEFLECTION of an ELECTRON BEAM by a MAGNETIC FIELD.

magnetic dependent resistor, *n.* any resistive material (mainly SEMICONDUCTORS) whose RESISTANCE value is altered by the presence of a MAGNETIC FIELD. See MAGNETORESISTANCE.

magnetic disk, *n.* a plastic DISK coated with magnetic powder that is used as an external storage medium for computers. The storage method is based on direction of magnetism (see MAGNETIC CORES) and the disk is spun while a READ/WRITE HEAD is put into contact or near-contact with its surface. This allows access to any part of the disk in a short time.

magnetic field, *n.* the space around any form of magnet in which force effects on FERROMAGNETIC materials can be detected.

magnetic flux, *n.* a 'flow' or FLUX (1) of magnetism. This is most easily measured in terms of the ELECTROMOTIVE FORCE that is generated when a circuit surrounding the flux is removed from the flux.

magnetic flux density, *n.* a measure of the strength of MAGNETIC FIELD in a material. Symbol: **B**; unit: weber/sq. metre. See also FLUX DENSITY.

magnetic focusing, *n.* a method of focusing an ELECTRON BEAM by using MAGNETIC FIELDS.

magnetic hysteresis, *n.* the NONLINEAR relationship between FLUX DENSITY in a material and the MAGNETIC FIELD that produces it.

In Fig. 47 on page 182, the initial part of the graph that starts at the origin is traced out when a magnetic field is applied to a material that is not initially magnetized. Increasing field strength leads to the condition of SATURATION, at which increases of field strength cause only comparatively small changes in flux density.

If the field is then reduced, the shape of the graph from the saturation point downwards is not the same as the shape when

Fig. 47. **Magnetic hysteresis**. The curve shows the once-only part of the trace for an unmagnetized material, and the saturation, remanance and coercive force points on the graph. The graph is normally plotted with units for **B** that are very much larger than the units for **H** in order to make the graph of reasonable size.

the field was being increased. There will be a flux density remaining in the material even when the external field is zero. This value of flux density is called the REMANENCE.

If the field is now reversed, and its strength increased, it now opposes the flux density direction, and the flux density decreases. The field value that is needed to reduce the flux density to zero is called the COERCIVITY, and is a measure of the permanence of the magnetism.

Increasing the field now reverses the direction of the flux density until saturation is reached in the opposite direction. Reduction of field strength from this point now causes another path to be traced, making the trace symmetrical. The area that is enclosed by the path of this HYSTERESIS LOOP represents the amount of energy lost in the whole cycle. Note that in hysteresis diagrams, the units are always chosen so as to produce diagrams of reasonable scale.

magnetic leakage, *n.* a loss of FLUX (1) from a MAGNETIC

CIRCUIT. Unlike current in a metallic circuit, flux is not totally confined to magnetic material, and the amount of flux that strays from the intended path is the LEAKAGE FLUX.

magnetic lens, *n.* a lens, for focusing an electron beam, produced by using magnets to form a magnetic field that will focus the beam. The magnetic lens may utilize permanent magnets, but it is more common to use electromagnets to form an ELECTROMAGNETIC LENS whose focus can be easily adjusted by varying the current in the electromagnet(s).

magnetic memory, *n.* a MEMORY system in which data is represented as direction or intensity of magnetization of a material. The advantage of any such system is that it is NONVOLATILE, i.e. the data is not erased when power is removed from the system.

magnetic moment, *n.* a quantity that is sometimes used to measure the strength of a magnet. The torque acting on a bar magnet in a field is the vector (cross) product of magnetic moment and the FLUX DENSITY of the surrounding field.

magnetic pick-up, *n.* a type of gramophone PICK-UP that makes use of electromagnetic induction. See MOVING-IRON PICK-UP, MOVING-COIL PICK-UP.

magnetic pole, *n.* a point around which magnetism is concentrated. Any magnet that has an air gap will have a pole on each side of the air gap.

magnetic recording, *n.* a method of recording electrical signals as variations of the MAGNETISM of a material. For audio recording, the material is a finely powdered metal oxide (iron oxide, chromium oxide) or metal (usually iron) coated on plastic tape. The tape is fed past a recording head at a steady speed. The head consists of a FLUX (1) path that is almost totally closed, but with a tiny gap that touches the tape. This causes an intense FIELD to cross the tape and so magnetize the particles on the tape. The signal to the tape head takes the form of audio current signals on a winding around the magnetic material. On playback, the tape is again drawn at the same constant speed past a similar head, often the same head. This time, the variations in magnetization of the tape cause a varying flux in the magnetic circuit of the head, and so induce varying voltages in the winding. See also MAGNETIC TAPE, PAPER TAPE.

Because the graph of tape magnetism plotted against head coil current is a nonlinear (HYSTERESIS) shape, some form of BIAS is needed to achieve acceptable results. This is achieved by using high-frequency signals. See also AZIMUTH ANGLE.

magnetic saturation, *n.* the point at which the magnetic FLUX DENSITY of a material ceases to increase perceptibly when the magnetizing force is increased. At this point, the PERMEABILITY of the material is virtually the same as the permeability of the air around it.

magnetic screening, *n.* the protecting of COMPONENTS against the effect of MAGNETIC FIELDS. This is necessary if unwanted magnetic fields are present near CATHODE-RAY TUBES, TRANSISTORS, INTEGRATED CIRCUITS, or INDUCTORS. The 'magnetic screening' is a closed box that is made from material of very high PERMEABILITY so that flux passes through the screening material in preference to any other path.

magnetic shunt, *n.* an alternative path for MAGNETIC FLUX consisting of a piece of high-permeability material whose position on a magnetic path can be varied so as to control the amount of flux in another path. This is the principle of the permanent magnet whose magnetization can be switched on and off.

magnetic tape, *n.* a plastic tape coated with magnetic material for the purpose of recording. Iron oxide is the most usual coating, but chromium (IV) oxide and metallic iron have also been used for high-quality recording. See MAGNETIC RECORDING, PAPER TAPE.

magnetic tuning, *n.* a tuning method for MICROWAVE cavities. Part of the RESONANT CAVITY is made of FERRITE, whose PERMEABILITY can be altered by the steady field from an electromagnet.

magnetism, *n.* a field effect that produces strong forces on ferromagnetic and paramagnetic materials. MAGNETIC FIELDS are produced by circulating currents. These can be currents in wire conductors, or the atomic-scale circulation of electrons.

A number of materials are affected to some extent by

magnetism. *Paramagnetic* materials will attempt to align their magnetic axes with the field, *diamagnetic* materials will attempt to place their magnetic axes at right angles to the field. FERROMAGNETIC materials are a form of paramagnetic materials, like iron, on which very strong forces act. Many ferromagnetic materials can be permanently magnetized.

magnetization, *n.* the effect of creating a magnetic FLUX DENSITY in the space around a material. Magnetization may be due to the presence of a PERMANENT MAGNET, or to the MAGNETOMOTIVE FORCE caused by electric current.

magnetize, *vb.* to make a material permanently or temporarily magnetic.

magnetomotive force, *n.* a cause of MAGNETIZATION. Symbol: *Fm*; unit: AMPERE-TURN. The magnetomotive force of a coil causes MAGNETIC FLUX in a MAGNETIC CIRCUIT.

magnetoresistance, *n.* a change of resistance caused by magnetism. See MAGNETIC DEPENDENT RESISTOR.

magnetostriction, *n.* a stress caused in a material by MAGNETIZATION. The forces between atoms in a magnetized material cause stresses that can affect the dimensions of the material. *Positive magnetostriction* causes an increase in length of a material when it is magnetized. *Negative magnetostriction* means that the length of a sample will decrease when it is magnetized. Alternating magnetic fields applied to either type of material will cause mechanical vibrations that are commercially used in ULTRASONIC generators. The familiar whistling sound from a TV receiver is caused by magnetostrictive vibrations of the core of the line-output transformer.

magnetron, *n.* the earliest type of high-power MICROWAVE oscillator. The principle is based on the creation of pulsed beams of electrons that travel in circular paths in a vacuum. By making the ELECTRON BEAM of each electron travel across the mouth of one of several identical tuned cavities, the cavities are set into RESONANCE at a microwave frequency. The oscillation reaches a peak when the speed of circulation of the electrons is such that one cycle of the electrons round the beam path takes the same time as one cycle of the microwave frequency. Stability of frequency is achieved by making connections (see

cavity

cathode

anode

flange — internal window

flange

waveguide

Fig. 48. **Magnetron**. A simplified cross-section through a magnetron. The strapping between alternate cavities is not illustrated.

STRAPPING) between alternate cavities. The microwave signal energy is tapped by a loop in one cavity that is coupled to an external WAVEGUIDE. See Fig. 48.

magnitude, *n*. the ABSOLUTE VALUE or amplitude of a signal expressed as a positive value.

mainframe, *n*. the largest type of computer.

mains power supply, *n*. see ALTERNATING CURRENT.

mains hum, see HUM.

mains monitor, *n*. a metering device that senses changes in the mains supply (see ALTERNATING CURRENT). This can, for example, be used to cause a computer to record important data onto MAGNETIC DISKS in the event of any sign of a supply interruption.

majority carrier, *n*. the charged CARRIER (2) (electron or hole) that is responsible for more than 50% of the current flow in a SEMICONDUCTOR. Compare MINORITY CARRIER.

major lobe, *n*. the longest LOBE in an aerial radiation pattern. This corresponds to the direction of transmission or reception for a DIRECTIONAL AERIAL.

make, *vb*. to close a CIRCUIT.

make-and-break circuit, *n*. a form of mechanical circuit

INTERRUPTER that converts steady current into pulses. See also CHOPPER.

manganin, *n*. a copper-manganese alloy that is used for constructing WIRE-WOUND RESISTORS. It is particularly suitable because of comparatively large RESISTIVITY, low TEMPERATURE COEFFICIENT of resistivity and small CONTACT potential with copper.

man-made noise, *n*. the NOISE that is caused by man-made DEVICES such as car ignition systems, thermostats, light switches, fluorescent lights, etc.

Marconi aerial, *n*. a simple vertical wire AERIAL.

mark, *n*. the part of an on/off cycle of voltage that is the on-time. If a voltage is switched on for 2ms and is off for 3ms, then the mark is the 2ms time for which the voltage is on. The off-time is called the *space*. The mark-space ratio in this case would be 2/3.

marker pulse, *n*. a PULSE that is used as a time reference in PULSE-TIME MODULATION and MULTIPLEXER systems.

mark-space ratio, *n*. the ratio of on-time (time for which voltage is supplied) to off-time for a rectangular pulse. The mark-space ratio for a perfectly square pulse is 1:1. See Fig. 49 on page 188. See also MARK, DUTY CYCLE.

maser, *n*. *acronym for* Microwave Amplification by Stimulated Emission of Radiation, a form of MICROWAVE amplifier that uses the electron energies in a gas or in a solid crystal. The electrons in the material are excited to a high energy level and the incoming signal is used to trigger the return to normal level, releasing energy. Solid crystal masers run at very low temperatures (liquid helium temperatures of around 4K) and offer very high power gain with very low noise. Gas masers are used as very precise microwave oscillators. Similar principles are used for LASERS.

mask, *vb*. to shield areas of a CHIP in order to make a process such as ETCHING or DIFFUSION follow a shape pattern.

masked ROM, *n*. a form of permanent ROM memory that consists of electrical connections. Each unit of the memory consists of a permanent connection to earth (logic 0) or to the positive supply terminal (logic 1), so that the data is fixed when

mark/space ratio $= \frac{1}{2}$

duty cycle $= \frac{1}{3}$

If mark/space ratio $= \frac{x}{y}$ then duty cycle $= \frac{x}{x+y}$

$$D = \frac{M}{M+1}$$

$$M = \frac{D}{1-D}$$

where M = mark/space ratio and D = duty cycle

Fig. 49. **Mark-space ratio.** The mark-space ratio for a pulse waveform, and how it is related to the duty cycle.

the memory IC chip is manufactured by a process called *masking*. This type of memory is NON-VOLATILE, because the retention of data does not depend on the power supply being maintained.

master oscillator, *n*. a high-stability OSCILLATOR that is used as the source of a CARRIER signal. The master oscillator output is to a BUFFER stage (or stages), to ensure that the effect of connecting a LOAD to the master oscillator is negligible.

master-slave flip-flop, *n*. a form of double FLIP-FLOP in which the first unit, the master, drives the second (slave). See J-K FLIP-FLOP.

matched termination, *n*. a cable TERMINATION at which no signal REFLECTION occurs. The termination is the load at the end of a TRANSMISSION LINE or WAVEGUIDE, and if correctly matched produces no STANDING WAVES in the line.

matching, *n*. obtaining equality of the magnitude of LOAD and OUTPUT impedance. This ensures maximum power transfer in the case of a fixed output resistance (see MAXIMUM POWER THEOREM).

maximum power theorem, *n*. a theorem for finding matching load value. For a given output impedance, the maximum power theorem shows that the maximum power is developed in a load whose resistance is exactly equal to the output resistance, and whose reactance is exactly equal and opposite to the reactance of the output. The converse is not true – if the load is fixed, then the maximum power in the load is achieved when the output resistance of the driving stage is as low as possible.

Maxwell's equations, *n*. the equations of electromagnetic waves that link magnetic field strength (**H**), the electric displacement (**D**), the magnetic flux density (**B**) and the electric field strength (**E**). The solution of the equations takes the form of a wave whose velocity is dependent on the PERMEABILITY and PERMITTIVITY of the medium in which the wave travels.

M-derived filter, *n*. a FILTER that has a reactive component in one arm and a RESONANT CIRCUIT in the other. See Fig. 50 on page 190.

mean life or **mean time before failure (MTBF),** *n*. the average working life of a COMPONENT. This may be measured under working conditions, or calculated from ACCELERATED LIFE TESTS taken under abnormal conditions. See also FAILURE RATE, RELIABILITY.

mean time before failure (MTBF), see MEAN LIFE.

mechanical resonance, *n*. a forced mechanical OSCILLATION at RESONANT FREQUENCY. Mechanical resonance can be a cause of failure of mechanical parts, but can often be useful, for example, in any device using a pendulum. It is also responsible for resonant peaks in MOTIONAL IMPEDANCE, but this can be turned to advantage if a large amount of power needs to be converted to mechanical form at one particular frequency.

medium frequency (MF), *n*. the RF band that covers the range of 300kHz to 3MHz approximately.

medium wave (MW), *n*. the (approximate) WAVELENGTH range of 100m to 1km.

mega-, *prefix*. denoting one million, 10^6. Symbol: M.

Fig. 50. **M-derived filter**. The series and shunt types of M-derived filter circuit.

Megger, *n*. *Trademark.* an instrument for measuring INSU-LATING RESISTANCE. The original trade name denoted an instrument that combined a handwound high-voltage gener-ator with a sensitive current meter. Modern versions use DC inverters and electrometers.

memory, *n*. a circuit for storing data in BINARY CODE, particularly for a computer. This applies to storage as current in one of a pair of transistors (STATIC RAM), charge in a capacitor (DYNAMIC RAM) or connections in an integrated circuit (MASKED ROM). Memory systems can also be constructed using magnetic effects, such as MAGNETIC CORE stores, BUBBLE MEMORY, MAGNETIC TAPE and MAGNETIC DISK.

The types of memory that depend on current or charge are generally volatile, because the data is lost when power is switched off. Magnetic and masked ROM memories are nonvolatile, because the stored data remains in store until replaced by other data.

See also ROM, PROM.

memory location, *n*. the binary or hexadecimal number ADDRESS that is required to gain access to a specific memory location.

mesa transistor, *n*. a form of silicon junction transistor construction. The BASE of the transistor is formed on a portion that is raised above the level of the COLLECTOR and EMITTER, like the small flat-topped hill called a 'mesa' (Spanish: table).

mesh, *n.* a NETWORK of CURRENT paths.

mesh current, *n.* the CURRENT in a network MESH. This can be used to form equations of network action, using KIRCHOFF'S LAWS or NORTON'S THEOREM.

mesh–PDA tube, *n.* a specialized form of POST–DEFLECTION ACCELERATION for INSTRUMENT TUBES. The DEFLECTION SENSITIVITY of an electrostatically deflected cathode-ray tube is very low if the accelerating voltage is high, of the order of 10kV. Modern oscilloscopes demand tubes that have very high deflection sensitivity, so that transistor deflection amplifiers can be used. At the same time the trace must be bright so that high-speed traces are visible, and this demands large accelerating potentials. The mesh-PDA tube solves the dilemma by placing a wire mesh of high transparency between the end of the DEFLECTION PLATES and the FINAL ANODE. The mesh serves to separate the fields, so that the region of the deflection plates can use low velocity electrons, that are then accelerated after passing through the mesh.

metal film resistor, *n.* a form of FILM RESISTOR that makes use of a thin metal film as its conductor.

metallized paper capacitor, *n.* a form of PAPER CAPACITOR that makes use of a metallizing coating on the paper, rather than on the use of metal strips.

metallizing, *n.* the process of coating a material with metal. This can be done chemically, by ELECTROPLATING (on metals), or by chemical reduction (on other surfaces). Another method is to evaporate the metal in a vacuum, as used for depositing thin films of aluminium. SPUTTERING is a third method in which the material to be coated is placed in a low-pressure gas in which a GAS DISCHARGE is operating with the metal that forms the coating material being used as one electrode. Sputtering is more suitable for depositing powdery films of metals. Combinations of methods can be used, so that it is fairly common to find an insulating material coated with a thin conducting film by sputtering, and then electroplated.

metal rectifier, *n.* a RECTIFIER that makes use of a metal-

semiconductor CONTACT. Copper-oxide and selenium rectifiers were used to a considerable extent at one time.

meter, *n.* a measuring instrument whose reading is usually in
the form of a needle positioned against a scale.

meter-protection diode, *n.* a DIODE used in pairs wired across
a meter movement. The principle is that the diodes form a
high-resistance path for voltages up to and exceeding the
normal voltage across the meter terminals. For a large overload
voltage, however, one or both diodes will conduct, thus
preventing damage to the meter. The protection diodes are
particularly effective in preventing damage from transient
pulses.

meter resistance, *n.* the INTERNAL RESISTANCE of a METER
movement, including any internal shunts.

metre, *n.* the basic SI unit of length. Symbol: m. The length of
the metre is specified in terms of the number of wavelengths of
light from a specified source.

Metrosil, *n. Trademark.* a type of nonlinear RESISTOR, seldom
used nowadays. The Metrosil has a very NONLINEAR current-
voltage characteristic, with current proportional to about the
fourth power of voltage. This made the device very useful as a
protection against voltage surges, and it was also used as a crude
form of high-voltage stabilizer. See also VARISTOR.

MF, see MEDIUM FREQUENCY.

mica, *n.* a natural INSULATOR, related to asbestos, that can be split
into very thin sheets. The silver form is preferable to the ruby
form for electronics use.

mica capacitor, *n.* a CAPACITOR made by metallizing mica
plates. Mica capacitors have low losses, low TEMPERATURE
COEFFICIENTS and good stability of characteristics.

micro-, *prefix.* denoting one millionth. Symbol: μ.

microelectronics, *n.* the design and construction of electronic
devices using INTEGRATED CIRCUITS.

micron, *n.* one-millionth of a metre, i.e. a micrometre.

microphone, *n.* a sound to electrical wave TRANSDUCER.
Sometimes shortened to *mike.* Many types of microphone have
been devised, starting with the carbon-granule type that was
used in early telephones. Most modern types are ELECTRO-

DYNAMIC RIBBON MICROPHONES, MOVING–COIL MICROPHONES, MOVING–IRON MICROPHONES. CAPACITOR MICROPHONES, which once seemed to be obsolescent, were revived when ELECTRETS became available commercially.

The main features of a microphone that might affect choice are sensitivity, directionality, size, quality and price. The sensitivity is measured in terms of peak-to-peak output for a given sound pressure wave, and is usually very low, particularly when compared to the human ear. Many microphone types are directional, and the way in which a microphone is housed can enhance the main lobe of sensitivity. Size varies considerably, but ribbon microphones tend to be larger than the other types.

The highest quality is obtained from ribbon microphones, mainly because the MECHANICAL RESONANCES can be at frequencies well above the audio range. As often happens, ribbon microphones are generally the most expensive, and capacitor microphones the cheapest. The enclosure in which the microphone is housed is at least as significant acoustically as the construction of the microphone itself.

microphony, *n.* an unwanted electrical signal generated in response to sound waves. Some electronic components, particularly plates of air-spaced variable capacitors, can vibrate when struck by sound waves, and cause MODULATION of electrical signals. Radio valves were particularly prone to this problem, which is seldom met with in receivers nowadays.

microprocessor, *n.* a VLSI integrated circuit that carries out computing actions. The microprocessor is an assembly of interconnected REGISTERS and GATES which is PROGRAMMABLE. A master CLOCK determines the speed at which instructions are executed, and the program is in the form of number codes stored in consecutive locations in memory. The microprocessor can then, given the correct starting location in memory, load in the instruction codes one by one and execute them. The processes that can be carried out include simple arithmetic (addition and subtraction of small numbers), LOGIC actions such as AND GATE, OR GATE, XOR GATE and INVERTER (1), and SHIFTING and ROTATION. All the operations of a computer are obtained from these few logic actions by suitable programming.

microprogram, *n.* the instructions that are built into a MICROPROCESSOR by the manufacturer. These instructions allow the microprocessor to carry out only the fixed set of actions under external program instruction that are described in the manufacturer's specification.

microstrip, *n.* a form of TRANSMISSION LINE, consisting of a metal ribbon that acts as a ground plane, separated by a ribbon of insulator from a narrower ribbon of conductor, the signal conductor. The CHARACTERISTIC IMPEDANCE depends on the width, and is typically between 10 and 50ohms.

microwave, *n.* the range of radio WAVELENGTHS from approximately 135cm down to fractions of a millimetre. These cannot easily be generated or amplified by the conventional electronic devices used for lower radio frequencies, and are transmitted more readily through WAVEGUIDES than along conventional copper conductors.

microwave cooker, *n.* a cooker in which food is the target of a microwave beam from a MAGNETRON. The frequency is 2.45GHz, because this corresponds to a resonance of the hydrogen atoms in water. Any water present in food will therefore be rapidly heated internally. Objects with a very low water content are not heated. Metal objects must not be present because they can damage the magnetron by reflecting power back into the system.

microwave generator, *n.* a DEVICE, vacuum or semiconductor, that is used as an OSCILLATOR at MICROWAVE frequencies. This includes KLYSTRONS, CARCINOTRONS, MAGNETRONS, GUNN DIODES, and Josephson junctions (see JOSEPHSON EFFECT).

microwave tube, *n.* any vacuum MICROWAVE device, including the KLYSTRON, TRAVELLING–WAVE TUBE, MAGNETRON.

mike, see MICROPHONE.

mil, *n.* a unit of length equal to one thousandth of an inch, equal to 0.0254mm.

Miller effect, *n.* the effect of NEGATIVE FEEDBACK from output to input of an amplifying device through stray or internal

CAPACITANCE. The capacitance is the total of inter–electrode capacitance and stray capacitance. For inverting amplifiers, the Miller effect makes this capacitance appear to be multiplied by the voltage gain.

Miller integrator, *n.* a wide–range INTEGRATOR circuit that depends for its action on a CAPACITANCE connected between the input and the output of an INVERTING AMPLIFIER. See Fig. 51.

Miller timebase, *n.* a TIMEBASE circuit that consists of a square–wave generator combined with a MILLER INTEGRATOR.

milli-, *prefix.* denoting one thousandth, 10^3. Symbol: m.

millimetric waves, *n.* the WAVELENGTHS in the range 1mm to 9mm.

MIL specification, *n.* a specification drawn up for equipment that is to be used by the US armed forces, either as original equipment or as spares.

minimization, *n.* the application of LOGIC theory to a LOGIC GATE circuit. Minimization applies logic theory to find redundant gates, and often allows a logic action to be carried out in a much simpler form. See KARNAUGH MAP.

minority carrier, *n.* the CARRIER (2), electron or hole, in a semiconductor that carries less than 50% of the current. Compare MAJORITY CARRIER.

mismatch, *n.* the inequality of OUTPUT IMPEDANCE and LOAD IMPEDANCE. Mismatch can cause loss of power, and REFLECTIONS along a line.

mixer, *n.* the frequency changer stage of a SUPERHETERODYNE RECEIVER. The mixer has two inputs, one at received signal frequency, which is modulated, and one from the local oscillator. The result of mixing is a signal at INTERMEDIATE FREQUENCY that carries the original modulation.

MKS system, *n.* a system of units used in science and engineering, based on the metre, second and kilogram as fundamental mechanical units, supplemented by the ampere for electrical work.

mnemonics, *n.* a set of simple words that are used to write programs for a MICROPROCESSOR. The term derives ultimately from the Greek for 'to remember', and the words are intended to remind the user of the action that is required.

Fig. 51. **Miller integrator.** (a) The basic circuit and (b) typical waveforms.

mode, *n.* **1.** the FREQUENCY and WAVEFORM of a resonating system. **2.** the classification of a WAVE in terms of its polarization (see POLARIZED, sense 1). The three modes are TEM WAVES, TE WAVES, and TM WAVES.

modem *n. acronym for* MOdulator–DEModulator, a device used to convert digital signals into a form suitable for long-distance transmission, and to reconvert received signals.

The modem is widely used for linking computers over telephone lines and via radio links (where this is permitted). The MODULATOR section translates the data bits of 0 and 1 into tone signals at two different frequencies representing 0 and 1. The data is then transmitted as a set of tones, using rates of transmission that are slow by computing standards. At the receiving end, the DEMODULATOR converts the received tones into data signals again. See also SERIAL TRANSMISSION.

modulation, *n.* the alteration of a CARRIER (1) wave so that it bears information. The most elementary form of modulation (often regarded as not being a form of modulation at all) is Morse code, in which the carrier is switched on and off. For carrying audio or video signals, AMPLITUDE MODULATION or FREQUENCY MODULATION is used. Any of these modulation methods will produce a signal that consists of a carrier and a set of SIDEBANDS, in which the sidebands carry the information. The most common forms of modulation are wasteful of transmitted energy, because only a fraction of the total radiated power is in the form of the sidebands that carry the information.

Several systems exist that suppress one sideband and/or the carrier in order to use the transmitter power more effectively. These SINGLE-SIDEBAND systems require special DEMODULATION circuits. The carrier frequency must be considerably higher than the highest frequency that will be modulated onto it. For MICROWAVE transmissions, it is generally easier to pulse the carrier on and off, and modulate the pulsing system. At the receiver, various types of demodulator are needed to recover the form of the original signal.

modulation factor, see DEPTH OF MODULATION.

modulation index, *n*. a figure used in calculating BANDWIDTH for frequency-modulated signals (see FREQUENCY MODULATION). The modulation index is obtained by dividing the maximum frequency change of the CARRIER by the maximum frequency of the modulated signal. The modulation index should be a small fraction.

modulator, *n*. any CIRCUIT that modulates a CARRIER.

moiré pattern, *n*. an image formed by light passing through two or more grids. Sometimes called *strobing* by camera operators. Moiré patterns are a problem in TV pictures, because of the use of scanning in lines, and the vertical bar structure of the aperture grille. The effect is that pictures that contain horizontal or vertical stripes appear to contain elaborate moving patterns, often coloured.

monitor, *n*. a VISUAL DISPLAY UNIT commonly used with computers.

monochromatic radiation, *n*. radiation consisting of one single frequency, or a small range of frequencies. An unmodulated CARRIER that is a perfect sine wave is a monochromatic radiation.

monochrome, *n.* a picture or display using shades of one colour only. Often referred to as black–and–white, but computers make use of monitors whose screen colour may be green or amber.

monolithic circuit, *n.* a CIRCUIT made in one piece, i.e., an INTEGRATED CIRCUIT fabricated from a single piece of silicon.

monophonic or **mono,** *adj.* (of a sound–reproducing system) using one sound channel only. Compare STEREOPHONIC.

monoscope, *n.* a form of TV SIGNAL-GENERATOR tube that is used to provide a pattern such as a test chart. Simple dot and bar patterns can be generated by signal generators, but the monoscope uses camera–tube techniques to generate a more elaborate picture signal. Monoscopes are being replaced by computer-generated test patterns.

monostable or **one-shot** or **single-shot,** *n.* a type of MULTIVIBRATOR with one stable state. A TRIGGER PULSE is used to place the monostable in its unstable state and, after a short time, the circuit switches back to its original state. The time is determined by a capacitor-resistor TIME CONSTANT. The device is used to generate a pulse of known width from a trigger pulse. See Fig. 52.

Morse code, *n.* an old-established system of communication. Morse code uses two signals, the short dot and the long dash, to code letters of the alphabet and digits. Morse can be used for communication along very long lines, and for radio signalling by switching a CARRIER on and off. The advantage of Morse is that it makes very efficient use of a low-power carrier and is highly noise-immune. It is nowadays mainly used for emergency systems only, but its influence on radio practice still lingers on in the form of the requirement for radio amateurs to take a test in Morse.

MOS, *n. acronym for* Metal–Oxide Semiconductor, see FIELD-EFFECT TRANSISTOR.

mosaic, *n.* a set of insulated conducting dots on an insulating surface (see INSULATE). The mosaic was a feature of early types of TV camera tubes in which the dots acted as CAPACITORS,

Fig. 52. **Monostable**. A typical monostable circuit. The duration of the pulse output is determined by the time constant CR.

storing CHARGE quantities that formed a charge image corresponding to the light image.

MOS capacitor, *n.* a metal–oxide semiconductor CAPACITOR formed on a chip by using doped (see DOPING) silicon for plates and silicon oxide as the INSULATOR. MOS capacitors are the basis of CHARGE–COUPLED DEVICES and of BUCKET–BRIGADE and DYNAMIC–MEMORY devices.

MOSFET, see FIELD–EFFECT TRANSISTOR.

MOS IC, *n.* an INTEGRATED CIRCUIT that is constructed using MOSFETS as the active components. See FIELD–EFFECT TRANSISTOR.

MOS transistor, see FIELD–EFFECT TRANSISTOR.

motherboard, *n.* a baseboard for a computer circuit used in small computers. The main parts of the computer are on a single board, called the 'motherboard'. This board is fitted with sets of sockets, each of which can connect to another board. All the computer signals are made available at each socket, so that the facilities of the computer can be greatly extended by plugging in extension boards.

The system is often referred to as having *open architecture*, in the sense that the computer can be extended by using boards made by suppliers other than the original manufacturer.

Computers of this design type, such as the Apple-2, can have very long working lives because it is always possible to upgrade the design rather than replace the machine.

motional impedance, *n.* a form of IMPEDANCE found in an electromechanical TRANSDUCER. A transducer such as a LOUD-SPEAKER converts electrical signals into mechanical motion. The current that a signal of constant voltage can pass will be greatest if mechanical motion is prevented, least if the motion is completely unimpeded. This means that the electrical imped-ance will also vary with the resistance to mechanical motion, particularly if there is mechanical resonance. Compare BLOCKED IMPEDANCE.

motor, *n.* a DEVICE that converts electrical energy into motion. Most motors convert to rotation, but linear motors convert AC energy directly into linear motion. See also UNIVERSAL MOTOR, INDUCTION MOTOR, SYNCHRONOUS MOTOR.

motorboating, *n.* a form of PARASITIC OSCILLATION at low frequencies. Motorboating in audio amplifiers produces a noise like a motorboat engine, hence the term. The cause is usually breakdown of a decoupling capacitor, or sometimes acoustic feedback.

moving-coil meter, *n.* the basic DIRECT CURRENT measuring METER. A COIL, attached to an indicating needle, is suspended from springs or from a taut fibre in the field of a permanent magnet. The shape of the field is radial over a large part of its area, because of the presence of a cylindrical magnetic core. Current flowing through the coil will cause torque that rotates the coil against the restoring torque of the springs or suspension. The angle of rotation is proportional to the current through the coil over a wide range of angle. The current range can be extended by using shunts, voltage ranges can be read using series resistors, and ALTERNATING CURRENT can be measured by adding a RECTIFIER bridge.

moving-coil microphone, *n.* a MICROPHONE in which the sound waves affect a moving COIL. The sound waves strike a diaphragm to which the coil is attached. The vibration of the coil then generates a signal voltage because the coil is placed in the field of a permanent magnet.

moving-coil pick-up, *n.* a form of PICK-UP for the groove type of disc recording. The stylus of the pick-up is attached to a small COIL that is located in the field of a permanent magnet. The vibration of the stylus causes vibration of the coil, inducing a signal. Because both coil and magnet must be very small, the signal amplitude is very low, measured in microvolts, and the output from this type of microphone requires considerable amplification. The OUTPUT IMPEDANCE of the microphone is very low, however, which makes it easier to avoid picking up interference.

moving-iron meter, *n.* a METER that makes use of the movement of a SOFT MAGNETIC MATERIAL. The magnetic material, called the ARMATURE, usually forms part of a FLUX (2) path in a soft MAGNETIC core, and is suspended from springs and attached to an indicating needle. A COIL is wound around the magnetic core, and CURRENT in this coil will cause flux. The flux will cause a force to act on the armature, pulling it into line with the flux. This force is opposed by the spring suspension, so that the angle of the turning of the armature is related to the amount of current. The instrument is nonlinear unless the armature is suitably shaped. The advantage of a moving-iron instrument is that it measures true RMS values of signals whose frequencies are within its range. The instrument cannot be used for high-frequency signals because of the high inductance of the coil. See also HOT-WIRE INSTRUMENT, MOVING-COIL METER.

moving-iron microphone, *n.* a MICROPHONE that uses the moving-iron principle. The vibrations of a diaphragm affect a soft magnetic armature that is placed in a FLUX (2) gap of a permanent magnet. A COIL wound round the magnet body converts variations of flux into signals.

moving-iron pick-up, *n.* a very popular form of gramophone pick-up that uses the moving-iron principle. The vibration of a stylus moves an ARMATURE that is part of a FLUX (2) circuit for a permanent magnet. A COIL wound around the magnet has a signal induced by the flux variations. The output is reasonably large, a few millivolts, and the impedance low enough to avoid interference problems. The linearity depends greatly on the design of the magnetic circuit.

MSI, *abbrev. for* medium scale integration, the scale of integration in which the number of active components on one chip is in the range 100 to 1,000. See LSI, VLSI.

MTBF, see MEAN LIFE.

MTI radar, *n.* moving-target indicator radar, a RADAR system that uses cancellation of returns from fixed targets so that only moving objects are displayed. Modern MTI systems use computer techniques to carry out the cancellation and display. See also CANCELLATION CIRCUIT.

mutiplexer, *n.* **1.** a CIRCUIT that allows the TRANSMISSION of several signals at once over a single channel communication system (a *multiplex* system). This can denote a CARRIER that is modulated in two ways, but more commonly denotes a circuit using PULSE methods. The original signals can be recovered by a DEMULTIPLEXER circuit. A single-channel system is sometimes called a *simplex* system. **2.** (in instrumentation systems) a hybrid digital/analogue device, in which one of a number of analogue signals is selected by means of a binary address and routed to a single output. **3.** (in logic circuits) a device in which one of a number of digital inputs is selected by means of a binary address and connected to a single output.

multiplier, *n.* a CIRCUIT or DEVICE that carries out a multiplying action. An ELECTRON MULTIPLIER multiplies the number of electrons in a beam. A FREQUENCY MULTIPLIER produces a harmonic of its input signal. An analogue multiplier produces an output whose amplitude is proportional to the product of the amplitudes of the inputs. A *digital multiplier* carries out the arithmetical operation of multiplication on a pair of binary numbers.

multistable, *adj.* (of an electronic COMPONENT or CIRCUIT) possessing more than one stable state, like the old gas-filled counter tubes (Dekatrons) and more modern RING-COUNTER circuits.

multistage, *adj.* (of an electronic CIRCUIT) possessing more than one unit, particularly of amplification.

multivibrator, *n.* a form of oscillator CIRCUIT for non-sine waves. The oscillator uses two INVERTING AMPLIFIERS that are cross-coupled. This means that the output of each amplifier is

Fig. 53. **Multivibrator**. The circuit is shown here in its astable form. This circuit is a fundamental type of SQUARE-WAVE generator.

connected to the input of the other. If both connections are made through capacitors, the multivibrator is free-running, and will generate a square wave for as long as power is applied. If one connection is direct, and the other through a capacitor, then the circuit is MONOSTABLE. With two direct couplings, the circuit becomes a FLIP-FLOP. See Fig. 53.

mu-metal, *n.* a nickel–iron alloy that has very high PERMEABILITY. Mu-metal is used for MAGNETIC SCREENING.

mush, *n.* the NOISE in a radio receiver that is being operated with too weak a CARRIER signal.

music centre, *n.* a combined radio, cassette recorder and gramophone, with amplifiers and loudspeakers.

music power, *n.* a figure for power output of an AMPLIFIER. The figure attempts to take into account the nonsinusoidal nature of music, and is always much greater than the true power figure for sine wave output. The term has fallen into disrepute because of its frequent misuse in advertising to suggest that an amplifier has much more power output than is truly the case.

muting, *n.* the suppression of a SIGNAL by any DEVICE or CIRCUIT that shuts off unwanted signals. One application is automatic muting of interstation noise in FM receivers. The muting circuit comes into operation when the carrier strength falls below a preset limit, and this is used to suppress the audio output, thus eliminating the loud rushing noise that is otherwise heard before a signal is tuned in.

mutual conductance or **transconductance,** *n.* the ratio of change of output current to change of input voltage for an ACTIVE COMPONENT. Symbol: *Gm*; unit: usually milliamperes per volt.

See also CONDUCTANCE.

mutual inductance, *n.* the quantity that relates the MAGNETIC FLUX in one inductor to the current in another nearby inductor. Symbol: *M*; unit henry. When mutual inductance exists between inductors, the inductors are said to be coupled and the amount of COUPLING is determined by the value of mutual inductance compared to the individual SELF-INDUCTANCE of the inductors, and by the presence of FERROMAGNETIC material. See also COUPLING COEFFICIENT.

Mylar, *n. Trademark.* a form of polyester plastic, used as an INSULATOR, particularly in CAPACITORS.

N

NAND gate, *n.* a type of LOGIC GATE. The gate output is logic 1 unless all of its inputs are at logic 1, when its output is logic 0. The NAND gate is easy to manufacture, and is extensively used in small-scale integrated circuits. The advantage of using NAND gates is that any gate circuit can be built up from NAND gates alone. The same is true of NOR gates. See Fig. 54. See also AND GATE, OR GATE, NOT GATE, KARNAUGH MAP, INVERTER (1).

nano-, *prefix.* denoting 10^{-9}, e.g., nanosecond, nanofarad. Symbol: n.

narrow-beam aerial, *n.* an aerial with a very narrow RADIATION PATTERN and negligible SIDE LOBES. A narrow-beam aerial has a large GAIN in its aimed direction, as compared to a

(a)
input A
input B

Q
output

(b)

A	B	Q
0	0	1
0	1	1
1	0	1
1	1	0

Fig. 54. **Nand gate**. (a) NAND gate symbol. (b) Truth table.

C

L

R

Fig. 55. **Natural frequency**. See main entry.

simple DIPOLE. This can permit good reception even in noisy conditions.

natural frequency or **resonant frequency,** *n*. the frequency of natural RESONANCE of a circuit or any other system that can oscillate. Any system that is set into oscillation by a brief stimulus will from then on oscillate at its natural frequency. An OSCILLATOR is most stable when the stimulus is so small that the frequency of oscillation is the natural frequency for the network.

A capacitor presents a high impedance to low-frequency alternating current, but has a small impedance at high frequency. The opposite is true for an inductor, which has a large impedance at high frequencies owing to the opposing voltage generated by rapid changes of current.

In a circuit containing inductive, capacitive and resistive devices (as shown in Fig. 55 on page 205), the impedance 'seen' by the voltage generator will be large at high frequencies (because of the inductor) and also at low frequencies (because of the capacitor). At some intermediate frequency there will be a minimum impedance, and this is called the 'resonant frequency' or 'natural frequency'. In the circuit in Fig. 55, which is called a *series resonant circuit*, resonance will occur when the angular frequency of the voltage generator ω is:

$$\omega = \frac{1}{\sqrt{LC}}$$

Resonance occurs at the frequency when the inductive and capacitive impedances are equal and opposite, so that they exactly cancel. Under these conditions the impedance is real, and has the value R as though the circuit only contained a resistor.

A circuit excited into oscillation by an impulse will resonate until all the energy contained within the circuit has been lost through damping (resistance in this case).

Resonant circuits are often used to 'select' signals near their resonant frequency. They are also used to construct oscillators.

See also RINGING.

NBS, *abbrev. for* National Bureau of Standards (US).

n-channel, *n.* a path of current constructed from an N-TYPE doped semiconductor. The term is usually applied to FIELD EFFECT TRANSISTOR construction in which the width of the channel is controlled by altering the BIAS on the surrounding material by means of a control electrode known as the GATE.

See also P-CHANNEL.

negative, *adj.* (of a material) possessing an excess of ELECTRONS. The term is applied to any material in which there is a surplus of electrons over protons, whether these electrons are free or bound. Note that an n-type semiconductor is not negative in this sense, because the number of electrons is exactly balanced by the number of HOLES. The distinguishing feature of an n-type semiconductor is that many of the electrons are free to move and can be used as current carriers. Compare POSITIVE.

negative bias, *n.* the application of a steady negative voltage or potential to a circuit or active device, e.g. the GATE of a FET, the base of a transistor or the GRID of a valve or CATHODE–RAY TUBE to which a negative potential is applied in order to control the flow of electrons. A sufficiently large negative bias will prevent electron flow, and this amount of bias is called CUTOFF. Compare POSITIVE BIAS.

Fig. 56. **Negative feedback**. The circuit method applied to a general-purpose amplifier. The circuit assumes the use of a balanced amplifier. If gain without feedback is very high, then gain with feedback is approx. $(R_1 + R_2)/R_2$. This is the inverse of the division ratio of the resistor chain.

negative feedback, *n.* the process by which a portion of the output of an amplifier is fed back to the input in such a way as to diminish the total input signal. This reduces the effective gain of the amplifier, but markedly increases its input impedance and reduces its output impedance. In addition, linearity is greatly improved. A system is said to be 'linear' when its output is related to the input by an expression of the form:

$$S_{out} = C S_{in} + B$$

when C and B are constants.

Negative feedback takes several forms. The feedback may be proportional to either the output voltage or the output current, and it may be presented to the input either in series or in parallel with the signal to be amplified. There are therefore four basic types of negative feedback: *series voltage feedback*, *parallel voltage feedback*, *series current feedback*, and *parallel current feedback*.

A further advantage of using negative feedback is that for an amplifier with high OPEN-LOOP GAIN (such as most OPER-ATIONAL AMPLIFIERS), the use of negative feedback means that the circuit gain is determined solely by the external (feedback) component values. See Fig. 56. Compare POSITIVE FEEDBACK.

negative ion, *n*. an atom that has gained one or (sometimes) more ELECTRONS and is therefore negatively charged. Because of the charge, the ion will experience force in an ELECTRIC FIELD, and if free to move will do so. Compare POSITIVE ION. An ion should not be confused with a HOLE.

negative logic, *n*. a logic voltage system in which the more negative voltage represents LOGIC ONE. Negative logic is seldom used nowadays. Compare POSITIVE LOGIC.

negative resistance, *n*. an unstable condition in which an increase of voltage across two points is accompanied by a decrease of current between the points. The term 'negative' is used because this is the opposite of the normal ohmic resistance. Any device that can produce negative resistance over a range of voltage levels can be used as an OSCILLATOR. If negative resistance can occur in an AMPLIFIER under certain circum-stances, the amplifier will be unstable under these conditions.

negative temperature coefficient (NTC), *n*. a figure that expresses by how much a quantity decreases as the ambient temperature increases. NTC capacitors are used to stabilize RF oscillator frequency, and NTC resistors are used for similar purposes in RC oscillators. Compare POSITIVE TEMPERATURE COEFFICIENT.

neon, *n*. a gaseous element used in display devices. The neon signal lamp consists of two small parallel ELECTRODES sur-rounded by low-pressure neon. The lamp glows orange-red at a POTENTIAL DIFFERENCE of around 70V only after the gas has

Fig. 57. **Neon.** (a) Neon construction. (b) A typical circuit for a neon indicator.

been ionized (see IONIZATION) by a higher potential difference called the STRIKING POTENTIAL. When the gas is ionized, an increase of current through the gas causes a drop in the potential across the electrodes, so that the characteristic is of a NEGATIVE RESISTANCE. See Fig. 57.

net loss, *n.* the overall loss of SIGNAL, usually expressed in DECIBELS, in any device or network, active or passive.

network, *n.* a circuit that consists of PASSIVE COMPONENTS, such as resistors, capacitors and inductors. Many types of electronic circuits can be divided into ACTIVE COMPONENTS, such as opamps or transistors, and passive networks.

neutral, 1. *adj.* being earthed, or connected neither to positive nor to negative potential. **2.** *n.* the return line of an AC mains supply.

neutralization, *n.* a form of connection or set of connections made in an amplifier STAGE in order to prevent OSCILLATION. A neutralizing connection generally consists of a capacitor connected between two stages of amplification, and is intended to counteract the effects of STRAY CAPACITANCE by shifting the signal phase in the opposite direction. Neutralization is particularly needed when a TRANSISTOR is being used for tuned radio-frequency amplification at a frequency near to the limit of its frequency response. See also UNILATERAL NETWORK.

neutron, *n*. a neutral elementary particle found in the nucleus of an atom. The nucleus also contains positively charged particles called PROTONS. A neutron has no charge, and its rest mass is 1.67482×10^{-27} kilogram, 1839 times that of an electron.

newton, *n*. the SI and MKS unit of force. Symbol: N. A newton is defined as the force required to produce an acceleration of 1 metre per second per second to a body of mass 1kg. In the earth's gravitational field the downward force on a 1kg mass is approximately 9.81 N.

Nichrome, *n*. *Trademark*. an alloy of nickel and chromium that has fairly high RESISTIVITY, and can be used at fairly high temperatures. It is extensively applied in heating elements, and can be used for WIRE-WOUND RESISTORS that will be operated with high DISSIPATION.

nicad cell, *n*. a nickel–cadmium cell or battery, a rechargeable form of alkaline electrolyte cell, used as a power source in portable equipment.

Nife cell, *n*. *Trademark*. a nickel–iron CELL or battery. This was an early (1901) design of rechargeable alkaline electrolyte cell, now mainly used for electric traction.

node, *n*. **1.** a joining point in a NETWORK, particularly a FILTER network, at which components are connected. See Fig. 58a. **2.** a point in a STANDING WAVE pattern at which there is no wave motion. See Fig. 58b. The position of maximum wave motion is called the ANTINODE. Nodes and antinodes are particularly important in AERIAL design, and in TRANSMISSION LINES.

noise, *n*. any unwanted SIGNAL, often signals of random frequency, phase and amplitude. See also MAN-MADE NOISE, RADIO NOISE, SOLAR NOISE, IMPULSE NOISE, THERMAL NOISE, SCHOTTKY NOISE, WHITE NOISE.

noise factor, *n*. the ratio of SIGNAL power to NOISE power. In TELEMETRY, this factor is measured for a radio receiver that is tuned to a desired signal, firstly with no MODULATION, so that the noise output of the receiver can be measured, then with full modulation so that the power of signal plus noise can be measured.

noise figure, *n*. the NOISE FACTOR expressed in DECIBELS.

no-load condition, *n*. the operation of an amplifier, oscillator

Fig. 58. **Node.** (a) Nodes in a ladder network. (b) Nodes in a standing-wave pattern.

or any other device without the LOAD that will normally be attached to it, i.e. no power is taken from the circuit. An amplifier should be stable and should not suffer damage under such conditions. An oscillator should show no frequency DRIFT.

nomogram, *n.* a form of chart that allows the values of a variable to be estimated without resorting to a mathematical formula. One form taken by a nomogram is a set of columns of values. By joining two columns with a straight line, values can be read from other columns that are intersected by the straight line. This can often be as precise as is needed, and allows very rapid estimates of quantities that would normally be time-consuming to calculate. See Fig. 59 on page 212. See also FORM FACTOR(2).

nondestructive test, *n.* any form of testing that does not damage the test specimen. X-RAY examination is one form of nondestructive test, as is ULTRASONIC scanning.

noninductive, *adj.* (of a wire winding) being wound so that its INDUCTANCE is a minimum. Often applied to WIRE-WOUND

1

70

20

3

50

10

4.0

line shows
that with
3cm wavelength,
the reflector
diameter of 4.0m
gives

50dB gain

100
wavelength (cm)

0
gain (dB)

.25
reflector diameter (m)

Fig. 59. **Nomogram**. The example shows a nomogram for the apparent power gain of a microwave parabolic reflector. The result is obtained simply by drawing a straight line between two condition values, and reading off the answer at the intersection. Only a few values have been shown to make the construction clear.

RESISTORS in which the required length of resistance wire is wound half in one direction and half in an opposite direction. The effect of this is to cancel most of the SELF-INDUCTANCE of the winding. For most purposes, the use of a metal FILM RESISTOR is a more satisfactory solution if inductance must be very low, but where high DISSIPATION or great accuracy is required, there may be no option but to use wire-wound construction.

nonlinear, *adj*. possessing a CHARACTERISTIC shape that is not a straight line. The term is usually applied to an AMPLIFIER or other analogue signal device in which a plot of signal out against signal in is not a straight line. Passive networks that do not contain metal-cored inductors are usually linear.

Nonlinearity in an amplifier is a cause of HARMONIC DISTORTION and INTERMODULATION. See also NEGATIVE FEEDBACK. Compare LINEAR.

nonlinear distortion, *n.* a type of distortion, such as HARMONIC DISTORTION and INTERMODULATION that is caused by NONLINEAR behaviour. The nonlinearity may be in an active device such as a transistor or IC, or in a passive device with HYSTERESIS, such as an iron-cored inductor.

nonreactive, *adj.* (of a component) having only RESISTANCE. The term is applied to a RESISTOR or a TRANSMISSION LINE in which the PHASE of voltage is always the same as the phase of current under normal working conditions. See also IMPEDANCE, REACTANCE, RESISTANCE.

nonresonant, *adj.* (of a component or circuit) having a frequency characteristic with no sudden changes. A nonresonant component or circuit (see APERIODIC CIRCUIT) can be used at any frequency with no risk of abrupt changes of phase or gain if the frequency is changed. See NATURAL FREQUENCY, RESONANCE.

nonsinusoidal, *adj.* (of a WAVEFORM) not being a sine wave, but (usually) a pulse or square wave.

nonvolatile, *adj.* (of memory storage) not depending on a power supply for the storage of data, i.e. any form of memory that uses MAGNETIC or ELECTROSTATIC storage that will be retained when power is no longer applied. Compare VOLATILE. See also EAROM, EPROM.

NOR gate, *n.* a form of logic gate whose output is at LOGIC ONE only when all of its inputs are at logic 0. For all other combinations of inputs, the output is logic 0. The gate can be imagined as a combination of OR GATE and INVERTER (1), but is always manufactured as a gate in its own right. Like the NAND GATE, NOR gates can be used in combination to provide the action of any other type of gate.

normalized figure, *n.* a figure that has been adjusted to fit a standard pattern. For example, RESONANCE curves are normalized around unity gain and resonant frequency. This means that the response is plotted with the peak gain shown as 1, and with the frequencies shown relative to the resonance fre-

Fig. 60. **Normalized figure**. A normalized response curve, in terms of percentage gain and centre frequency.

quency, rather than using actual measured values of gain and frequency for any one particular circuit. Normalization is encountered to a considerable extent in FILTER design, and in PROPAGATION calculations. See Fig. 60.

Norton's theorem, *n.* the current equivalent of THEVENIN'S THEOREM for finding an EQUIVALENT CIRCUIT. This states that any two-terminal LINEAR NETWORK to which a signal is applied can be simulated by the behaviour of a current GENERATOR in parallel with a resistor.

NOT gate, see INVERTER (1).

n-p-n transistor, *n.* a BIPOLAR TRANSISTOR with a BASE of p-type material, and EMITTER (1) and COLLECTOR of n-type. The n-p-n structure is the predominant one for silicon transistors.

NTC, see NEGATIVE TEMPERATURE COEFFICIENT.

NTSC, *abbrev. for* National Television Standards Committee (US). This is the committee that decides on technical standards for TV broadcasting in the US, notable for the 1951 colour TV standard that is named NTSC after the committee. See also PAL, SECAM.

n-type, *adj.* (of a SEMICONDUCTOR material) being doped (see DOPING) with an electron-rich impurity. This causes the material to conduct predominantly by the movement of

negative electrons. See also P-TYPE, TRANSISTOR, SEMICON-
DUCTOR.

nucleus, *n*. the central part of an atom. The nucleus is positively
charged, and contains most of the mass of an atom.

null detector, *n*. a DEVICE that detects when a signal has zero
amplitude, often used in conjunction with the NULL METHOD of
measurement to indicate balance. See also BRIDGE.

null method, *n*. a measuring method in which adjustments are
made in order to produce a NULL-DETECTOR reading. BRIDGES
are the best-known null methods, because when a bridge
circuit reaches its balanced condition, the signal or DC voltage
across the detector is zero. This makes it unnecessary to use a
detector that is calibrated in any way, and only high sensitivity
is required. The size of the quantity that is being measured is
calculated from the values of the other components in the
bridge circuit and so is unaffected by any calibration error of
the meter instrument.

numerical control, *n*. the control of any SYSTEM by digital
signals, often denoting the control of machinery by using
digital signals from a computer.

Nyquist diagram or **vector response diagram,** *n*. a plot of
a NORMALIZED FIGURE of gain against phase shift for an
amplifier. This shows the relationship between gain and
feedback in an amplifier and is used as a measure of stability. See
Fig. 61 on page 216. See also NYQUIST CRITERION.

Nyquist criterion, *n*. a method of determining if an amplifier
will be unconditionally stable. This depends on whether the
plot of a NYQUIST DIAGRAM encloses the point $-1,0$ on the
conventional normalized form of the diagram.

Fig. 61. **Nyquist diagram**. A typical Nyquist plot for an amplifier. This shows gain as a complex variable (see COMPLEX NUMBER) plotted on real and imaginary axes. The solid line (unconditionally stable) and the dotted line (unstable) represent the transfer function G, taking phase into account. If the plot indicates instability, the gain of the amplifier must be reduced around the critical frequencies.

O

OCR, see OPTICAL CHARACTER READER.

octave, *n*. a doubling or halving of FREQUENCY. A change in response (such as of a FILTER) is often quoted as the number of decibels of attenuation or amplification per octave.

off–line, *adj*. (of part of a computer system) disconnected from the computer system. An off-line device is normally active in the sense that power is applied to it, although it is prevented from communicating with the rest of the computer system. Compare ON–LINE.

offset, *n.* a deviation from correct or normal VOLTAGE or CURRENT. The offset of an OPERATIONAL AMPLIFIER is the BIAS that is needed on one input to make the output reach earth voltage when the other input is at earth voltage.

ohm, *n.* the SI unit of electrical RESISTANCE. The resistance in ohms between two points is defined as the DC voltage divided by the DC current flowing between the points. Symbol: Ω.

See also CONDUCTANCE, REACTANCE, IMPEDANCE.

ohmic, *adj.* (of a material or a component) obeying OHM'S LAW, having a constant value of RESISTANCE at a steady temperature. If the value of resistance varies with applied voltage or current, then the resistance is *nonohmic*.

See also THERMISTOR.

ohmic contact, *n.* an electrical contact with a steady value of CONTACT RESISTANCE.

ohmic loss, *n.* a power loss caused by DISSIPATION in a resistor as distinct from radiation loss or HYSTERESIS loss, for example.

ohmmeter, *n.* an instrument for measuring RESISTANCE. Simple ohmmeters use a CELL of constant voltage to pass a CURRENT through the unknown resistor, and measure this current. The disadvantage is a nonlinear reading scale. More elaborate ohmmeters use measuring BRIDGE circuits.

See also MEGGER.

ohm-metre, *n.* the unit of RESISTIVITY. The resistivity of a material is the RESISTANCE between opposite forces of a cubic metre of that material at a steady temperature. Symbol: Ω m.

Ohm's law, *n.* the principle that the RESISTANCE of a metallic conductor is constant at a constant temperature. For metallic and other ohmic conductors we can use the relationship $V = R \times I$ between (DC) current and voltage because the quantity R (resistance) is a constant. Nonohmic conductors do not have any constant resistance value, and the $V = RI$ relationship can be used only if the value of R under the conditions is known.

ohms-per-volt, *n.* a figure used to compare the sensitivity of DC VOLTMETER movements that shows the series resistance of the voltmeter for any voltage range. For example, if a meter is quoted as having 30K per volt, then on its 10V range, the resistance of the meter is 30 × 10k-ohms.

oil-break switch, *n.* a form of SWITCH whose contacts are immersed in oil. This suppresses ARCING when the contacts separate.

omnidirectional aerial, *n.* an aerial whose RADIATION PATTERN is the same in all (horizontal) directions.

one-shot, see MONOSTABLE.

on-line, *adj.* (of a part of a computer system) being switched on or connected to the remainder of the SYSTEM. Compare OFFLINE.

opamp, see OPERATIONAL AMPLIFIER.

open architecture, see MOTHERBOARD.

open circuit, *n.* a disconnection in an electrical CIRCUIT through which no CURRENT flows.

open-circuit impedance, *n.* a measurement of the IMPEDANCE of a NETWORK. The open-circuit impedance at the input of the network is the impedance that it has with the output open circuit. The open circuit impedance of the output is the impedance value that it has when the input is open circuit.

open-circuit voltage, *n.* the output signal voltage of an OPEN CIRCUIT or device when no LOAD is connected.

open-collector device or **open-ended device** or **open-collector output,** *n.* a digital device in which the active pull-up transistor of the output stage is omitted. Many digital device outputs are driven by a pair of transistors, and the output is held at 1 or 0 by a conducting transistor or MOSFET (see FIELD-EFFECT TRANSISTOR). However, if a number of device outputs have to be connected together, this kind of active output is undesirable, since it may lead to an active low voltage being connected to an active high voltage with disastrous consequences. To avoid this problem open-collector devices are used. The output can only be made FALSE, which is a low voltage, or disconnected, and it is the responsibility of the user to provide a pull-up transistor so that in its disconnected state the output appears to be high. The pull-up resistor limits current and prevents any damage when conflicting outputs are connected. Open-collector devices can degrade the speed and noise immunity of a logic signal, and this can be avoided by the use of a TRI-STATE DEVICE.

The outcome of any logical analysis can have one of two results: TRUE or FALSE. In digital electronics, HIGH and LOW voltages represent TRUE and FALSE states respectively. The exact voltage levels corresponding to TRUE and FALSE depend upon the type of digital device used. However, TRUE is normally represented by +5V, and FALSE by 0V. See also PUSH-PULL.

open-loop gain, *n.* the GAIN of an amplifier when no FEEDBACK loop is connected.

open wire, *n.* an uninsulated wire, as on an overhead line.

operating point, *n.* a graph point that represents operating conditions. On a graph of output voltage plotted against input voltage for a device (a TRANSFER CHARACTERISTIC), for example, the operating point is the point in the graph that represents the static DC-bias condition with no signal applied. See Fig. 62.

Fig. 62. **Operating point**. The operating point for a linear amplifier stage. The graph is a plot of collector voltage against base voltage for a transistor operating with a load. The operating point is chosen to be in the middle of the linear portion.

operational amplifier (opamp), *n.* a very high-gain linear DC-coupled DIFFERENTIAL AMPLIFIER with a single-ended output. The gain of an opamp will typically be between 10^5 and

Fig. 63. **Operational amplifier**. See main entry.

10^6. An opamp will have a high INPUT IMPEDANCE of $1M.\Omega$ or more, and a low OUTPUT IMPEDANCE of between 50Ω and $5k\Omega$. Most opamps use a split power supply, typically $\pm15V$. The symbol for an opamp is shown in Fig. 63a, and it will be noticed that a pair of inputs are provided. The output becomes positive when the $+$ input is more positive than the $-$ input, and vice versa.

An ideal opamp will have an output which is able to change instantaneously in response to the input. Practical opamps cannot do this; the rate at which the output can change is called the SLEW RATE.

Almost all opamp circuits can be analyzed using two simple rules:

I. The voltage between the $+$ and $-$ inputs is zero (to a very good approximation).

II. The inputs draw no current.

Consider the application of these rules to the circuit in Fig. 63b:

(a) The $+$ input is grounded, so Rule I states that the $-$ input must also be at earth potential.

(b) Therefore the whole of V_{in} appears across R_1, and the whole of V_{out} appears across R_2. Since Rule II states that the inputs cannot accept current, the current through R_1 must have an equal magnitude but an opposite sign to that through R_2.

In other words, $V_{in}/R_1 = -V_{out}/R_2$. The gain of this current V_{out}/V_{in} is therefore equal to $-R_2/R_1$.

This illustrates a common feature of opamp circuits. Because the intrinsic gain of the device and its input impedance are so high, Rules I and II can be applied, and the gain of an opamp circuit is determined solely by the input and feedback components.

For further details of opamp circuits see Ref. 2.

opposition, *n.* a SIGNAL which is a mirror–image of another signal. Two signals of identical frequency and waveshape are said to be *in opposition* if their amplitudes at any instant are equal and opposite. The word *antiphase* is sometimes used, but for asymmetrical waves, a 180 degree phase shift does not produce an opposition (or inverted) wave.

optical axis, *n.* the straight line connecting the centres of lenses in an optical SYSTEM.

optical character reader (OCR), *n.* a DEVICE that can scan printed characters and give a digital output to a computer. The scanning may be manual or automatic, and the output is usually in ASCII code form.

optical fibre, *n.* a thin strand of transparent glass used to contain and transmit optical signals by total internal reflection. The very small size of an optical fibre means that large numbers can be packed into the space occupied by a single conventional cable. Much higher data rates can be achieved using optical fibres rather than conventional conductors.

optical image, *n.* an image in light, using dark and shade, or colour of various degress of SATURATION. A TV CAMERA TUBE would convert an optical image like this into a CHARGE image, and so into an electron–beam image.

optimum bunching, *n.* the bunching of electrons in a beam so that each bunch is separated by free space. See KLYSTRON, BUNCHER.

opto–electronics, *n.* the study and the use of optical elements in electronic circuits. Opto–electronic devices such as PHOTODIODES and PHOTOTRANSISTORS can be used to build hybrid electronic-optical circuits, in which an electrical signal is connected to light pulses, passed along an OPTICAL FIBRE, and reconnected to electrical impulses at the other end. Some forms of signal processing can be carried out on a signal while it is in its optical form; for example, filtering, mixing and switching. Recent developments of extremely high-speed optical switches have led to the possibility of optical computers being constructed, and research is currently being undertaken in this area.

Oracle, *n. Trademark.* a TELETEXT system operated by the Independent Broadcasting Authority (UK). Identical technically to the BBC CEEFAX service.

OR gate, *n.* a LOGIC circuit that gives a LOGIC ONE output when any one, several or all of its inputs is at logic 1. The NOR GATE is the preferred type for manufacturing convenience. The action of the OR gate is inclusive, meaning that the output will be logic 1 no matter whether there is one logic 1 input or more than one. For some applications it is necessary to exclude the case of more than one input being at logic 1, in which case the EXCLUSIVE-OR GATE is needed. See Fig. 64.

Fig. 64. **Or gate.** (a) Logic diagram. The logic of the gate is that the output is zero only when all inputs are zero. (b) Truth table.

orthicon, *n.* an obsolete type of TV CAMERA TUBE, first superseded by the IMAGE ORTHICON, then by the VIDICON.

oscillating current, *n.* a CURRENT that varies in a periodic manner with time.

oscillating voltage, *n*. a VOLTAGE that varies in a periodic manner with time.

oscillation, *n*. the production of a periodic VOLTAGE or CURRENT.

oscillator, *n*. a CIRCUIT that produces an AC signal output from a DC supply. Any circuit that has a negative value of AC resistance over a range of VOLTAGES can be considered to be an oscillator. Connecting a RESONANT CIRCUIT to this NEGATIVE RESISTANCE will result in a tuned oscillator whose output is close to a sine wave in shape. If the oscillating conditions only just produce negative resistance over a short range, the waveshape will be a reasonably accurate sinusoid. If the negative resistance is large, or if no tuned circuit is connected (see APERIODIC CIRCUIT), the output will be of square shape, as the oscillator output swings between BOTTOMING and CUTOFF. A few devices, such as TUNNEL DIODES, have a negative resistance portion of their characteristic.

The other approach to oscillators is to produce a more controllable negative resistance characteristic by using an amplifier with POSITIVE FEEDBACK, so that the output signal from the amplifier provides enough input signal to sustain oscillation. This approach is the basis of common oscillator circuits such as the COLPITTS OSCILLATOR, FRANKLIN OSCILLATOR and HARTLEY OSCILLATOR.

oscilloscope, see CATHODE-RAY OSCILLOSCOPE.

outgassing, *n*. the removal of absorbed gas from the metal, ceramic and glass of a THERMIONIC VALVE. This is done by an EDDY CURRENT HEATER while the valve is being evacuated. At later stages, outgassing can be assisted by running the valve filament and possibly passing anode current. Transmitting valves use no GETTER to absorb traces of gas, so it is particularly important to perform the outgassing very thoroughly while the valve is still connected to the vacuum pumps.

out–of–phase signal, a SIGNAL whose phase is not in PHASE with respect to another signal. Out-of-phase is sometimes used to imply that the signal is INVERTED (see INVERSION), but the two shapes are not identical for signals other than sine waves.

output, *n.* the final signal-delivering STAGE of an electronic circuit. Compare INPUT (1).

output gap, *n.* the part of a MICROWAVE device from which the microwave signal is taken.

output impedance, *n.* a COMPLEX NUMBER expressing the amplitude and phase relationship between voltage and current at the OUTPUT of a DEVICE or CIRCUIT.

output meter, *n.* a METER that can be connected to the OUTPUT of a CIRCUIT to measure the power at the output.

output transformer, *n.* a TRANSFORMER that is used at the OUTPUT of a CIRCUIT for COUPLING and IMPEDANCE MATCHING. Output transformers were at one time used in domestic audio amplifiers, but are seldom seen nowadays because of the developments in power transistors. The form of output transformer used in AMPLITUDE MODULATION is known as a *modulation transformer*.

overall efficiency, *n.* the ratio of power supplied by a DEVICE to the power required to operate it.

overbunching, *n.* the separation of bunched electrons after optimum bunching has been achieved. See KLYSTRON, BUNCHER.

overcoupling, *n.* an excessive coupling (see CRITICAL COUPLING) between RESONANT CIRCUITS that will cause the amplitude-frequency graph to show a dip at the frequency of resonance. Compare UNDERCOUPLING.

overcurrent trip, *n.* a safety DEVICE that opens a CIRCUIT when excessive CURRENT flows.

overdamped, *adj.* (of a RESONANT CIRCUIT or mechanical system) being DAMPED to an extent that prevents oscillations completely and causes a voltage or movement to die away too slowly. Compare UNDERDAMPED.

overdriven stage, *n.* an amplifying STAGE that has too large an INPUT signal. This causes distortion of the output, and sometimes causes a DEAD TIME, so that no output signal is produced.

overdubbing, *n.* a separate recording of a piece of music from one instrument on a multitrack tape that can be used to replace another track made at an earlier time.

over-horizon propagation, *n.* the broadcasting of a radio signal over the visible horizon. PROPAGATION over the near horizon can be due to signal refraction in the lower atmosphere but for greater distances, the propagation is carried out by reflections from the IONOSPHERE. Modern satellites allow a different form of over-horizon propagation by the rebroadcasting of transmissions that are beamed up to the satellite from earth.

overlapping gate, *n.* a form of construction for CHARGE-COUPLED DEVICES.

overload, *vb.* to take more than the related power from a DEVICE or CIRCUIT. Overloading may cause a deterioration in the OUTPUT (such as an unacceptable waveform shape), or possibly damage to the device or circuit.

overload level, *n.* the amount of output power at which OVERLOAD starts.

overmodulation, *n.* the excessive AMPLITUDE MODULATION of a CARRIER so that the carrier amplitude is reduced to zero at each modulation trough. See Fig. 65.

carrier
minimum

zero
carrier

carrier
maximum

(a)   normal modulation   (b)   overmodulation

Fig. 65. **Overmodulation**. The effect of overmodulation on an amplitude-modulated signal is to reduce the carrier amplitude to zero. This will cause very severe distortion of the received signal.

overscan, *n.* the application of excessive SCAN amplitude, particularly to a TV CAMERA TUBE. This is done to ensure that the whole of the active surface is used at times when the camera is working with a test signal. Using overscan avoids any danger of marking the normal picture area with a burned-in image.

overshoot, *n.* an excessive transient portion of PULSE amplitude. At the leading edge of a pulse, the voltage may momentarily rise above the normal amplitude level of the top of the pulse. This transient is the 'overshoot'. Compare UNDERSHOOT.

oxidation, *n.* a chemical process in which an element is combined with oxygen (one constituent of the air) to form a compound called an 'oxide'. The oxides of metal are generally insulators, and the oxidation of silicon to produce non-conducting silicon oxide is an essential part of the production process of MOSFETS (see FIELD-EFFECT TRANSISTOR) and INTEGRATED CIRCUITS. The term is also used more widely in chemistry to denote any process in which electrons are removed from an ion, whether this process involves oxygen or not.

oxide masking, *n.* the use of a layer of SILICON (IV) oxide to protect the underlying silicon. The oxide layer can be selectively etched with acid to allow the silicon to be treated.

P

PA, see POWER AMPLIFIER, PUBLIC ADDRESS.

packing density, *n.* **1.** the number of ACTIVE COMPONENTS per unit area in an INTEGRATED CIRCUIT. **2.** the number of molecules or atoms per unit volume in a crystalline material.

pad, *n.* **1.** a connection to an INTEGRATED CIRCUIT. **2.** *Trademark.* a computer network controller. **3.** an ATTENUATOR circuit with a fixed division ratio.

pair, *n.* a TRANSMISSION LINE with two conductors. The conductors may be parallel (twin-line), twisted, or in coaxial form.

paired cable, *n.* a CABLE made from sets of twin conductors.

pairing, *n.* a TV display fault that accentuates the appearance of scanning lines on the screen (see SCAN). Pairing occurs as the result of a synchronizing fault that prevents correct INTERLACE action. As a result, the even–numbered lines are in the same screen positions (or very close to) the odd–numbered lines. This makes the screen appear to have much lower vertical resolution. See Fig. 66.

even-numbered lines — odd-numbered lines

normal interlace

even odd

pairing

Fig. 66. **Pairing**. The effect of pairing on the lines that appear on a TV screen.

PAL, *n. acronym for* Phase Alternate Line, the standard European COLOUR TELEVISION coding system. Like the SECAM system, PAL was devised to correct faults that were evident in the much earlier (1952) US NTSC system. Of these faults, the most troublesome was the effect of PHASE variations in the colour SIGNALS, which caused frequent and random colour variations in the received picture. This led to the joke that NTSC was an abbreviation for never twice the same colour.

In the PAL system, devised by Telefunken in Germany, the luminance (**Y**) signal is transmitted normally, and the colour information is coded into two signals, the **U** and **V** signals. The **U** signal (whose AMPLITUDE is proportional to **B-Y**), is transmitted by modulating a SUBCARRIER in phase, and the **V** signal (proportional to **R-Y**) is modulated on to the subcarrier at 90 degree phase. The **V** signal is inverted on alternate lines, hence the name of the system. The phase of the synchronizing burst signal is also alternated to $+45$ degrees and -45 degrees relative to a reference OSCILLATOR. At the TELEVISION RECEIVER, the alternation of the burst phase is used to identify (by generating an IDENT SIGNAL) the phase of the **V** signal, and to invert it when necessary. Because of the inversion, phase changes in transmission can be cancelled. The cancellation is done by delaying the colour signals for one line duration, and adding them to the colour signals for the next line. The colour signals are thus always averaged over two lines, in one of which the **V** signals will have been inverted during transmission. The main disadvantage of both PAL and SECAM systems is that the vertical RESOLUTION is halved as compared to the NTSC system because of the averaging of the contents of adjacent lines.

PAM, see PULSE AMPLITUDE MODULATION.

panoramic receiver, *n.* a RECEIVER that automatically tunes to a number of selected FREQUENCIES in sequence. Panoramic receivers are used to monitor international distress frequencies, or to monitor signals from a number of users of different frequencies.

paper capacitor, *n.* a CAPACITOR whose DIELECTRIC is paper, usually impregnated with insulating oil. The metal conductors can be aluminium foil ribbons, or aluminium metallized coatings (see METALLIZED PAPER CAPACITOR). The sandwich of conductors and paper is rolled into the form of a cylinder with another layer of paper. Values of capacitance in the region of 1nF to $0.5\mu F$ can be achieved in a reasonable size, and the voltage rating can be high, typically 100V to 1kV.

paper tape, *n.* a now little-used method of permanent storage for computer data. The data is recorded by punching holes across the width of the tape, using up to eight preset positions. Each line of holes represents one character of a data file. The system is very slow, and has been superseded for all but important archives by MAGNETIC DISK storage. See also MAGNETIC TAPE, MAGNETIC RECORDING.

parabolic reflector or **microwave dish,** *n.* a concave mirror of parabolic cross-section that is used as a receiving or transmitting aerial for radio waves in the form of a parallel beam. For transmission, the signal source (often the horn end of a waveguide) is located at the focus of the REFLECTOR, so that waves from the horn are reflected into a beam whose area of cross section is the same as that of the reflector. For reception, waves hitting the reflector are focused on to a small area at which the first receiver stage is placed. Small parabolic reflectors are now being sold for domestic use, to pick up direct satellite broadcasts.

parallel, *adj.* (of a circuit or component) being connected in a way that makes it possible to share CURRENT across a common POTENTIAL DIFFERENCE. Resistors in parallel form a total resistance that is smaller than any of the single values. Capacitors in parallel form a capacitance that is the sum of individual capacitance values. Cells in parallel with the same voltage output form a battery with higher current rating, but the same voltage output as a single cell.

parallel-loading, *n.* the loading (see LOAD) of a RESONANT CIRCUIT by connecting a resistor in PARALLEL. The lower this value of resistance, the greater the loading or damping (see DAMPED).

parallel-plate capacitor, *n.* a CAPACITOR consisting of a pair of PARALLEL conducting plates separated by an INSULATOR called the DIELECTRIC. For such a structure, capacitance can be calculated from the dimensions of the plates and the thickness and relative PERMITTIVITY value of the DIELECTRIC. Most practical forms of capacitor are variations on this basic design.

parallel resonant circuit, *n.* a RESONANT CIRCUIT that uses an inductor connected in parallel with a capacitor.

parallel-T network, see TWIN-T NETWORK (1).

parallel transmission, *n.* a connection between a COMPUTER and a PERIPHERAL that consists of a number of lines, one for each digital bit in the data unit. Parallel transmission is fast and is used for connecting the computer to disk systems. It is also widely used for connecting printers to computers, using the standard developed by Centronics Inc., and for digital network control using the IEEE protocol developed by Hewlett-Packard.

parameter, *n.* a quantity whose value is fixed only for one particular example. The parameters of a TRANSISTOR, for example, include quantities such as the forward-current transfer ratio (current out/current in). This parameter may be constant for one particular transistor and set of conditions, and may have a different value under different test conditions, or in the next transistor that is tested.

parametric amplifier, *n.* a form of AMPLIFIER that is used mainly for MICROWAVES. The parametric amplifier uses a circuit that contains a device, such as a VARACTOR, for which a PARAMETER (capacitance in this example) is electrically variable. By using a signal to vary the parameter at a suitable frequency, a combination of amplification and frequency mixing can be achieved. The action of varying the parameter is called *pumping*.

paraphase amplifier, *n.* an amplifier that converts SINGLE-ENDED signals (unbalanced signals whose sum amplitude is always zero) into balanced form (see BALANCED AMPLIFIER). The simplest form of pharaphase amplifier is the transistor with equal loads in the emitter and the collector circuits. See Fig. 67.

parasitic aerial or **parasitic radiator** or **passive aerial,** *n.* an AERIAL element that does not receive or transmit signals and is used only to make an active aerial directional. See also REFLECTOR, DIRECTOR.

parasitic oscillations, *n.* the unwanted OSCILLATIONS caused by POSITIVE FEEDBACK in an AMPLIFIER. The feedback is usually through STRAY CAPACITANCE or inductance, and so is at a very high frequency. In some cases, such as audio amplifiers, the existence of parasitic oscillations may not be suspected as they can occur above the audio range. See also MOTORBOATING.

parasitic radiator, see PARASITIC AERIAL.

parasitic stopper, *n.* a RESISTOR used to suppress PARASITIC OSCILLATIONS. When parasitic oscillations cannot be stopped by using screening, changes in layout, or other methods of avoiding STRAY CAPACITANCE and INDUCTANCE effects, parasitic stoppers may be used. These are resistors connected into the path of the oscillation to cause damping (see DAMPED). Stoppers are usually resistors of 100R to 1K value wired as close to the electrodes of an active device as possible.

partition noise, *n.* a form of NOISE in multi-electrode devices. In the days when pentode valves were used in receivers,

Fig. 67. **Paraphase amplifier**. A simple form of paraphase amplifier that produces both in-phase and inverted signals.

partition noise arose because of random fluctuations in the electron currents to the various electrodes.

pass band, *n.* the range of frequencies that a FILTER will pass from input to output without attenuation. The range is usually defined in terms of the frequencies that are attenuated by -3dB as compared to the central frequency of the band. Compare REJECTION BAND.

passivation, *n.* the protection of a SEMICONDUCTOR surface from unwanted contamination.

passive aerial, see PARASITIC AERIAL.

passive component, *n.* a COMPONENT that cannot cause a POWER gain. Components such as resistors, capacitors, and linear inductors (including transformers) are all 'passive'. Nonlinear action along with a power supply, such as in a MAGNETIC AMPLIFIER, can cause a component to be classed as an ACTIVE COMPONENT.

passive substrate, *n.* an INSULATION layer on which a semiconductor can be formed or attached.

patchboard or **plugboard,** *n.* a board that contains sockets that are connected to circuits or devices. Experimental interconnections of CIRCUITS can then be arranged by connecting sockets with patch cords.

See also BREADBOARD.

patch cord, *n*. **1.** a CABLE with a plug at each end, used for patching on a PATCHBOARD. **2.** an extension cable, especially one that allows a board taken from a circuit to be run externally for fault-finding purposes.

patching, *n*. **1.** the making of connections temporarily on a PATCHBOARD or BREADBOARD. This is done to test a circuit idea, to make measurements without the need to have to construct a circuit or printed circuit board. Patching is feasible only for comparatively low-frequency circuits because of the large STRAY CAPACITANCES and INDUCTANCES of a patchboard system. **2.** in the US, a connection between a radio link and a telephone system.

PCB, see PRINTED CIRCUIT BOARD.

p-channel, *n*. a conducting channel in a FIELD-EFFECT TRANSISTOR that uses P-TYPE doping.

See also N-CHANNEL.

PCM, see PULSE CODE MODULATION.

PD, see POTENTIAL DIFFERENCE.

PDA, see POST-DEFLECTION ACCELERATION.

PDM, see PULSE-DURATION MODULATION.

peak clipping, see CLIPPER.

peak factor, *n*. the ratio of peak amplitude to ROOT MEAN SQUARE value.

peak forward voltage, *n*. the maximum permitted voltage across a RECTIFIER when current flows in the forward direction. The rectifier may be a DIODE, or a JUNCTION in a bipolar transistor.

peak inverse voltage, *n*. the maximum permitted voltage across a RECTIFIER when bias is reversed, with no current flowing. This is a very important quantity for a semiconductor junction such as a diode, because if the peak inverse voltage is exceeded, the diode or junction may break down. Unless the amount of reversed current can be limited, the diode or junction will then be destroyed.

peak limiter, see CLIPPER.

peak load, *n*. a LOAD that causes maximum possible power to be dissipated from a circuit.

peak point, *n.* the start of a NEGATIVE RESISTANCE region in the CHARACTERISTIC of a UNIJUNCTION or TUNNEL DIODE.

peak-riding clipper, *n.* a form of self-adjusting CLIPPER. A peak-riding clipper charges a CAPACITOR to the value of the peak voltage of the signal, and uses this voltage as a clipping voltage. In this way, brief interference pulses can be clipped, but fluctuations in the peak amplitude of the wanted signal will not cause clipping of the signal.

peak-to-peak amplitude, *n.* a measurement of AMPLITUDE, particularly for an ASYMMETRICAL WAVEFORM, that extends from the positive peak value to the negative peak value. See Fig. 68 on page 234.

peak value, *n.* an AMPLITUDE measured to one peak of a WAVEFORM from the zero voltage or from a steady BIAS level.

peak white, *n.* the level of AMPLITUDE of TV signal that corresponds to peak output of light on the screen.

pedestal, *n.* a SQUARE WAVEFORM on which another pulse can be placed. The pedestal provides the starting voltage for the main pulse. See Fig. 69 on page 234.

percentage modulation, *n.* a measurement of linear AMPLITUDE MODULATION. The 'percentage modulation' is the amplitude of modulating signal divided by the amplitude of carrier signal, expressed as a percentage.

perfect crystal or **ideal crystal,** *n.* a CRYSTAL in which each atom is precisely in position, with no impurity particles to disturb the geometrical and chemical perfection.

perfect transformer or **ideal transformer,** *n.* a TRANSFORMER with no STRAY CAPACITANCE nor stray inductance, no EDDY CURRENTS, no HYSTERESIS in its core, and hence 100% COUPLING of signal and no LOSS.

period, *n.* the duration of one CYCLE of a waveform, equal to the inverse of frequency.

periodic, *adj.* (of a WAVEFORM, oscillation, coincidence or effect) occurring at regular intervals.

peripheral, *n.* any DEVICE external to the main system, i.e. devices that can be connected to a computer, are controlled by the computer, but are not necessarily part of the computer. Examples include disk drives and printers.

Fig. 68. **Peak-to-peak amplitude.** (a) For a symmetrical wave, the peak-to-peak amplitude is simply twice the peak amplitude. (b) For a pulse or any other asymmetrical waveform, the peak-to-peak amplitude is the only relevant measurement.

Fig. 69. **Pedestal.** A pulse superimposed on a pedestal. The addition of a pedestal is a method of ensuring, for example, that the pulse peak voltage cannot fall below the triggering level.

permalloy, *n.* a nickel–iron alloy that has high PERMEABILITY and unusually low HYSTERESIS loss.

permanent magnet, *n.* a MAGNET made of material that has retained magnetism. The essential feature of a material for permanent magnets is high RETENTIVITY. The magnet can be demagnetized by heating or by applying a strong enough alternating field which is then slowly reduced to zero. Permanent magnets are self-demagnetizing to some extent unless the flux path is kept closed by the use of a KEEPER.

permeability, *n.* the ratio of flux density (**B**) in a material to the magnetic field strength (**H**) that causes it. Symbol: μ; unit: henry per metre. All materials have a value of permeability, but for most materials this value will be close to the value of the permeability of free space, about 1.25×10^{-6} henry/metre. For FERROMAGNETIC materials, the values of permeability can be much higher, but are variable. Since the value of permeability of a ferromagnetic material is proportional to the slope of the HYSTERESIS curve at any point, the value can vary from about the free-space value (at SATURATION) to a very large value (many tens of thousands of times greater than the free space value) in the middle of the hysteresis curve. The permeability of a ferromagnetic material is usually quoted as the RELATIVE PERMEABILITY, and the conditions under which it is measured must be stated.

permeability of free space, *n.* the magnetic constant for a vacuum. The symbol is μ_0 (pronounced mew–nought) and the value in modern units is approximately 1.25×10^{-6} henry/metre. The speed of light or any other electromagnetic wave in space is given by:

$$c = \frac{1}{\sqrt{(\epsilon_0 \mu_0)}}$$

where c is the wave velocity and ϵ_0 (pronounced epsilon-nought) is the PERMITTIVITY OF FREE SPACE. See also PERMITTIVITY, PERMEABILITY.

permeability tuning or **slug tuning,** *n.* the tuning of a RESONANT CIRCUIT by varying the position of a core in a coil.

Permendur, *n. Trademark.* a cobalt–iron magnetic alloy. The important characteristic of Permendur is its very high SATURATION flux density.

Perminvar, *n. Trademark.* a nickel–cobalt–iron alloy. Its notable characteristic is a very constant value of RELATIVE PERMEABILITY over a wide range of applied magnetic field strengths.

permittivity, *n.* a characteristic of an INSULATOR, defined as the ratio of electric displacement (**D**) to electric field strength (**E**) in a material. Electric displacement is a quantity describing the behaviour of charge in a DIELECTRIC subjected to an electric field. Symbol: ϵ; unit: farad per metre. More practically, the permittivity value appears in the expression for the capacitance of a PARALLEL–PLATE CAPACITOR:

$$C = \frac{\epsilon A}{d}$$

in which C is capacitance in farads, A is plate area in square metres, d is plate spacing in metres, and ϵ is the permittivity of the dielectric. If the dielectric is air or vacuum, then the value of permittivity is the PERMITTIVITY OF FREE SPACE, ϵ_0.

permittivity of free space, n. the value of PERMITTIVITY for a vacuum. Symbol: ϵ_0. The permittivity and the PERMEABILITY of a medium determine the speed of electromagnetic waves in that medium. See PERMEABILITY OF FREE SPACE.

persistence, n. the phenomenon of light being emitted from a PHOSPHOR screen for some time after it has been struck by an electron. See AFTERGLOW, LONG–PERSISTENCE SCREEN.

perveance, n. a characteristic of a vacuum valve. Perveance measures the DC conductivity of the valve per unit area of cross-section of the ANODE.

PFM, see PULSE–FREQUENCY MODULATION.

phase, n. a time difference between two identical WAVEFORMS of the same FREQUENCY. Phase difference is expressed either as a fraction of a CYCLE or, more usually, as a PHASE ANGLE. When the term is used to denote a single wave, the phase angle between current and voltage is meant.

phase angle, n. a measurement of the difference in the PHASE of two waves. The phase angle between two waves, in degrees, is found by expressing the phase as a fraction of the cycle time and multiplying this figure by 360. If the phase angle is to be expressed in radians, then the time fraction must be multiplied by 2π.

phase constant, n. the PHASE shift per unit length of line caused by a TRANSMISSION LINE.

phase control, n. a method of using a THYRISTOR to control power in an AC circuit. In a phase-control system, the point of switching on the thyristor in each cycle can be varied with respect to the phase of the voltage.

phase-correction circuit, n. a CIRCUIT that restores the original PHASE (of voltage relative to current) of a signal to compensate for the effect of another network.

phase delay, *n*. the amount of PHASE shift per unit frequency of a wave.

phase deviation, *n*. the difference in PHASE ANGLE of a phase-modulated wave compared to a standard (reference) phase. See PHASE MODULATION.

phase difference, *n*. the difference in PHASE between two waves expressed in terms other than PHASE ANGLE, e.g. time difference or fraction of a cycle.

phase discriminator or **phase-sensitive discriminator,** *n*. a form of demodulator for phase-modulated signals (see PHASE MODULATION). The phase discriminator produces an output voltage that is proportional to the phase difference between the input signal and a reference signal.

phase distortion, *n*. the unwanted PHASE DIFFERENCE between current and voltage of a waveform. Phase distortion is caused by the presence of reactive components in the current path.

phase inverter, *n*. **1.** a signal waveform inverter, such as an INVERTING AMPLIFIER. **2.** a circuit that changes the phase of a signal by 180 degrees. In common usage, the term usually denotes **1.**, but **2.** is the more correct definition.

phase-locked loop, *n*. a CIRCUIT in which the PHASE of a LOCAL OSCILLATOR is locked to the phase of an incoming signal (see LOCK-IN). This implies that the frequencies of the two signals are also equal. The locking action is carried out by using a PHASE DISCRIMINATOR to generate a signal proportional to the phase difference between the signals, and then using this signal to correct the oscillator frequency until phase equality is reached.

phase modulation (PM), *n*. the MODULATION of the PHASE of a CARRIER by a SIGNAL. The phase change of the carrier is made proportional to the amplitude of the modulating signal. The carrier amplitude remains constant, and the frequency of the variation is the same as the frequency of the modulating signal. The effect of phase modulation is indistinguishable from that of FREQUENCY MODULATION.

phase-sensitive detector, see PHASE DISCRIMINATOR.

phase shift, *n*. a change in the relative PHASES of two quantities;

the term usually denotes a change in the phase of voltage relative to current in a single wave.

phase-shift oscillator, *n.* a form of OSCILLATOR that uses an INVERTING AMPLIFIER. The phase of the output signal is shifted by 180 degrees, using a CR network, and connected to the input. For a sine wave, the phase shift has the same effect as an inversion, so that the feedback is positive for the frequency at which the phase shift is 180 degrees. The output of the phase-shift oscillator is a sine wave only if the gain is maintained at the minimum level needed for oscillation. See Fig. 70.

phase splitter, *n.* a CIRCUIT that produces a WAVE and its inverse, used mainly as a DRIVER for a BALANCED AMPLIFIER.

phase velocity, *n.* the apparent speed of a WAVE peak in a group of waves in a dispersing medium. If the GROUP VELOCITY is less than the wave speed, the phase velocity is greater than the wave speed.

phasing, *n.* **1.** the adjusting of two signals so as to be in PHASE. **2.** the correct time adjustment of a synchronizing signal.

phonon, *n.* a mechanical wave QUANTUM used in connection with heat transfer and the propagation of acoustic waves.

phono plug, *n.* a popular type of plug (and socket) for audio use, particularly in the US. The plug is of coaxial design with a 3mm diameter pin and 9mm diameter shield.

phosphor or **fluorescent screen,** *n.* a material used for coating CATHODE-RAY TUBE screens. Phosphors are metal compounds, usually sulphides or silicates of heavy metals, that have been 'activated' by DOPING with other metals, notably silver. The effect is that incoming radiation, either as ultraviolet or electron beams, will cause light to be emitted by the phosphor. The emitted light is always at a lower energy level than that of the incoming radiation.

Phosphors can be manufactured for many colours of visible light (and for infrared and ultraviolet) by suitable choice of materials. The white phosphor for monochrome television use is a mixture of phosphors, with a predominantly blue cast. Phosphors for colour TV use must be reasonably well matched, so that the ratio of beam currents for equal brightness is not too great. The red phosphor is normally the least efficient.

Fig. 70. **Phase-shift oscillator**. The waveform is very sensitive to the GAIN of the STAGE, here shown adjustable. For serious use, the gain would be automatically controlled.

photocathode, *n.* a thin layer of material that emits ELECTRONS in a vacuum when struck by light. Photocathodes are based on materials such as antimony, caesium, rubidium, potassium and sodium. These are easily prepared as thin films by evaporation, but can exist only in a vacuum. For use in PHOTOCELLS and PHOTOMULTIPLIERS, the photocathodes are made after the tube has been evacuated.

photocell or **electric eye** or **photoelectric cell,** *n.* a DEVICE that will provide an electrical OUTPUT from a light INPUT (1). See also PHOTOCONDUCTIVE CELL, PHOTOELECTRIC EFFECT.

photoconductive cell, *n.* a form of PHOTOCELL that uses a material whose conductivity is affected by light. Many semiconductors are photoconductive, but the materials that are used most frequently in photoconductive cells are cadmium sulphide and silicon (for small detectors) and antimony trisulphide or lead (IV) oxide for TV camera tubes (vidicons).

photoconductivity, *n.* a variation of CONDUCTIVITY caused by light in which the conductivity of the material increases when it is illuminated.

photoconverter, *n.* a form of ANALOGUE/DIGITAL CONVERTER that uses PHOTOCELLS, one for each BIT of a binary number, and beams of light whose position varies according to an input. The input can be from a rotating shaft or a sliding object, and the beams of light are obtained by shining a light through masks carried on the moving objects.

photocurrent, *n.* an electric CURRENT produced in a PHOTOCELL by the action of light.

photodetector, *n.* any electronic DEVICE that gives an electric OUTPUT when struck by light.

photodiode, *n.* a SEMICONDUCTOR diode that is light sensitive. The diode is operated with REVERSE BIAS, and is contained in a transparent material. When illuminated by light, a reverse current flows. The current is very small (to avoid damaging the device), but the speed of response of most photodiodes is rapid.

photoelectric effect, *n.* the EMISSION of electrons from materials exposed to energetic radiation such as light. The velocity of the emitted electrons depends on light frequency, and their quantity on light intensity. For any given photoemissive material, there will be a threshold frequency below which no emission can be obtained no matter how intense the radiation.

photoemission, *n.* the EMISSION of electrons due to the impact of electromagnetic radiation. See PHOTOELECTRIC EFFECT.

photoemissive cell, *n.* a form of photocell that makes use of PHOTOEMISSION.

photolithography, *n.* a method of making PRINTED CIRCUITS and INTEGRATED CIRCUITS. A material is coated with PHOTORESIST, a light-sensitive form of lacquer. The material is now treated like a photographic plate, and exposed to an image, often using ultraviolet rather than visible light. The effect of the exposure is to harden the lacquer selectively, so that washing the material will remove only the unexposed lacquer. This results in a lacquer image that is resistant to mild acids. The material that is not lacquer-coated can then be etched with acid, or otherwise chemically treated. Finally, the lacquer can be removed with solvents or by heating.

The technique is stretched to its limits in the manufacture of INTEGRATED CIRCUITS, mainly because the distance between conducting lines in modern ICs is equal to a few wavelengths of light.

photomultiplier, *n.* a combination of a PHOTOCATHODE and a set of secondary multipliers, or DYNODE CHAIN. The current output of a photomultiplier is very much greater than that of a photocathode. However, the signal from a photomultiplier can be subject to NOISE as the DARK CURRENT is multiplied as well as the wanted photocurrent.

photon, *n.* a discrete amount of radiated energy that behaves like a particle. The energy of a photon of a given radiation is found by multiplying the frequency of the radiation by Planck's constant, *h*.

photoresist, *n.* the photosensitive lacquer that is used in PHOTOLITHOGRAPHY. The original photoresist was the gelatine-chromium (IV) oxide mixture that once formed the basis of the gum-bichromate photographic system. Nowadays a form of lacquer is used.

photosensitivity, *n.* the sensitivity of a material to light. In electronics, photosensitivity is usually applied to materials that give an electrical response to light.

phototransistor, *n.* a TRANSISTOR provided with a transparent covering over the base region which renders it light sensitive. The phototransistor is operated with no connection to the base. Base current is created by the PHOTOEMISSION effect of light striking the base region. The base current is then amplified by the normal transistor effect. The sensitivity is much higher than that of a photodiode, but the response time is longer.

phototube, *n.* a tube, normally evacuated, that makes use of a PHOTOCATHODE to emit electrons. The electrons may be collected by an anode at a positive voltage, or multiplied by a DYNODE CHAIN, as in a PHOTOMULTIPLIER.

photovoltaic cell, *n.* a DEVICE that generates a VOLTAGE when exposed to light. The first photovoltaic cells used the element selenium, but these have been replaced by junctions formed between metals and a semiconductor (usually silicon).

photovoltaic effect, *n.* the generation of a VOLTAGE at the junction of two materials when struck by light.

pi-attenuator, *n.* an ATTENUATOR section with one series element and two parallel elements resembling the Greek letter π.

241

PIC, *abbrev. for* proportional-integral control, a form of
FEEDBACK control in which a signal proportional to the error
amount is superimposed upon a ramp obtained by integrating
the output.

pick-up, a gramophone TRANSDUCER. The pick-up converts
the mechanical vibration of a stylus that tracks the groove of a
recording into an electrical output. The pick-up is usually in
the form of a plug-in cartridge that can be attached to a TONE-
ARM that holds the cartridge and guides it across the record
surface.

    The methods of converting vibration into electrical signals
range from the PIEZOELECTRIC PICK-UP, for high output and
relatively low quality, to the MOVING-COIL PICK-UP for the
lowest output and the highest quality. These systems may
become obsolete with the introduction of digital COMPACT DISC
systems.

pico-, *prefix.* denoting 10^{-12}. Symbol: p.

picture element or **pixel,** *n.* the smallest part of a TELEVISION
picture display that can be separately controlled. For TV
reception purposes, this size is governed by the scanning
frequencies, and (for colour) by the colour system and aperture
grid dimensions.

picture frequency, *n.* the rate of transmission of a complete
picture in television. See FRAME, RASTER.

picture noise, *n.* the effect on a picture of a noisy signal. NOISE
in a TV signal causes a speckled appearance on the picture. On a
colour signal, noise is most noticeable on areas of saturated red.

picture signal, *n.* the video COMPOSITE SIGNAL that carries all
the picture information.

picture tube, *n.* a television CATHODE-RAY TUBE. The tube uses
a large, usually rectangular, tube face, and is very short. The
deflection is obtained using coils around the neck of the tube,
often shaped so as to obtain the very large deflection angle that
is required. The tube is operated at a comparatively high
accelerating voltage of about 14kV for monochrome, 24kV for
colour signals. The picture intensity variations are obtained by
using the incoming video signals to control the electron beam

current. A single electron gun is used for a monochrome tube, three guns for colour tubes.

piezoelectric crystal, *n.* a CRYSTAL, such as quartz or barium titanate, that produces a voltage when stressed, and changes dimensions when a voltage is applied. The crystals are cut so that the effect is most marked between two parallel faces, and these faces are metallized (see METALLIZING), usually with silver. The crystals can then be used as electromechanical TRANSDUCERS.

piezoelectric cutter, *n.* a sound-recording DISC cutter. The audio signals are applied to a PIEZOELECTRIC CRYSTAL that carries a cutting stylus. The cutter is forced to cut a spiral groove in a disc by being attached to a form of screw-cutting lathe. As the audio signal causes vibration of the stylus, the cut groove is modulated. Two cutters set 90 degrees apart are needed for stereo recording.

piezoelectric loudspeaker, *n.* a type of treble loudspeaker or TWEETER. The piezoelectric tweeter uses a PIEZOELECTRIC CRYSTAL that is attached to a small diaphragm. When an audio signal is applied to the faces of the crystal, the diaphragm is vibrated.

piezoelectric pick-up, *n.* a PICK-UP for conventional gramophone records that uses a PIEZOELECTRIC CRYSTAL. The early crystal pick-ups used materials such as Rochelle salt that were unstable, and often failed in hot moist weather. Later types used 'ceramic' cartridges, with materials such as barium titanate. These produced fairly high outputs (tens of millivolts), but never with the linearity that may be obtained using pick-ups of the magnetic type, such as MOVING-IRON PICK-UPS or MOVING-COIL PICK-UPS.

piezoelectric strain gauge, *n.* a method of obtaining an electric signal proportional to strain in a material. The piezoelectric strain gauge uses a PIEZOELECTRIC CRYSTAL attached using epoxy resin to a part of a structure. Changes in the stress in the structure appear as voltage signals from the piezoelectric material.

pinch-off, *n.* the reduction of CURRENT to zero in the channel of a FIELD-EFFECT TRANSISTOR. Pinch-off occurs when the channel contains no free conductors because of the bias at the GATE (1).

pincushion distortion, *n.* the DISTORTION of a TV picture from a rectangular shape to a shape in which the sides are curved inwards. Compare BARREL DISTORTION.

p-i-n diode, a DIODE with a thin layer of intrinsic (high resistance) semiconductor between the P-TYPE and the N-TYPE layers. Used as a microwave source (IMPATT diode) and as a photodiode (the depletion layer diode).

pinout, *n.* a chart that shows the pin connections for an INTEGRATED CIRCUIT.

PIPO register, *n.* a parallel-in, parallel-out REGISTER, constructed from a connected chain of FLIP-FLOP units. Each unit has a separate input and a separate output. The units can load inputs and deliver outputs together, but there is no shifting of bits from one unit to another unless by external connections. See Fig. 71. Compare PISO REGISTER, SIPO REGISTER, SISO REGISTER, FIRST-IN/FIRST-OUT BUFFER, FIRST-IN/LAST-OUT BUFFER.

Fig. 71. **PIPO register**. The arrangement of a typical PIPO register, showing four bit units.

Pirani gauge, *n.* a form of gauge for measuring low gas pressures in a partial vacuum that operates by measuring the heat conduction through gas, and is suitable mainly for the lower levels of vacuum.

See also IONIZATION GAUGE.

PISO register, *n.* a parallel-in, serial-out REGISTER, constructed

Fig. 72. **PISO register**. The arrangement of a typical PISO register showing four bit units.

from a connected chain of FLIP–FLOPS used for connecting data from parallel to serial form. A PISO register can accept one bit of a parallel input at each unit, but outputs are obtained in serial form from one end only by clocking (see CLOCK) the register. See Fig. 72.

Compare PIPO REGISTER.

pixel, see PICTURE ELEMENT.

planar process, *n.* a process for forming SEMICONDUCTOR junctions that uses a layer of silicon oxide on the surface of pure silicon to ensure that diffusion processes affect only semiconductor surfaces that have been exposed by etching away the oxide layer.

plane-polarization, *n.* a type of polarization in which waves of light or other electromagnetic radiation have an electric component that is always in a fixed direction, the plane of polarization.

See POLARIZED (1).

plan-position indicator (PPI), *n.* a form of RADAR display in which the position of the receiver is indicated by the centre of the display tube. Distances from the radar receiver are proportional to distances from the centre of the tube face, and directions are read from a scale of compass positions around the tube face.

plasma, see IONIZATION.

plasma display, *n.* a form of ALPHANUMERIC display that uses the glowing gas of a plasma (see IONIZATION).

plasma oscillations, *n.* the OSCILLATIONS of the current CARRIERS in a plasma (see IONIZATION). These cause severe radio–frequency interference.

plastic–film capacitor, *n.* a capacitor of the rolled type that uses plastic film in place of paper (see PAPER CAPACITOR). The main types are polyester (mylar) and polystyrene.

plate, see ANODE.

plateau, *n.* a part of a graph that remains horizontal over a considerable range of values.

plated–magnetic wire, *n.* a wire of nonmagnetic material such as copper, which is covered with a magnetic coating deposited by ELECTROPLATING.

plated–through connection, *n.* a connection from one side to the other in a double-sided PRINTED CIRCUIT BOARD. A hole is drilled through the board, and metal is deposited on the sides of the hole to link the copper strips on each side of the board.

plug, *n.* a male connector for connecting signals or power. Compare SOCKET.

plugboard, see PATCHBOARD.

plug–in, *adj.* (of part of a circuit) being connected or disconnected by a PLUG and SOCKET.

plumbicon, *n.* a form of VIDICON that uses a lead (IV) oxide photoconductor.

plumbing, *n.* a slang term for MICROWAVE signal connections through waveguides.

PM, see PHASE MODULATION.

p–n junction, *n.* an area of contact between a P-TYPE and an N-TYPE semiconductor within a CRYSTAL. The JUNCTION cannot be created simply by bringing two materials together, because there must be no discontinuity in the crystal structure at the junction. At any such junction, a rectifying effect will be obtained. Current will flow easily in the forward direction of the junction, with the p-type material at a higher positive voltage than the n-type material. No current flows until a threshold voltage is reached, after which the current-voltage graph is exponential. In the reverse direction, current is negligible, until the voltage reaches a level at which the junction breaks down.

p-n-p transistor, *n.* a TRANSISTOR that is formed using P-TYPE material for the EMITTER (1) and COLLECTOR regions, and n-type for the BASE. In use, both the collector and the base must have negative bias with respect to the emitter. See also N-P-N TRANSISTOR.

point-contact diode, *n.* an early form of semiconductor DIODE construction. A point-contact diode uses a metal wire ending in a sharp point, which makes contact with a small piece of semiconductor material. The diode was used mainly for demodulation of high-frequency low voltage signals.

poison, *n.* an impurity in a material that prevents normal action. Compare DOPING, a deliberate addition of impurity in order to obtain specific effects.

polarity, *n.* **1.** a variety of charge (positive or negative). **2.** a magnetic direction (north or south). **3.** a method of connecting certain components, e.g., electrolytic capacitors, to avoid damage.

polarized, *adj.* (of an electromagnetic wave, an electronic component, or a connector) **1.** having the electric field portion of an electromagnetic wave with a defined amplitude in a defined direction, which is taken as the direction of polarization. In a very few cases (see TM WAVE), the direction of the magnetic portion of the wave is considered. **2.** having a fixed charge, such as possessed by an ELECTRET, or requiring a potential of stated polarity on each of two connectors, like an ELECTROLYTIC CAPACITOR. **3.** making connection between a plug and a socket in such a way that only one method exists of inserting the plug in the socket, e.g. the 13A mains plug and socket used in the UK.

pole, *n.* **1.** a point on the complex S-plane (see POLE-ZERO DIAGRAM). **2.** a centre of charge or magnetism. **3.** a terminal, especially a cell or battery terminal.

pole-zero diagram, *n.* a graph showing the voltage responses (*poles*) and current responses (*zeroes*) of a circuit. For example, the natural response of a second-order system is determined by the roots of its characteristic equation. In general these roots are COMPLEX NUMBERS.

As an example, consider the locus of roots for a series RLC (resistor, inductor, capacitor) circuit as R varies. The characteristic equation of such a circuit is

$$LS^2 + RS + 1/C = 0$$

and the roots are

$$S = -R/2L \pm j(1/LC - R^2/4L^2)^{\frac{1}{2}} = a \pm j\omega$$

where S = a complex frequency, $j = \sqrt{-1}$, and ω is angular frequency. When $R = 0$, $S = \pm j\omega_n$, defining values of the undamped NATURAL FREQUENCY. When $R > 0$, a real part of S appears and the values of S are complex conjugates.

The governing equation of the RLC circuit is

$$L\frac{dI}{dt} + RI + \frac{1}{C}\int I dt = V$$

If the current I is exponential, i.e., $I = I_0 e^{St}$, this becomes

$$LSI + RI + \frac{1}{SC}I = V$$

and we can define impedance $Z(S)$ as

$$Z(S) = \frac{V}{I} = SL + R + \frac{1}{SC}$$

The magnitude of $Z(S)$ can be plotted as a height above the S plane. Typically, the impedance function plotted in three dimensions (a, ω and $|Z(S)|$) has the appearance of an exponential-sided cone. The tip(s) of the cone(s) are called 'poles', and signify components of the natural voltage response of a circuit. Points at which the magnitude of $Z(S)$ is zero are called 'zeroes', and signify components of the natural current response of a circuit. The pole-zero concept is a powerful tool for determining the natural forced behaviour of any linear circuit. The reader is recommended to study an advanced textbook on this topic for further details. See Ref. 2 for further details.

polyester-film capacitor, *n.* a rolled capacitor that uses polyester in place of paper. See PAPER CAPACITOR.

polyphase supply, *n.* an electrical supply that uses more than two PHASES. The usual form is three phase, in which the currents in the three lines are 120 degrees out of phase with each other.

polyphase transformer, *n.* a TRANSFORMER with several windings that can be connected to a polyphase supply.

polystyrene-film capacitor, *n.* a type of CAPACITOR that uses the same form of construction as a PAPER CAPACITOR, but using polystyrene film in place of paper.

port, *n.* **1.** an INPUT/OUTPUT circuit, particularly for a computer system. A port must include storage, because there can be no certainty that the input or output will take place at a time when it can be used. In addition, a port includes a method of interrupting (see INTERRUPT) the action of the MICROPROCESSOR so as to trigger the reading of an input. **2.** a terminal on a device.

position sensor, *n.* a device, sometimes based on the HALL EFFECT, that can sense the position of a mechanical device. Other examples include optical-shift position sensors, and ultrasonic proximity detectors.

positive, *adj.* (of a material) having a deficiency of ELECTRONS. The term is applied to any material in which the number of electrons is less than the number of protons. Compare NEGATIVE.

positive bias, *n.* the application of a steady positive potential to a circuit or active component terminal such as the GATE (1) of a field-effect transistor. Compare NEGATIVE BIAS.

positive feedback or **regeneration,** *n.* the process of sending back a portion of the output to the input of an amplifier in such a way as to reinforce the input signal (see FEEDBACK). Positive feedback increases gain, narrows bandwidths, increases distortion, and can cause oscillation. Compare NEGATIVE FEEDBACK.

positive ion, *n.* an atom that has lost one or (sometimes) more ELECTRONS and is therefore positively charged. Because of the charge, the positive ion will experience a force in an electric field opposite in direction to that experienced by an electron. Compare NEGATIVE ION.

positive logic, *n.* the logic system in normal use in which a positive voltage represents level 1, and zero or negative voltage represents level 0. Compare NEGATIVE LOGIC.

positive temperature coefficient (PTC), *n.* a figure that expresses by how much a quantity increases in value as the temperature increases. Compare NEGATIVE TEMPERATURE COEFFICIENT.

post-deflection acceleration (PDA), *n.* the acceleration of an electron beam in a CATHODE-RAY TUBE after the deflection of the beam. The method applies to electrostatically deflected tubes as used for oscilloscopes and other instruments. For high deflection sensitivity, the electron velocity must be low, for high brightness the velocity must be high. In a PDA tube, the accelerating voltage as far as the DEFLECTION PLATES is low. Following the deflection plates, the beam is accelerated to a high velocity so as to produce a bright trace.

The separation of the low-velocity and high-velocity regions can be very complete, as in the MESH PDA TUBE system. An alternative is the SPIRAL PDA tube, in which an anode at the deflection plates is connected to the final anode by a thin spiral of high-resistance graphite. This allows a graduated accelerating field to be created between the end of the deflection region and the screen.

pot, see POTENTIOMETER.

potential, see ELECTRIC POTENTIAL.

potential barrier, *n.* the difference in VOLTAGE between two points that forms an obstacle to the movement of a charged particle. A negative electrode, for example, forms a potential barrier to an electron.

potential difference (p.d.), *n.* the difference in ELECTRIC POTENTIAL between two points. Symbol: U or V or ΔV; unit: volt. Potential difference is defined as the amount of work done per unit charge when a charge is moved from one point to the other, along any path.

potential divider, *n.* a series arrangement of RESISTORS. A voltage is applied over the whole set, and fractions of the voltage can be obtained at each point where two resistors are

Fig. 73. **Potential divider**. See main entry.

connected. The division formula is expressed as:

$$V_{out} = V_{in} \frac{R_2}{R_1 + R_2}$$

For alternating signals, capacitors or inductors can be used to form potential dividers. See Fig. 73. See also COLPITTS OSCILLATOR, COMPENSATED ATTENUATOR.

potential gradient or **electric field strength,** *n*. the POTENTIAL DIFFERENCE between two points divided by the straight-line distance between the points. Unit: volts per metre.

potentiometer (pot), 1. a variable resistor having a moving contact that can be placed at any point between the terminals of a resistive coil or carbon track. **2.** an instrument for measuring ELECTRIC POTENTIAL using a tapped voltage divider.

powdered–iron core, see DUST CORE.

power, *n*. the rate of the production or dissipation of energy. Symbol: *P*; unit: watt. In DC circuits, power is calculated from the product of POTENTIAL DIFFERENCE and CURRENT, $V \times I$. For AC systems, the quantities must be measured in ROOT MEAN SQUARE terms and be in phase.

power amplifier (PA), *n*. **1.** a STAGE that provides output POWER to a LOAD. **2.** the final RF AMPLIFIER that provides POWER to the aerial from a transmitter. **3.** the audio power amplifier stage that delivers the signal to the loudspeaker(s).

power component, *n*. the in-phase component of current or voltage.

power efficiency, *n*. the ratio of output power to input power, particularly for a TRANSDUCER.

power factor, *n*. the fraction by which the product $V \times I$ for AC signals must be multiplied to obtain true POWER. The power factor is equal to the cosine of the phase angle between voltage and current.

power gain, *n*. the ratio of POWER output to power input for any device or circuit.

power pack, *n*. a circuit that converts AC mains supply voltage into low-voltage DC for an electronic device. The conventional power pack will consist of a mains transformer, RECTIFIERS, and smoothing, possibly with voltage stabilization stages. See also RESERVOIR CAPACITOR.

power supply, *n*. the source of POWER for an electronic circuit that can be mains, battery, solar cell, or other methods.

power transistor, *n*. a TRANSISTOR that is designed to handle large currents and dissipate heat efficiently. A power transistor usually has a large area of collector in good thermal contact with a metal casing. This allows the transistor to dissipate a large steady power providing that the case can be cooled by conduction or convection. See HEAT SINK.

PPI, see PLAN–POSITION INDICATOR.

PPM, see PULSE–POSITION MODULATION.

pre-amplifier (preamp), *n*. a STAGE or set of stages of low-noise voltage amplification, used in audio amplifiers in particular. In audio amplifiers, the preamp handles all the selection and mixing of inputs at various voltage levels. The system is arranged so that the output will be of about the same amplitude for any selected input. The output of a preamplifier is normally connected to the input of a POWER AMPLIFIER stage.

pre-emphasis, *n*. a selective boosting of high audio frequencies. Pre-emphasis is used before transmitting FM signals, and before recording on tape or on disc. In all these systems the noise tends to be concentrated mainly at high frequencies, and using a pre-emphasized signal, the receiver or playback stages can cut treble or high frequencies (DE-EMPHASIS), and the noise

along with it. This restores the treble to its correct level, and
reduces noise.

E 6 series	E 12 series	E 24 options
20%	10%	5%
1·0	1·0	1·0
		1·1
	1·2	1·2
		1·3
1·5	1·5	1·5
		1·6
	1·8	1·8
		2·0
2·2	2·2	2·2
		2·4
	2·7	2·7
		3·0
3·3	3·3	3·3
		3·6
	3·9	3·9
		4·3
4·7	4·7	4·7
		5·1
	5·6	5·6
		6·2
6·8	6·8	6·8
		7·5
	8·2	8·2
		9·1

Fig. 74. **Preferred values**. Three of the preferred number
series for component values. Any multiple or submultiple of
these numbers can be used.

preferred values, *n.* a set of standardized figures between 1 and
10. These are based on a logarithmic scale, and are used to select
values for RESISTORS and CAPACITORS. The principle is that if a
set of values in a tolerance range of, say, 20% is selected, then no
value of resistance or capacitance can possibly be rejected. A
nominal 2K2 resistor, for example, in the 20% tolerance range,
could have a value of up to 2K64, or down to 1K76. The next
value of 3K3 could be as low as 2K64, and the previous value of
1K5 could be as high as 1K8. A range of resistors or capacitors
can therefore be manufactured, and values selected for 5%
accuracy. The remaining components can then be selected to

provide a set of 10% components, and the remainder can be sold as 20% tolerance. See Fig. 74.

pre-pulse trigger, *n*. a TRIGGER PULSE for a CATHODE–RAY OSCILLOSCOPE. In a system, such as a radar transmitter, in which a master pulse is generated and used to trigger all the subsequent effects, it is useful to provide a pulse that immediately precedes the main pulse. This makes it possible to trigger an oscilloscope timebase just before the main pulse arrives, so that the shape of the whole of the main pulse can be displayed. If the main pulse is used for triggering, its leading edge cannot be seen on the oscilloscope display.

Prestel, *n*. *Trademark*. an information service for computers that makes use of the telephone network.

PRF, see PULSE–REPETITION FREQUENCY.

primary electron, *n*. an electron obtained from a cathode of any type. Compare SECONDARY ELECTRON.

primary radiator, *n*. the main element in an AERIAL. For a TRANSMITTER, the primary radiator is the electrically connected aerial element. For a receiving aerial, the primary radiator is the element that is connected to the RECEIVER.

primary service area, *n*. the area of good reception around a TRANSMITTER. The primary service area is served by the ground wave, and interference from reflected waves is small. This ensures a good standard of reception, day or night.

primary standard, *n*. a national or international standard of measurement, such as the National Physical Laboratory (UK) current balance for the ampere. SECONDARY STANDARDS are calibrated from instruments of this type for everyday use, as primary standards may take a long time to set up and use.

primary voltage, *n*. the AC or signal VOLTAGE across the primary winding of a transformer.

primary winding, *n*. the WINDING to which the input signal for a transformer is connected. In the conventional iron–cored transformer, the primary winding is wound immediately next to the core. For modern toroidal transformers, primary and SECONDARY WINDINGS are often interchangeable. See also TERTIARY WINDING.

printed circuit, *n*. a CIRCUIT in which the interconnections between components consist of copper strips on an insulated board. The components are introduced by drilling holes for terminating leads, threading the leads through and soldering them to the copper strips. The pattern of connections on the board is printed on by PHOTOLITHOGRAPHY, and the unwanted metal is etched away in ferric chloride or ammonium persulphate. Double-sided boards have a pattern printed on each side, with PLATED-THROUGH CONNECTIONS between each side. Connections to the board are made using EDGE CONNECTORS, or by soldering sockets to the board. The advantages of printed circuits include uniformity, since the boards can be mass-produced, and the ease of automated assembly.

printed circuit board (PCB), *n.* a board prepared by PHOTOLITHOGRAPHY ready for the insertion of components. The board material is usually SRPB (silicon–resin bonded paper) or fibreglass, and the copper sheet is bonded to the board as part of the manufacturing process for the board. The bonding must be sufficiently heat-resistant to allow DIP-SOLDERING of the whole board when the components have been threaded into place.

print-through, *n.* a transfer of MAGNETISM from one layer of magnetic tape to another. Print-through causes the effect of *pre* or *post-echo*. This means that a loud sound can cause a faint copy to be heard just before and just after the correct position on the tape. Print-through is minimized if tape is frequently wound from reel to reel.

probe, *n.* **1.** a lead for injecting or extracting signals, e.g. the sharp-pointed or clip-ended lead of a test instrument such as a voltmeter, signal generator or (particularly) an oscilloscope. **2.** a conductor that is inserted permanently into a RESONANT CAVITY (of a microwave device) to inject or extract signals.

PRO-ELECTRON code, *n.* a system of coding TRANSISTORS and other SEMICONDUCTOR devices. The PRO-ELECTRON code uses letters and numbers. The first letter is a material code, with A = germanium, B = silicon. The second letter denotes the device type, such as C for audio voltage amplifier, F for RF amplifier. A last letter of X,Y or Z is used to denote an industrial device. The number that follows is the maker's development number. The advantage of the PRO-ELEC-TRON code is that the type of device can be deduced from the code, unlike the US system of serial numbers.

program, *n.* a set of instructions for a computer or a MICROPROCESSOR.

programmable, *adj.* capable of being controlled by a stored set of instructions, usually in number form.

PROM, *n. acronym for* Programmable Read–Only Memory, a form of permanent NONVOLATILE memory for a computer. The data stored on the chip can be read by the computer, but no new data can be written while the chip is in the computer. The chip can be removed from the computer, erased and reprogrammed if changes are needed. See also EAROM, EPROM, ROM.

propagation, *n.* the spreading of a radio wave from its source to all the points at which it can be received.

propagation coefficient, *n.* a quantity that measures the attenuation and phase change, per metre, caused by a TRANSMISSION LINE.

propagation delay, *n.* the time delay between the PROPAGATION of a signal into a line and the reception of the signal at the other end. Also used of a broadcast signal to mean the (much shorter) delay caused by the time taken for the wave to move from transmitter to receiver.

propagation loss, *n.* the energy loss from a signal beam in the course of PROPAGATION by radio, cable or optical fibre.

propagation prediction, *n.* a prediction of ionospheric weather conditions. Prediction of changes in the IONOSPHERE is possible with reference to the condition of the sun, and past experience of changes. In this way, predictions of propagation conditions for various wavebands can be made in advance, so that important communications can be routed through channels that will be least affected by the expected changes.

proportional control, *n.* a control system that makes use of NEGATIVE FEEDBACK. The output of the system is measured, and the result of the measurement is used to correct the controlling signal.

proportional counter, *n.* a form of radiation detector. The detector is biased so that the amount of current that is produced is proportional to the energy of the ionizing radiation.

protective gap, *n.* a spark gap that is used to protect high-voltage equipment. Any sudden voltage surge will cause a spark at the protective gap rather than causing breakdown of insulation or other irreversible damage to electronic circuits.

protective relay, *n.* a RELAY that will disconnect a circuit if a fault occurs. See also CONTACT BREAKER, OVERCURRENT TRIP.

proton, *n.* a stable, positively charged elementary particle, found in the nucleus of an atom. The number of protons in an atom is equal to the number of electrons (equivalent to the atomic number of the element). The nucleus of an atom also contains neutral particles called NEUTRONS. The charge of a proton is 1.6022×10^{-19} coulomb; this charge is of equal magnitude but opposite sign to that of an ELECTRON. The rest mass of a proton is 1.67252×10^{-27} kilogram, 1,836 times that of an electron.

proximity effect, *n.* a form of INTERFERENCE between signal conductors. High-frequency signals are carried by currents that flow on the outsides of conductors. If two such conductors are close to each other, the repulsion of the electrons can cause the effective area of the conductors to be restricted, making the apparent resistance higher.

PTC, see POSITIVE TEMPERATURE COEFFICIENT.

PTFE (Trademark: **Teflon),** *abbrev. for* polytetrafluoro-ethylene, a plastic material with very high resistivity, low dielectric loss, low coefficient of friction, and which is almost unaffected by moisture. PTFE is extensively used in high-voltage insulation and in cable connectors.

PTM, see PULSE–TIME MODULATION.

p-type, *adj.* (of a semiconductor material) being doped with ACCEPTOR material. P-type material conducts by HOLE mobility, rather than by ELECTRON mobility. See also N-TYPE.

public address (PA), a sound–reinforcing system for large numbers of listeners that uses microphones, amplifiers and loudspeakers. Problems of PA systems include echos and acoustic feedback, lack of intelligibility, and NOISE.

pulling, *n.* the disturbance of OSCILLATOR frequency by another signal at a nearby frequency. Unless an oscillator is very stable, it can be made to synchronize with a strong signal at a close frequency. Pulling is minimized by isolating an oscillator as much as possible from other circuits. This can be done, for example, by using a separate stabilized supply, encasing the oscillator section in metal, and by connecting its output through a buffer stage.

pullup resistor, *n*. a RESISTOR that is intended to BIAS an electrode to a positive potential, usually that of the supply positive terminal. Several types of logic ICs need pullup resistors if their outputs are not connected directly to another input or if a number of outputs are connected.

pulsating, *adj*. anything oscillating in size, brightness or other quantity.

pulse, *n*. a single cycle of abrupt VOLTAGE or of CURRENT change. The usual pulse form consists of a sharp rise of voltage, followed by a drop to the original level, the BASE LEVEL. In most systems, pulses are used in a pulse train, meaning that the pulses repeat at regular intervals. The intended shape of a pulse is usually rectangular, but due to effects of STRAY CAPACITANCES and inductances, this shape is modified to give the effects of OVERSHOOT, DROOP and RINGING (2). A perfect rectangular pulse would require no time to change its voltage value, but in practice the requirement to charge and discharge stray capacitance means that a definite rise time and fall time can be measured. These times are usually measured between the 10% and 90% amplitude points. The width of the pulse is the time for which its amplitude exceeds the 90% level.

A pulse may be of current rather than of voltage. Pulse shapes other than rectangular are sometimes used, such as triangular and cosine-squared pulses.

pulse–amplitude modulation (PAM), *n*. a form of MODU-LATION based on PULSES at MICROWAVE frequency. The signal to be transmitted is used to modulate the amplitude of pulses in a pulse train. DEMODULATION is very simple (a LOW-PASS FILTER is used), but this type of transmission is very susceptible to interference.

pulse–code modulation (PCM), a form of MODULATION

based on the transmission of DIGITAL signals. The signal's amplitude is sampled at intervals by an ANALOGUE/DIGITAL CONVERTER. The output of the converter is used to generate a series of pulses, so that a set of pulses is sent for each point on the waveform of the signal. At the receiver, these signals are decoded, and the signal recovered from a digital-to-analogue converter.

pulse discriminator, *n.* a CIRCUIT that selects PULSES of a particular specification on the basis of their amplitude, width or repetition frequency.

pulse-duration modulation (PDM) or **pulse-width modulation (PWM),** *n.* a form of MODULATION using a SIGNAL to modulate the width of PULSES. The width or duration of each pulse is proportional to the amplitude of the modulating signal at that instant. DEMODULATION can be carried out by a simple INTEGRATOR.

pulse-forming line, *n.* a line or cable with a reflecting TERMINATION that is used to control the pulse width in a pulse generator that is terminated with a short circuit or an open circuit that will reflect a PULSE back along the line. The length of the line will determine the time needed for a pulse to be propagated down the line and then reflected back, and this time delay can be used to control the pulse width in a pulse generator circuit. An artificial LUMPED PARAMETER line is often used.

pulse-frequency modulation (PFM), *n.* a form of MODULATION in which the repetition frequency of PULSES is proportional to the amplitude of the modulating signal at any instant.

pulse generator, *n.* a CIRCUIT that generates PULSES, usually for testing pulse circuits. For comparatively long pulses, MULTIVIBRATORS can be used, but for pulses in microwave systems, pulse generators based on PULSE-FORMING LINES are more useful.

pulse-height analyser, *n.* a measuring instrument for received PULSES. The analyser shows how many received pulses fall into each group of amplitude.

pulse modulation, *n.* a form of modulation using a train of pulses to carry information. At MICROWAVE frequencies, conventional modulation of oscillators is almost impossible, and most oscillators are operated by pulsing. Only a form of modulating the pulses, then, can allow these frequencies to be used for communications. To take advantage of the large bandwidths that are available at microwave frequencies, MULTIPLEXER systems that allow more than one signal to modulate a pulse train are particularly useful. All pulse modulation systems operate on the basis that the pulse repetition rate will be very much greater than the frequency of the signal that is being modulated, so that the pulses carry a sample of the signal.

pulse-position modulation, *n.* a form of PULSE MODULATION using displacement of a pulse from its standard time position. This requires a clock signal to be available both at the transmitter and at the receiver, so that the deviation of the pulse from its correct timing can be detected.

pulse regeneration, *n.* the restoration of a PULSE to its original specification. All circuits and transmission systems will distort the shape and timing of a pulse. A regeneration system restores the original shape and timing. The regeneration system often consists of a PULSE GENERATOR that is triggered by the imperfect pulse. All digital devices incorporate pulse regeneration, so that a degraded input pulse results in a 'perfect' output pulse.

pulse-repetition frequency (prf), *n.* the rate at which PULSES are transmitted, in terms of pulses per second. The normal KILO- and MEGA- prefixes will be used with the unit of pps (pulses per second), so a rate of 5kpps means 5 thousand pulses per second.

pulse shaper, *n.* a CIRCUIT that alters PULSE shape. The INTEGRATOR and DIFFERENTIATOR circuits are pulse shapers, and a pulse regeneration circuit will consist of, or contain, a pulse shaper.

pulse spacing, *n.* the time between pulses in a PULSE train.

pulse-time modulation (PTM), a general title for any MODULATION system that affects timing rather than amplitude of pulses. See PULSE–DURATION MODULATION, PULSE–FREQUENCY MODULATION, PULSE–POSITION MODULATION.

pulse-width modulation, see PULSE–DURATION MODULATION.

pumping, *n*. **1.** the alteration of a PARAMETER in a PARAMETRIC AMPLIFIER. **2.** the irregular rise and fall in noise level of the sound from a tape that has been recorded with an unsatisfactory noise-reduction system.

punch-through, *n*. a breakdown of a region in a TRANSISTOR. Punch-through in a bipolar transistor means that the base region is destroyed by excessive collector-base voltage, so that the base no longer controls the collector–emitter current. A similar effect occurs in field–effect transistors in which current punches through the substrate layer, bypassing the gate.

puncture voltage, *n*. the value of voltage that breaks down an insulator, particularly the DIELECTRIC of a capacitor.

purity, *n*. the purity of colour in a COLOUR TELEVISION tube. 'Purity' means that when a single colour is displayed, it should appear as the same colour with the same amount of saturation over the whole of the screen. The main cause of impure displays is accidental magnetization of metal components in or around the tube.

purity error, *n*. any cause of impure colour. See PURITY.

purple plague, *n*. a common fault in very early TRANSISTORS. This was caused by the use of gold and aluminium together, so forming an alloy that diffused into the SEMICONDUCTOR.

push–pull, *adj*. (of digital devices and amplifier output stages) having a pair of transistors or MOSFETS (see FIELD–EFFECT TRANSISTOR) that are used alternately to drive the output high (LOGIC ONE) or low (logic 0). See also OPEN–COLLECTOR DEVICE, TRI–STATE DEVICE.

pyroelectric, *adj*. (of a material) generating a voltage from a temperature gradient. Pyroelectric materials are used in fire alarms and other applications. Some types of plastic film are strongly pyroelectric, and also several types of CRYSTAL.

Q

Q band, *n*. a MICROWAVE band in the wavelength range of approximately 6.5mm to 8.3mm, corresponding to the frequency range of 36 to 46GHz.

Q code, *n.* a code used by radio amateurs, particularly on the MORSE CODE bands. The code uses a letter Q followed by other letters to indicate standard questions and answers.

Q factor, *n.* the magnification factor or quality factor of a RESONANT CIRCUIT, used for describing the behaviour of a circuit near RESONANCE. The sharpness of response or selectivity of a circuit to sources of different frequency depends on the Q value. Q factor can be defined as the value of the resistive parallel paths divided by the impedance of the inductive parallel path at the frequency in question. Q factor can be estimated graphically, from a plot of the ratio of output voltage to input voltage, or output current to input current, against frequency. Q factor is found as the frequency at resonance divided by the width of the resonance peak at -3dB points.

Q meter, *n.* an instrument for measuring the Q-FACTOR values of a RESONANT CIRCUIT.

quadrature, *n.* the state of a VOLTAGE or CURRENT having a phase difference of 90 degrees to some reference phase. If, for example, the current wave has a phase angle of 90 degrees with respect to the voltage wave, the two are in quadrature.

quadripole, *n.* a network, particularly a balanced FILTER network, having four separate signal terminals.

quantization, *n.* the SAMPLING of a signal to produce a number of values per second, an essential part of ANALOGUE/DIGITAL CONVERTER operation.

quantum, *n.* a discrete amount of energy. A PHOTON is the quantum of electromagnetic energy and momentum absorbed or emitted in a single process by a charged particle.

quantum yield, *n.* a measure of the efficiency of a PHOTOCATHODE, equal to the average number of electrons produced for each photon of suitable energy.

quarter-wave match, *n.* a LINE (1) that is a quarter of a wavelength long, used for matching two other lines.

quartz crystal, *n.* the silicon-oxide crystal, found naturally, that is used as an electromechanical resonator. The crystal is cut to shape, and opposite sides are metallized (see METALLIZING). The crystal will then act as a TRANSDUCER of radio frequencies to mechanical vibrations and vice versa, and exhibits the

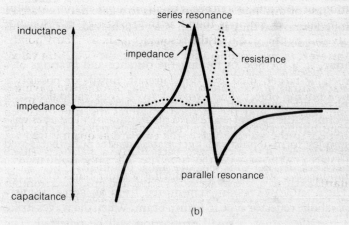

(a)

L, C_c and R are equivalent values of crystal

C_s = stray capacitance

(b)

Fig. 75. **Quartz crystal**. (a) The equivalent circuit and (b) characteristics of a typical quartz crystal. The two resonant frequencies are usually very close in frequency to each other. The equivalent Q-FACTOR is very large, of the order of 50,000.

behaviour of a tuned circuit with very high Q FACTOR. Such crystals are used to control the frequency of transmitters, to generate precise frequencies for timing (as in a digital watch) or for SYNCHRONOUS DETECTION, and in FILTERS with a narrow pass band or stop band. See Fig. 75.

quench, *vb.* to de-ionize an ionized gas. The term can imply that ions in a gas-filled tube such as a GEIGER–MÜLLER TUBE have been made to recombine, so that the gas is no longer conductive.

quiescent current, *n*. the steady current (BIAS current) that flows when no signal is applied to a circuit.

R

race hazard, *n*. a problem in unsynchronized LOGIC GATE circuits. PULSES that form the inputs to a gate may be subjected to delays that are not the same for two different pulse paths. Because of this 'race', the two inputs to a gate may not arrive together, so that the gate action is never achieved. Race hazards are avoided by SYNCHRONOUS operation.

radar, *n*. a method of finding the distance and bearings of a metallic target, such as a ship, aircraft, missile or possibly a nonmoving object. The term is derived from 'radio detection and ranging', and the method measures the time between transmitting a wave pulse and receiving the reflected echo. The simplest form of pulse radar generates a master pulse that is used to start a CATHODE-RAY TUBE timebase. The pulse is also used to modulate a MAGNETRON, producing a short burst of waves. These MICROWAVES are transmitted from an aerial, using a parabolic reflector type to form a beam. When the waves strike a metallic target, a small proportion will be reflected. The returning wave is picked up in the same aerial, amplified, demodulated to form a voltage pulse and displayed on the CRT screen. Because of the use of a timebase triggered by the initial pulse, the distance from the start of the sweep on the CRT screen represents the distance of the target.

A more common modern system is to use a PLAN–POSITION INDICATOR display, so that both distance and bearings can be displayed. Lower-power radar systems use continuous wave or FM systems, and the spread of moving objects can be measured using DOPPLER radar.

radar indicator, *n*. a CATHODE-RAY TUBE display for a RADAR system.

radial-beam tube, *n*. a vacuum electron tube intended for specialized purposes.

radiation pattern, *n*. a diagram that represents the effectiveness of an AERIAL. For a transmitting aerial, it shows lines of constant field strength. For a receiver aerial, it shows lines of equal sensitivity. The usual pattern for a simple directional aerial is a figure-of-eight, with unequal sized LOBES. The required direction is along the axis of the major lobe, and the rear lobe is often undesirable and represents wasted power in a transmitter.

radiation resistance, SEE AERIAL RESISTANCE.

radio, *n*. **1.** the technology of communication with electronically produced electromagnetic waves. **2.** any device that transmits or receives sound signals with these waves, and for a frequency in this range.

radio astronomy, *n*. the process of locating and analysing radio SIGNALS originating from stars or other distant bodies. This has become an important branch of astronomy, because many of the celestial sources of radio waves do not correspond to visible objects.

radio beacon, SEE BEACON.

radio compass, *n*. a form of radio direction finder that makes use of a DIRECTIONAL AERIAL to locate the direction of a radio BEACON or other transmitter in a known location.

radio frequency (RF), *n*. a FREQUENCY in the accepted practical radio range. This covers the frequency range from about 100kHz to about 300GHz. At the lower end of the range, radiation is very difficult unless extremely long aerials can be used. At the upper end of the range, electronic methods for generating signals can no longer be used.

radio-frequency heating, *n*. the heating of objects by radio-frequency currents. The two main methods are induction heating (see EDDY CURRENT HEATERS) for metals and DIELECTRIC HEATING for insulators.

radio noise, *n*. the unwanted NOISE signals that affect radio broadcasts. Noise can be natural or man-made. Natural noise consists of radiation from the movement of ions in the ionosphere and upper atmosphere along with signals directly from the sun and from other radio sources in space. Man-made noise includes interference from other transmitters, car ignition systems, fluorescent lights, electrical machines and other sources of radiation at radio frequencies. See also NOISE.

radio pill, *n.* a pill-shaped capsule that contains a miniature TRANSMITTER. Most radio pills also contain TRANSDUCERS to measure such quantities as acidity, pressure, etc. in the digestive tract of the body. These measurements are modulated onto the signal, so that a RECEIVER can plot conditions as the pill moves.

radio receiver, *n.* a RECEIVER for radio signals that carry sound modulation. The sound signals for entertainment radio will be either amplitude or frequency modulated onto the carrier. Military and other communications equipment will often use SINGLE-SIDEBAND techniques. Frequency modulation is used only for the transmissions on VHF bands, because of the large bandwidth that is needed. The almost universal receiver is the SUPERHETERODYNE, in which the received signal from the aerial is tuned, and may be amplified in one stage, but then converted to an INTERMEDIATE FREQUENCY for subsequent amplification. The demodulated IF signal is passed to the audio frequency stages, including any volume and tone controls, and so to the loudspeaker. At the demodulator, DC signals for gain and frequency control will be extracted. Special SYNCHRONOUS DETECTION techniques will need to be used if the transmission is of the single-sideband type.

FM receivers often make provision for STEREOPHONIC signal reception. Radio receivers can also be bought as TUNERS, containing only the RF, IF and first audio stages. These offer a higher quality of reception (of FM/stereo) and are intended for use with high-quality (Hi-Fi) amplifier and loudspeaker systems. High-quality reception of medium wave broadcasts is impossible because of the large number of (legal) transmitters that operate at closely spaced frequencies, plus various pirate transmitters that in some districts make the use of medium wave reception difficult.

radiosonde, *n.* an airborne measuring device employing data transmission by radio from the upper atmosphere. Radiosondes are used by meteorologists, and employ balloons to carry small transmitters and transducers to the required height. The transmitters send back data on atmospheric conditions, and are ultimately lost.

radiotelescope, *n.* an instrument for receiving radio signals from space. The main aerial types are parabolic dishes or arrays. The rest of the receiving equipment follows conventional radio receiver designs.

radio wave, see CARRIER.

radio window, *n.* the range of FREQUENCIES that are not reflected by the IONOSPHERE and can therefore be used in RADIO ASTRONOMY. The range is roughly from 15MHz (20m wavelength) to about 50GHz (6mm wavelength).

RAM, see RANDOM ACCESS MEMORY.

ramp, *n.* a steadily rising or falling voltage, such as the linear SWEEP portion of a timebase.

random–access memory (RAM), *n.* a form of electronic MEMORY that allows data to be read to or written from any location independently of others. A *serial-access memory* allows access to a unit of data only by shifting other units out. Random access permits only the wanted unit to be affected. This is done by allocating a number, the address number, to each unit of data. A set of address connections to the memory can be used to convey an address number, so that when an address number is placed in binary form on the lines, the correct data unit is made available. Another connection is used to select between reading or writing. Compare READ–ONLY MEMORY.

range, *n.* the distance between TRANSMITTER and RECEIVER. The term is often used to denote the maximum range, the greatest distance at which reliable communication can be established.

range tracking, *n.* a form of RADAR system that allows a moving target to be followed, but reduces other echos. The echo from the target is used to generate a gating signal for the target echo.

raster, *n.* a scanning pattern on a TV screen. Conventional TV uses a SCAN pattern of horizontal lines that slope slightly. Each screen line starts on the left–hand side of the screen and sweeps across to the right, moving downwards slightly as it does so. The line pattern is produced by using a horizontal TIMEBASE waveform, and the vertical movement from a vertical (FIELD) timebase. These timebase signals are applied to different sets of DEFLECTION COILS arranged around the neck of the tube. In this way, a pattern of parallel lines is traced out on the screen. In a complete picture, two sets of lines are used, interlaced. This means that the first set of lines, the even-numbered lines, will be spaced so as to occupy the vertical dimension of the screen. The second set, the odd-numbered lines, will then occupy the spaces between the first lines. The reason for this pattern is to satisfy the contradictory requirements of good vertical resolution, lack of flicker and small bandwidth. By using two interlaced patterns of 310 lines each (UK system), each of 1/50 second duration, the screen flicker is at 50Hz, but the resolution is of a 620 line picture (for monochrome), and the bandwidth is that of a 25Hz repetition rate. The electron beam is suppressed (see BLANKING) during the flyback time to prevent random noise from appearing on the raster.

rating, *n.* a specification of maximum operating conditions. The ratings (of voltage, current, frequency, temperature, etc.) for a component or assembly are determined by the manufacturer.

ratio adjustor, see TAPCHANGER.

ratio detector, *n.* a form of FM DEMODULATOR. The ratio detector is useful only if there is no trace of amplitude modulation in the signal, and has to be preceded by a limiter stage to ensure this. See also FREQUENCY DISCRIMINATOR.

rat-race junction, see HYBRID JUNCTION.

reactance, *n.* the ratio of SIGNAL voltage to signal current in an ideal CAPACITANCE or INDUCTANCE. Ideal in this case means with no measurable series resistance and infinite parallel resistance. The value of reactance depends on the signal frequency as well as on the value of capacitance or inductance. A pure reactance also causes a 90 degree phase shift between voltage and current. For a capacitor, the phase of current leads phase of voltage, and for an inductor, the phase of current lags the phase of voltage. See Fig. 76. See also IMPEDANCE, RESISTANCE. For further details, see Ref. 2.

reactance chart, *n.* a form of NOMOGRAM that is used to show

Fig. 76. **Reactance**. The reactance of capacitors and inductors, showing (a) value formulas, (b) the general reactance-frequency graph. The mnemonic for phase relationship is CIVIL, i.e., Capacitor, I before V; V before I in L (inductor).

reactance for different values of capacitance, inductance and frequency.

reactance transformer, *n.* an IMPEDANCE–matching circuit that uses REACTANCE.

reactivation, *n.* the reviving of electron EMISSION from the cathode or filament of an electron tube (vacuum valve). This usually involves running at higher than normal temperature for some time, often with grid current being passed.

reactive current or **idle current,** *n.* the component of current whose phase angle is at 90 degrees to the phase of voltage.

reactive load, *n*. any LOAD that causes a phase angle between the current and the voltage of a signal wave applied to it, i.e., a load that contains REACTANCE.

reactive voltage, *n*. the component of voltage whose phase angle is at 90 degrees to the phase of current.

reactive volt-amperes, *n*. the product of voltage and current when a phase angle exists. The dissipated power is less than this value, and is found by multiplying the reactive volt-amperes figure by the power factor (the cosine of the phase angle).

reactor, *n*. a COMPONENT that is REACTIVE, such as a capacitor or inductor.

read, *vb*. to copy stored information, particularly in a computing storage system. A nondestructive read process will allow the copy to be made in the form of a voltage on a line without any effect on the stored information. Compare WRITE. A DESTRUCTIVE READ process destroys the stored information in the course of copying it. For example, the stored charge image in a TV camera tube is read by measuring the electron current needed to discharge it.

read-only memory (ROM), *n*. a form of MEMORY for microprocessor or computer use. The usual form of ROM permits random access to any unit, but allows reading only. This form of memory is NONVOLATILE, and is used for all programs that must be present from the instant of switching on.

Compare RANDOM-ACCESS MEMORY.

read-out pulse, *n*. a PULSE applied to a magnetic core MEMORY system that allows a selected part of the memory to be read.

read-write head, *n*. the TRANSDUCER of a tape or magnetic disk recording system.

See MAGNETIC RECORDING.

receiver, *n*. a device that processes radio signals from an AERIAL into their final form (audio, video, digital code, etc.). Compare TRANSMITTER.

reception, *n*. the interaction between an electromagnetic wave and any form of aerial that results in a signal being received.

Compare TRANSMISSION.

reciprocal theorem, *n*. a theorem relating to networks.

Imagine two points, A and B in a linear network. If a (signal) voltage V at point A causes a (signal) current I at point B, then a voltage V at point B will generate a current I at point A.

recombination, n. the removal of CHARGE carriers from a semiconductor or an ionized gas. Recombination can occur when an ELECTRON and a HOLE meet and release energy, so that the electron is no longer mobile, and the hole no longer exists. Both electrons and holes may also be trapped by impurity atoms.

record, n. **1.** a permanent store of data. **2.** a gramophone record. See RECORDING OF SOUND.

recorder, n. a piece of recording equipment, for example, a tape (including cassette) recorder, or (in data recording), a multichannel tape recorder.

See also CHART RECORDER.

recording, n. the storing of data in permanent form.

recording of sound, n. the use of a system of TRANSDUCERS to convert sound into electrical signals that can be recorded. The main systems are mechanical–analogue, mechanical–digital, magnetic, and optical. The mechanical–analogue system uses the vibration of a stylus to modulate the shape of a groove that is cut into a gramophone DISC. The mechanical digital system uses an ANALOGUE/DIGITAL CONVERTER, and records the digital signals by pitting the surface of a disc with a laser beam. The storage density is very high, and the system permits the highest standard of SOUND REPRODUCTION that has been achieved to date, the COMPACT DISC system. The magnetic systems use either analogue or digital recording on magnetic tape. The optical system is used only for film soundtracks, in which the width or density of a strip of film is modulated by the audio signals. Optical systems suffer from poor signal to noise ratios, and noise-reducing techniques such as the DOLBY SYSTEM are very useful. Tape systems that use slow–moving, narrow tapes also suffer from noise problems, and the same solutions are used.

See also DBX.

recording of video, n. the use of a system for recording and replaying video signals, usually on tape (see VIDEO CASSETTE).

control track

video tracks

sound-recording track

Fig. 77. **Recording of video**. The arrangement of the recording head tracks on a typical videotape. The soundtrack is at one edge, and a control track at the other edge. The video-recording tracks run diagonally across the tape.

The recording of video signals on tape requires processing of the signals to reduce their bandwidth. The video-recording heads are moved to sweep along and across the tape, so that the speed of the tape can be comparatively low while permitting the speed of the head relative to the tape to be high. The tape is considerably wider than conventional audio-recording tape.

The sound track is separately recorded, usually on a strip that runs longitudinally, though on some modern machines much higher-quality sound reproduction is obtained by using an additional track swept with the video head. Video recording of a much higher standard is also possible on discs, using the same laser read and write techniques as are used for compact (audio) discs. At the time of publication, these systems allow only reading by the user, but read-write laser discs are under development. See Fig. 77.

rectifier, *n*. a COMPONENT, such as any type of DIODE, that passes current easily in one direction only. A rectifier, used in a half-wave or full-wave circuit will convert AC into UNIDIRECTIONAL CURRENT. This can be used to charge a RESERVOIR CAPACITOR in order to obtain smooth DC.

rectifier instrument, *n*. a measuring instrument that can be used with AC because it contains a RECTIFIER. The rectifier-bridge circuit is normally used.

rectifier voltmeter, *n*. a VOLTMETER that can measure sine wave AC values (see ROOT MEAN SQUARE) because it incorporates a RECTIFIER. The rectifier may be switchable, so that the voltmeter can be used for either DC or AC.

rectifying contact, *n.* a CONTACT between two materials that has a rectifying action. The difference between the forward and the reverse resistance values may be small, but the presence of the rectifying contact can cause nonlinear effects in a signal.

red gun, *n.* one gun of a COLOUR CRT. The red gun is the gun whose electrons will pass through the APERTURE GRILLE to strike only the parts of PHOSPHOR that glow red.

redundancy, *n.* a deliberate or natural duplication. Redundancy in a circuit means that additional components are provided that will take over from other components in the event of failure. This idea can extend to complete systems, such as on-board computers for space or aircraft systems. Redundancy in a signal means information that is not needed. In a TV signal, for example, over 90% of the data that is transmitted on one frame is also transmitted on the next frame, unless there is a change of scene. Some types of narrow bandwidth systems operate by removing redundancy from signals.

reflected current, *n.* the signal current reflected from a faulty termination of a TRANSMISSION LINE.

reflected impedance, *n.* an IMPEDANCE whose effect can be measured in a circuit, but which is connected to that circuit by means of a transformer, line or other coupling. The reflected impedance of the secondary of a transformer is the amount of impedance measured at the primary that is due to the presence of the secondary load.

reflected power, *n.* the POWER that is not absorbed by a LOAD, and which is returned to the generator. This applies typically to a TRANSMISSION-LINE system that is not correctly matched. In a microwave system, reflected power can cause overheating and failure of the microwave generator.

reflected wave, *n.* **1.** a wave reflected in a TRAVELLING-WAVE TUBE. **2.** Another name for SKY WAVE.

reflection, *n.* a reversal in the direction of travel and phase of a WAVE, usually by striking a metal or other conducting surface, or from a discontinuity in a transmission line or other medium.

reflection coefficient, *n.* the ratio of reflected current to forward current in a line. The two currents will not, in general, have the same PHASE.

reflection error, *n.* an error in RADAR or RADAR COMPASS systems caused by false REFLECTIONS of signals.

reflection factor, *n.* a measure of MATCHING in a TRANSMISSION LINE. The reflection factor is the ratio of the current sent to a reflecting load to the current that would be sent to a perfectly matched load. The factor is often converted into DECIBELS.

reflector, *n.* an element of a DIRECTIONAL AERIAL. The reflector is placed behind the active portion of the aerial, which is usually a DIPOLE. Its action is to reflect signal back to the dipole and so greatly reduce the size of the rear LOBE. The reflector can be made of metal sheet, or even from wire mesh. The length of the reflector is always greater than that of the dipole, usually by a factor of about 10%, and the spacing between reflector and active element is of the order of a quarter of a wavelength.

reflex circuit, *n.* a circuit that is used as an AMPLIFIER for a pair of signals at different frequencies. The technique is now obsolete — it was used as a way of economizing on valves in early radio receivers.

reflex klystron, *n.* a form of KLYSTRON in which the beam is reflected back after bunching. The effect is to make the device into a MICROWAVE oscillator, whose frequency is determined by the cavity dimensions and by the voltage applied to the reflecting electrode. Reflex klystrons were once the only available devices for use as local oscillators in microwave receivers, but have now been almost completely superseded for low power applications by GUNN DIODES.

reform electrolytic, *vb.* to apply steady POTENTIAL DIFFERENCE across an ELECTROLYTIC CAPACITOR until the leakage current reaches a minimum. Reforming is sometimes needed after an electrolytic capacitor has been stored unused for a long period, or after exposure to cold conditions. The reforming voltage re-establishes the film of aluminium oxide that acts as the insulator.

refresh, *vb.* to regenerate the condition of a signal. A refresh operation has to be used in storage devices that use destructive readout. The term is applied nowadays mainly to DYNAMIC RAM, which uses MOS capacitors to store data in the form of charges. Because of unavoidable leakage from these capacitors, the memory must be refreshed by recharging at intervals of, typically, one millisecond.

regeneration, see POSITIVE FEEDBACK.

regenerative receiver, *n*. an early type of RECEIVER that achieved very high GAIN and SELECTIVITY by using RF positive feedback. See also SUPER-REGENERATION.

register, *n*. an assembly of connected FLIP-FLOPS in which loading, storage or serial shifting (see SERIAL MEMORY) can be performed. Registers are used in microprocessors and in the CPU sections of large computers. The use of registers is to store data, in particular the results of arithmetic and logic actions on data.

regulator, *n*. a CIRCUIT that can maintain a constant value of either VOLTAGE or CURRENT under a wide range of conditions.

reignition voltage, *n*. the VOLTAGE that is needed to start CURRENT flowing in a gas-filled device. If there is a trace of IONIZATION remaining from previous current flow, the reignition voltage will be lower than the usual cold striking voltage.

rejection band or **stop band,** *n*. the range of frequencies that a FILTER will reject. Compare PASS BAND.

rejector, *n*. a CIRCUIT with very high IMPEDANCE at one frequency. The term usually denotes a PARALLEL RESONANT CIRCUIT used as a band-stop filter.

relative permeability, *n*. the ratio of the permeability of a material relative to the PERMEABILITY OF FREE SPACE. Symbol: μ_r.

relative permittivity, *n*. the ratio of the permittivity of a material relative to the PERMITTIVITY OF FREE SPACE. Symbol: ϵ_r. The relative permittivity value is equal to the value of absolute permittivity of the material divided by the permittivity of free space.

relaxation oscillator or **aperiodic oscillator,** *n*. a form of untuned oscillator in which the active devices pass current only for brief intervals. MULTIVIBRATORS, UNIJUNCTION oscillators and BLOCKING OSCILLATORS are all relaxation oscillators. The output waveform of such an oscillator is aperiodic, and consists of steep-sided waveforms with comparatively long periods of steady voltage, either at zero or supply voltage.

relaxation time, *n.* the recovery time for a CAPACITOR following a sudden change of charge.

relay, *n.* an electromechanical SWITCH. A current flowing through a coil causes a magnetic field that attracts an armature. The armature moves, opening or closing switch contacts that are mechanically connected to it. Many uses of relays have now been taken over by purely electronic components, such as THYRISTORS and TRIACS. In some cases, however, wiring regulations still insist on the use of mechanical relays.

relay driver, *n.* a CIRCUIT that provides current to the coil of a RELAY. When a TRANSISTOR is used as a relay driver, a diode must be connected so as to absorb the pulse of back-emf that will be generated when current is switched off.

reliability, *n.* a measure of confidence in the ability of a DEVICE to keep working. Unlike mechanical devices, the reliability of electronic equipment is too high to measure in terms of probability. A more useful measure is the inverse, FAILURE RATE.

reluctance, *n.* a magnetic circuit quantity comparable with RESISTANCE. See FLUX, MAGNETOMOTIVE FORCE.

remanence or **residual magnetism,** *n.* the retained MAGNETISM of a magnetic material. The remanence is the FLUX DENSITY remaining in material that has been magnetized to saturation, after which the magnetizing field has been removed. See also MAGNETIC HYSTERESIS.

remote control, *n.* the control over a DEVICE at a distance, either by wire signals or by radio.

repeater, *n.* a form of signal BOOSTER. A repeater in a telephone line amplifies the audio signals to compensate for attenuation in the lines. Repeaters can be made that are bidirectional, operating in either direction, or which restore the original waveform of signals such as pulses.

reset, *vb.* to restore anything to its original setting. As applied to a register means to clear, making each output logic 0.

Fig. 78. **Reservoir capacitor**. (a) A half-wave power supply circuit. (b) The action of the reservoir capacitor. (c) The supply waveform when the load draws a substantial current. (d) The approximate formula for ripple voltage.

reservoir capacitor, *n*. an essential part of AC to DC conversion. The reservoir capacitor is charged by a conducting rectifier to the peak voltage of the waveform. When the input voltage to the rectifier drops, the reservoir capacitor supplies current to the load until the rectifier can conduct again. See Fig. 78.

residual charge, *n*. the small amount of CHARGE that remains in a CAPACITOR after a spark discharge.

residual current, *n*. a CURRENT that continues to flow for a

277

short time (measured in nanoseconds) after voltage has been reduced to zero. The effect is caused by the momentum of the CHARGE CARRIERS.

residual magnetism, see REMANENCE.

resistance, *n*. the ratio of DC voltage to DC current for a conductor. Symbol: R; unit: ohm. The inverse of resistance is CONDUCTANCE.

See also OHM'S LAW.

resistance–capacitance (R–C) coupling, a method of transferring signal from one amplifier STAGE to another. A resistor is used as a load in the output stage of one device, and a capacitor is used to transfer AC signal without affecting the DC level of the next stage.

resistance pressure gauge, *n*. a form of pressure gauge that measures pressure by its effect on a resistor.

resistance strain gauge, *n*. a STRAIN GAUGE that uses a wire element. The wire is bonded to the material under test, and changes in strain cause variations in the wire length and cross section that alter its resistance. Semiconductor strain gauges are easier to use because of their much greater sensitivity, but are more costly.

resistance thermometer, *n*. an instrument for measuring temperature electrically. The resistance of any metallic conductor changes with temperature, becoming greater as temperature rises. Resistance thermometers use wire coils (nickel alloy or platinum) as sensors, and the resistance is usually measured in a BRIDGE circuit, using COMPENSATING LEADS.

resistance wire, *n*. a wire that is made from high–RESISTIVITY material. Typical materials are nickel–chromium alloys such as nichrome or constantan.

resistive component, *n*. the COMPONENT of an IMPEDANCE for which voltage is in phase with current.

resistivity, *n*. a quantity that measures the amount of RESISTANCE due to a material and independent of the dimensions of a sample of the material. Symbol: ρ; unit: ohm-metre. The figure of resistivity for a material is independent of shape or size and can be used to calculate the resistance of any specimen of that material. For a sample with area of cross section A and length d, and with resistance R, the resistivity is given by RA/d. Compare CONDUCTIVITY.

resistor, *n.* a COMPONENT that is used for its RESISTANCE. In the past, most resistors were manufactured from carbon composition, a baked mixture of graphite and clay. These have been almost completely superseded by carbon or metal FILM RESISTORS. WIRE-WOUND RESISTORS are used for comparatively low values of resistance where precise value is important, or for high dissipation. They are unsuitable for RF use because of their reactance.

See also VARIABLE RESISTOR.

resistor-transistor logic (RTL), *n.* an obsolete system of logic circuitry for INTEGRATED CIRCUIT use. These circuits use integrated resistors and transistors to form logic GATES (2).

resolution or **definition,** *n.* the ability of a display system to show fine detail, particularly cathode-ray and LCD displays.

resolution of potentiometer, *n.* a measure of the ability of a variable POTENTIOMETER to produce a small voltage change by a small adjustment. When wire-wound potentiometers are used, the smallest percentage change in resistance is given by the change from one turn of the winding to the next. For continuous metal-film potentiometers, this restriction does not apply, and greater resolution can be obtained.

resonance, *n.* the maintenance of OSCILLATION with minimum driving signal. A RESONANT CIRCUIT will show little response to signals until a signal close to the natural resonant frequency is used. At the resonant frequency, maximum current flows in the resonant circuit components for minimum input signal. There is usually current or voltage magnification, so that the circuit acts as a form of selective amplifier for one frequency.

resonance bridge, *n.* a form of BRIDGE circuit in which one arm consists of a series-tuned circuit. The bridge can be balanced only at the resonant frequency of the tuned circuit. From the balance conditions, the resistance of the tuned circuit can be found.

resonant cavity, *n.* a closed space surrounded by metal that acts as a RESONANT circuit for MICROWAVES.

resonant circuit or **tuned circuit,** *n.* a circuit that will resonate at some frequency. 'Lumped' resonant circuits use a capacitor and an inductor, but resonance can also occur in a quartz crystal, in a transmission line, and in a cavity.

resonant frequency, see NATURAL FREQUENCY.

resonant line, *n*. a TRANSMISSION LINE whose inductance and capacitance resonate at the operating frequency.

restore, *vb*. to return to original conditions.

retentivity, *n*. the quantity that measures the amount of retained magnetism of a magnetic material after an applied field has been removed. The units are as for flux density, webers per square meter. See also MAGNETIC HYSTERESIS, COERCIVITY.

reverberation unit (reverb. unit), *n*. a form of ULTRASONIC DELAY LINE used to provide artificial echo in a sound recording.

reverse AGC, *n*. a form of AUTOMATIC GAIN CONTROL that uses NEGATIVE BIAS. Reverse AGC is used when the gain of the amplifier stages is reduced by reducing their operating current. Compare FORWARD AGC.

reverse bias, *n*. a BIAS that opposes the flow of current in a device. Compare FORWARD BIAS.

reverse direction, *n*. the direction of high resistance to current flow through a device.

RF, see RADIO FREQUENCY (RF).

RF heating, *n*. eddy current heating (see EDDY CURRENT HEATER) or DIELECTRIC HEATING using radio frequencies.

rhombic aerial, *n*. a four-sided wire structure that acts as a DIRECTIONAL AERIAL.

ribbon microphone or **induction microphone,** *n*. a form of dynamic-induction MICROPHONE. A thin metal ribbon is stretched between the poles of a high-flux magnet. Vibration of the ribbon by sound waves causes an induced signal voltage that can be amplified. The microphone uses no separate diaphragm, so greatly reducing unwanted resonances, and is particularly suitable for high-quality work. The output is very small, but because of the low impedance it is not difficult to avoid interference pick-up. See also VELOCITY MICROPHONE.

right-hand rule, *n*. see FLEMING'S RULES.

ring counter, *n*. a form of digital counter that uses FLIP-FLOPS connected in a circular arrangement, so that the last flip-flop's output is connected to the input of the first flip-flop.

ringing, *n.* **1.** the oscillation of a resonant circuit caused by a pulse signal (SHOCK EXCITATION). **2.** unwanted oscillations appearing in a pulse.

ripple, *n.* the proportion of AC remaining in a steady voltage from a power supply. The ripple is due to the fluctuations of voltage across the RESERVOIR CAPACITOR as it is charged and discharged. For a full-wave rectifier system, the ripple frequency is twice supply frequency, but for a half-wave circuit, the ripple will be at supply frequency. The ripple waveform is generally a sawtooth rather than a sine wave.

ripple counter, *n.* a form of digital counter that consists of a chain of FLIP-FLOPS. The input pulses are used to switch the first flip-flop, and the output of this flip-flop is used to toggle the next in the chain. The number of pulses is shown in terms of the digital number stored by the outputs of each flip-flop. As each flip-flop input is the output of the previous stage, incrementing the count by one will cause a successive series of charges to 'ripple-through' the device.

ripple factor, *n.* the percentage of RIPPLE in a DC supply. This is expressed as the percentage of ROOT MEAN SQUARE ripple, assuming that the ripple is a sine wave – which it may not be.

ripple filter, *n.* an integrating or smoothing circuit that removes RIPPLE. The circuit is a simple form of LOW-PASS FILTER, using series inductance or resistance and parallel capacitance.

ripple frequency, *n.* the frequency of RIPPLE, in terms of supply frequency. If a bridge rectifier is used, ripple occurs at twice the supply frequency, if a half-wave rectifier is used, ripple is at supply frequency.

rise time, *n.* the duration of a pulse LEADING EDGE. This is usually taken as the time for the voltage to change from 10% to 90% of the pulse peak voltage.

RMS, see ROOT MEAN SQUARE (RMS).

robotics, *n.* the study of machines with some form of intelligence. The term 'robot' generally denotes any machine that has been programmed to carry out a set of repetitive mechanical actions with minimum human intervention.

ROM, *n. acronym for* Read–Only Memory, a form of memory for computers. The ROM operates with random access, but can be read only, not written. This makes it suitable for programs and other data that have to be available at the instant of switching on. ROMs for modern systems are manufactured by IC masking, making permanent connections within an IC to logic 0 or 1, along with memory addressing circuits so that the state of each connection can be read. Semipermanent programs can be stored in PROM form.

See also EPROM, EAROM.

root mean square (RMS), *n.* **1.** the square root of the average of the squares of a set of numbers or quantities. **2.** the root of the mean value of the square of wave amplitude. The root is used to find the DC equivalent of an AC quantity. The principle is that power can be correctly calculated for the AC circuit using RMS values (providing that PHASE SHIFTS are correctly taken into account). For a sinusoid, the RMS value is equal to peak value divided by $\sqrt{2}$. A different factor must be used for other waveforms.

See also TRUE RMS.

rotary encoder, *n.* an ANALOGUE/DIGITAL CONVERTER for a rotating shaft, which often uses an optical source/sensor arrangement and a slotted disk.

rotating–anode tube, *n.* a form of X-RAY TUBE in which the ANODE can be rotated to avoid overheating.

rotation or **endaround shift,** *n.* a serial memory or REGISTER action in which the most significant bit from the end of a memory or register is loaded in at the least significant end, the remaining bits being shifted one place to make room.

rotator, *n.* a portion of a WAVEGUIDE that changes the plane of polarization of the waves.

rotor, *n.* the rotating part of a motor or generator. Compare STATOR.

RS232, *n.* an internationally agreed standard for serial data transmission. It specifies high and low voltage levels, timing, and control.

R–S flip–flop, *n.* the simplest type of FLIP–FLOP, constructed from AND and NOT gates. An output is obtained if one input

R	S	Q	Q̄
0	1	1	0
1	1	1	0
1	0	0	1
1	1	0	1
0	0	not generally used	

Fig. 79. **R-S flip-flop.** The form of an R-S flip-flop constructed from NAND gates. The 1,1 input is a holding input. The circuit can also be constructed from NOR gates, and the holding input is the 0,0, with the 'forbidden' input 1,1.

at the two terminals, R and S, is at LOGIC ONE. The output is then stored for as long as both inputs are held at logic zero. The R–S flip-flop was superseded by the J–K FLIP–FLOP except for the purpose of switch debouncing. See Fig. 79.

rumble, *n.* a low-frequency NOISE. The term usually denotes low-frequency audio signals caused by mechanical vibrations of the motor of a gramophone disc player.

runaway, *n.* a loss of control, e.g., THERMAL RUNAWAY, the loss of control of temperature. If the temperature of a transistor increases to such an extent that the base current is no longer able to control collector current, the current and temperature will increase until the junctions are destroyed. Thermal runaway is very rare with modern silicon transistors.

S

saddle–shaped field, *n.* the shape of the ELECTROSTATIC FIELD required of an ELECTRON LENS to focus a beam of electrons. The field can be obtained from a set of three electrodes, with the central electrode at a lower potential than the other two. See Fig. 80 on page 284.

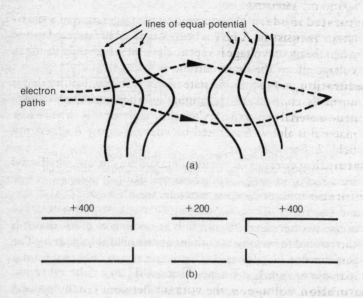

lines of equal potential

electron
paths

(a)

+ 400   + 200   + 400

(b)

Fig. 80. **Saddle-shaped field.** (a) The saddle-shaped field of
lines of equal potential, and the electron paths (dotted) in
such a field. (b) A cross section of a typical electrode
structure, that will produce a field shape as shown in (a).

sag, *n*. the decay of amplitude of a square PULSE. If the input to a
circuit is a perfect square pulse, sag on the output pulse is caused
by poor low–frequency response. The amount of sag is quoted
as a percentage of peak amplitude.

sampling, *n*. the making of measurements at intervals.
Sampling is an essential part of ANALOGUE/DIGITAL CONVERTER
operation and the conversion will be useful only if the sampling
rate is high enough. A minimum sampling rate of twice the
sample frequency is often quoted, but in practice a minimum of
five or ten times is used. See also SHANNON'S SAMPLING
THEOREM.

saturable reactor or **transductor,** *n*. an INDUCTOR whose
inductance value can be considerably changed by passing DC

through another coil wound on the same core. See also MAGNETIC AMPLIFIER.

saturated mode, *n*. the constant-current operation of a FIELD-EFFECT TRANSISTOR. A FET is being operated in saturated mode when the DRAIN voltage is kept at a level at which only the GATE voltage affects the drain current.

saturation, *n*. **1.** a limiting state of any variable quantity that is normally controlled by changing another quantity. A magnetic material is saturated when the magnetic flux density of a material is almost unaffected by changes in the magnetizing field. **2.** See HUE.

saturation current, *n*. a state of maximum current, unaffected by a rise of voltage. See SATURATED MODE.

saturation resistance, *n*. the RESISTANCE between COLLECTOR and EMITTER (1) of a saturated bipolar TRANSISTOR. SATURATION occurs because the resistance falls to such a low value that the current is determined by the load resistor rather than by the base current.

saturation signal, *n*. a SIGNAL that overloads a radar RECEIVER.

saturation voltage, *n*. the VOLTAGE between COLLECTOR and EMITTER (1) of a saturated bipolar TRANSISTOR. For a silicon transistor, this is typically less than 200mV.

SAW, see SURFACE ACOUSTIC WAVE.

sawtooth oscillator, *n*. an OSCILLATOR whose output is a voltage or current wave of sawtooth shape. The sawtooth oscillator is a form of RELAXATION OSCILLATOR.

sawtooth waveform, *n*. the output WAVEFORM from a SAWTOOTH OSCILLATOR. An ideal sawtooth waveform consists of the linear SWEEP section, a brief FLYBACK, and a waiting period between the end of the flyback and the start of the next sweep.

S band, *n*. a MICROWAVE band, with wavelength range from 5.77cm to 19.3cm, corresponding to the frequency range of 1.55GHz to 5.2GHz.

scale of integration, *n*. a description of the number of DEVICES that can be obtained on a single CHIP. The integration scales range from SSI (small scale), through MSI, LSI to VLSI (very large scale integration).

scaler, *n*. a form of PULSE-count divider. A scaler gives a pulse output after a fixed number of input pulses have been received. Most scalers are decade (ten pulses in for one out) or binary (two, four, eight or sixteen pulses in for one out).

scan, *n*. the movement of an ELECTRON BEAM across a target or screen (scanning). Television requires both a horizontal and a simultaneous vertical scan. See also RASTER.

scanner, *n*. **1.** a detector system for radioactive material. The term usually denotes a detector of radio tracers in the body, allowing a map to be made of suspect tissue. **2.** a slang term for a TV outside-broadcast van.

scanning, see SCAN.

scanning yoke, *n*. an arrangement of DEFLECTION COILS for a TV or radar CATHODE-RAY TUBE.

scattering loss, *n*. the loss of energy from an electron or light or radio BEAM by irregular reflections. Loss by scattering is particularly noticeable when the wavelength of the radiated energy is close to the dimensions of scattering particles, e.g. the effect of fog on light. The use of metal strips (called chaff or window) to confuse radar is an example of deliberate scattering of electromagnetic waves. An electron beam is scattered when it passes through matter.

schematic, see CIRCUIT DIAGRAM.

Schmitt trigger, *n*. a form of level-triggered BISTABLE CIRCUIT. The output of a Schmitt trigger remains low until the input voltage reaches a critical level. The output then switches high. The input voltage must then be lowered to a different and lower critical level in order to switch the output voltage low again. The Schmitt trigger is a particularly useful circuit for PULSE REGENERATION. See Fig. 81.

Schottky diode or **hot-carrier diode,** *n*. a DIODE that uses a metal-semiconductor JUNCTION, usually aluminium–silicon. The diode has a very low forward voltage for conduction, fast switching speed, and fast cutoff on reverse bias. Schottky diodes are incorporated into a range of digital logic ICs (the TTL LS series) in order to achieve faster switching with lower values of current.

Schottky noise or **shot noise,** *n*. a form of NOISE caused by the

Fig. 81. **Schmitt trigger**. (a) The Schmitt trigger circuit. (b) Its CHARACTERISTIC. The characteristic exhibits hysteresis that can be very useful, particularly for digital circuits. Schmitt triggers are available in IC form.

random emission of electrons, particularly in vacuum devices.

scintillation, *n*. **1.** the flash of light in some types of CRYSTAL when struck by an ionizing particle. **2.** the random variation of amplitude in a radio signal that has been transmitted over a long distance.

scintillation counter, *n*. a detector and counter of IONIZING RADIATION. The active elements consist of a scintillating crystal and a PHOTOMULTIPLIER. The flash of light produced by the CRYSTAL for each ionizing particle is detected by the photo-

287

multiplier, and the output pulse from the photomultiplier is amplified and used to operate a SCALER or COUNTER. The colour of light from the scintillation counter depends on the energy of the particle that produced it, and the pulse amplitude from the photomultiplier is also affected by the energy of the radiation. This makes it possible to analyse the output of a scintillation counter in more detail than is possible if a GEIGER–MÜLLER TUBE detector is used.

SCR, see THYRISTOR.

scrambler, *n.* a DEVICE for making telephone communications secure. The signal is treated, for example by inverting the frequency bands, so that it makes no sense to any listener who does not have an unscrambler for decoding.

screen, *n.* the endplate of a CATHODE-RAY TUBE, or the metal shield against electric or magnetic fields. See FARADAY CAGE, MAGNETIC SCREENING.

screen burn, see ION BURN.

screening, *n.* the encasing of a CIRCUIT with metal to reduce the effect of MAGNETIC or ELECTRIC FIELDS. The screening is usually against external fields, but can be used to prevent internal fields from escaping. For electrostatic screening, the metal should be a good conductor, and earthed. For magnetic screening, the metal must be of very high PERMEABILITY, and in the form of a complete loop.

screened pair, *n.* two insulated signal–carrying wires surrounded by a conducting braiding. A screened pair is very commonly used for stereo audio signals, with one wire for each channel and the braiding used for the earth connection.

SCS, see SILICON–CONTROLLED SWITCH.

search coil, *n.* a small COIL that is used along with a ballistic galvanometer as a method of measuring flux. This method of measuring flux has been largely superseded by the use of HALL-EFFECT devices.

SECAM, *n. acronym for* Système Electronique Couleur Avec Mémoire, the name of the French COLOUR TELEVISION transmission system that differs in several respects from the NTSC and PAL systems. In the SECAM system, the colour difference signals, **R-Y** and **B-Y**, are sent alternately. The signals are frequency modulated onto the SUBCARRIER, and a delay line is used at the receiver to allow both sets of signals to be available. The use of sequential signals effectively halves the vertical resolution, as the summing of signals does in the PAL system, and the use of frequency modulation causes marginally more visible dot-patterning on monochrome receivers than the PAL system. PRE-EMPHASIS is used to reduce the effect of the frequency variation of the subcarrier.

secondary cell, *n.* a CELL whose chemical action is reversible. The cell will provide electric energy until the chemical action is almost complete, at which point the action can be reversed by connecting the cell to a source of POTENTIAL DIFFERENCE that is higher than the normal output potential difference of the cell. This recharging action can be continued until the chemicals in the cell have been completely restored to their original state, allowing the cell to be used again. See also LEAD-ACID CELL.

secondary electron, *n.* an ELECTRON that has been emitted from a material in a SECONDARY EMISSION process. Compare PRIMARY ELECTRON.

secondary emission, *n.* the EMISSION of electrons from a material because of electron bombardment (of PRIMARY ELECTRONS). The effect occurs only for a limited range of accelerating voltage of the primary electron beam, between the crossover voltages. Below the first crossover voltage (30 to 100V usually) primary electrons land or are reflected. Above the second crossover voltage (in the region of 2,500 to 4,000 volts), primary electrons penetrate the material and are retained. In the secondary emitting region more electrons are emitted, with low velocities, than land. If the material is an insulator, it will become positively charged as a result of the secondary emission. See Fig. 82 on page 290.

secondary radar, *n.* a radar system in which reflections are not used. See IFF, INTERROGATING SIGNAL, TRANSPONDER.

secondary standard, *n.* a standard of measurement that can be used for calibrating instruments. A secondary standard, some-times confusingly known as a substandard, is calibrated from a PRIMARY STANDARD that may be a cumbersome and impractical

Fig. 82. **Secondary emission**. A typical secondary-emission graph for a material, showing the voltages of the first and second crossovers. Between these crossover points, more electrons are leaving the surface than land. If the substance is an insulator, its voltage will stabilize at cathode potential for bombardment at a voltage lower than that of the first crossover. For a bombarding voltage of a value between that of the crossover points, the surface will stabilize at the anode voltage. For bombardment using a voltage greater than that of the second crossover, the insulator potential will stabilize at the second crossover potential. This is one reason for using an aluminized screen for a cathode-ray tube, because in the absence of aluminizing, the screen surface is at the second crossover potential rather than at the anode potential.

device. The secondary standard then becomes the practical implementation of the standard.

secondary voltage, *n*. the AC voltage across the SECONDARY WINDING of a TRANSFORMER.

secondary winding, *n*. the TRANSFORMER winding across which an output of AC is taken. In the older core type of transformer, the secondary winding was the outside winding, wound over the primary winding. In modern toroidal and shell-construction transformers, the secondary and PRIMARY WINDINGS are interchangeable, and the only difference is in function.

See also TERTIARY WINDING.

see-saw circuit, *n*. an INVERTER with unity gain. The see-saw

Fig. 83. **See-saw circuit**. The see-saw circuit, or PARAPHASE AMPLIFIER in a direct-coupled form. The resistors marked as R are equal, and the output is an inverted copy of the input, with the same amplitude.

circuit uses 100% NEGATIVE FEEDBACK in an INVERTING AMPLI-FIER, and its main application is for inverting a signal to apply to a balanced amplifier. See Fig. 83.

selective fading, *n.* a form of FADING in which some frequencies of a signal are affected more than others, causing severe distortion that cannot be remedied by devices such as AUTOMATIC GAIN CONTROL.

selective interference, *n.* a form of INTERFERENCE, such as deliberate jamming, that affects one or a few particular frequencies.

selectivity, *n.* the ability to select a particular FREQUENCY. The simplest measurement of selectivity is the BANDWIDTH of the circuit or complete device.

See also Q FACTOR.

selenium, *n.* an element related to sulphur that was one of the first known SEMICONDUCTORS. It exhibits PHOTOCONDUCTIV-ITY, and when in contact with a metal acts as a PHOTOVOLTAIC CELL.

selenium rectifier, *n.* a RECTIFIER that uses selenium–iron junctions. Selenium rectifiers were once extensively used for power supplies. They have now been replaced with the smaller and more efficient SILICON DIODES. An incidental advantage of this is the elimination of the hazard of the poisonous fumes from burning selenium that used to be a predominant smell in electronics workshops.

self-capacitance, *n*. the STRAY CAPACITANCE between adjacent turns of wire in a coil. This causes a coil to have a self-resonant frequency, and an equivalent single value of capacitance can be calculated from the inductance value and the resonant frequency.

self-excited, *adj*. (of an oscillator) being self-starting. Some very stable oscillators are not self-starting, and need an applied signal to start oscillation.

self-inductance, *n*. the quantity that relates the MAGNETIC FLUX of an inductor to the current flowing in the windings of that inductor. Symbol: *L*; unit: henry. For a given size and shape of conductor in the absence of FERROMAGNETIC material, the inductance value is constant.

self-sealing capacitor, *n*. a CAPACITOR that resists damage by excessive voltage. If the DIELECTRIC is punctured, the local heating oxidizes the metal electrode around the puncture, restoring the insulation.

SEM, *abbrev. for* scanning-electron microscope. See ELECTRON MICROSCOPE.

semiconductor, *n*. a material whose CONDUCTIVITY can be controlled by the presence of IMPURITIES. The conductivity of a doped semiconductor (see DOPING) may be one or more orders of magnitude lower than that of a conductor. Semiconductors can be elements, such as selenium, germanium, silicon, or compounds such as gallium arsenide, antimony trisulphide, or cadmium sulphide. In the pure state, semiconductors are reasonably good insulators, but they have a NEGATIVE TEMPERA-TURE COEFFICIENT of RESISTIVITY, unlike metals.

Traces of impurity have a very considerable effect on resistivity, lowering the value to levels that can approach the resistivity values of some metals. In addition, the type of MAJORITY CARRIER, electron or hole, can be determined by the type of material that is used as an impurity, or doping material. See INTRINSIC, DONOR, ACCEPTOR, DIFFUSION, JUNCTION (2).

semiconductor diode, *n*. a DIODE that makes use of a

SEMICONDUCTOR material. JUNCTION (2) diodes make use of the contact between n-type and p-type semiconductors, POINT-CONTACT DIODES use a metal point contact to a semiconductor surface, and SCHOTTKY DIODES use a metal in contact with a larger area of semiconductor.

semitransparent cathode, *n.* a PHOTOCATHODE that is partly transparent to the light that causes EMISSION. Such a material can be used in the form of a thin film on a glass plate, with light striking the surface from the glass side, and electron emission from the other side. Such photocathodes were used in early types of TV CAMERA TUBES, and are still used in PHOTOMULTIPLIERS.

sensitivity, *n.* the ratio of OUTPUT change to INPUT (1) change for a measuring device. For a measuring instrument, sensitivity is quoted in terms of the amount of input for FULL-SCALE DEFLECTION, or the amount of input for unit deflection. For example, a milliammeter may be quoted as 1.0mA for fsd, and an oscilloscope amplifier as 1V per cm. For a radio receiver, the sensitivity would be quoted as the minimum input signal in microvolts that is needed to ensure a useful signal-to-noise ratio.

sense wire, *n.* the wire that threads a MAGNETIC CORE and detects a change of magnetization in the old but still-used core-storage system of computer memory.

sensor or **input transducer,** *n.* any type of measuring or detecting element or TRANSDUCER. A sensor will detect changes in the quantity to which it is sensitive (light, temperature, strain, rotation, etc), and transmit this change as an electrical signal.

sequential control, *n.* the control of any device by a sequence of instructions. MICROPROCESSOR-controlled equipment uses sequential control, and the controlling sequence of instructions is known as the program.

sequential field, *n.* an early type of COLOUR TELEVISION system. In a sequential field system, a complete picture in each primary light colour was transmitted and shown in sequence. The rate of display had to be fast enough to appear as one picture to the eye. Field-sequential methods, in which three complete fields are used per picture, are not compatible with MONOCHROME reception, but are still used for narrow-bandwidth colour TV. See also LINE-SEQUENTIAL TELEVISION.

sequential logic, *n*. a LOGIC system in which the output depends on the sequence in which inputs occur rather than the instantaneous combination of inputs. The FLIP-FLOP is a sequential device, because its output, unlike that of a GATE, is usually determined by the sequence of past inputs rather than a present input. For example, an R-S FLIP-FLOP with both inputs at zero can have an output that is 1 or 0, depending on what the *previous* input was. Contrast this with a gate, in which the output is determined completely by the current inputs.

serial counter, see ASYNCHRONOUS COUNTER.

serial memory, *n*. a MEMORY that makes use of devices such as FLIP-FLOPS connected in series. A set of flip-flops in series (a SERIAL REGISTER) can be clocked by a common PULSE so that an input at one end can be shifted through the register by clocking. The data bit moves along by one flip-flop for each clock pulse. Data stored in such a register can be obtained only by clocking out all the previously stored data. Modern computers make more use of RANDOM-ACCESS MEMORY systems.

serial transfer, *n*. the movement of digital data in binary form along a single cable. Each bit is transferred as a logic 0 or 1 signal along the cable, and for a group of bits, the transfer is controlled by a master clock rate. See also SERIAL TRANSMISSION.

serial transmission, *n*. the transmission of digital data along a single serial link. The transmission can be SYNCHRONOUS or ASYNCHRONOUS, and both types rely on generating identical clock pulse rates. In the synchronous system, the sending terminal sends out a synchronizing character, a set of 1s and 0s. This is used by the receiver to achieve synchronization, and from that time on, the two are held in synchronization by transmitting either data or the synchronizing character. In the asynchronous system, data is sent at intervals, with nothing on the line when there is no data. Each group of data (usually each byte) carries its own synchronizing signals in the form of a start bit and two stop bits.

series, *n.* the connection of COMPONENTS so that the same current flows through each in turn. See also PARALLEL.

series feedback or **current feedback,** *n.* a form of FEEDBACK in which some of the output current waveform is fed back to the input.

series network, *n.* a NETWORK in which components are connected in series with the signal.

series-parallel, *adj.* (of a CIRCUIT or NETWORK) having some components in series with the signal and others in parallel.

series resonance, *n.* a RESONANT CIRCUIT in which the impedance becomes a minimum at resonance. The series connection of an inductor and a capacitor is the simplest series resonant circuit. At resonance, the impedance of this circuit is solely resistive, and voltage is in phase with current.

series stabilization, *n.* a method of stabilizing CURRENT or VOLTAGE that uses a controller, such as a transistor, in series.

service area, *n.* the area within which a TRANSMITTER can be usefully received. The area is shown as a set of field-strength contours on a map, and is often divided into primary and secondary regions. Outside the secondary region, reception is unsatisfactory because of severe fading, or interference from other transmitters.

servo, *n.* any mechanical system that is electrically controlled, particularly a motor that is remotely controlled and will duplicate the movements of a master generator shaft.

seven-segment display, *n.* a method of displaying digits and some letters with seven bar shapes. The seven-segment display is extensively used for LIGHT-EMITTING DIODE and LIQUID-CRYSTAL DISPLAYS, particularly for calculators. The alternative is a DOT-MATRIX type of display. See Fig. 84 on page 296.

shaded-pole motor, *n.* a type of AC motor in which a phase shift is created in the field by a copper ring placed over part of the field core. The presence of this PHASE SHIFT creates a rotating field, and the metal rotor will try to keep in step with the rotation at the frequency of the AC supply.

shading, *n.* an unwanted AMPLITUDE change in a TV SIGNAL. This usually causes a uniformly-lit scene to appear to contain shadows when the image is viewed.

Fig. 84. Seven-segment display. The form of a seven-segment display, showing the conventional lettering system for the segments. Some displays include decimal points in addition to the segments.

shadow, *n.* the ATTENUATION of radio signals caused by obstructions between the TRANSMITTER and the RECEIVER. Hills, power lines and large metal objects can all cause shadowing, and the effect can be particularly severe at the higher frequencies.

For TV signals, improvements can sometimes be achieved by using a DIRECTIONAL AERIAL pointed to a local reflection, but in very bad cases, it may be necessary to use a REPEATER of some sort. A passive repeater, consisting of a receiving aerial on one side of a hill connected to a transmitting aerial on the other, is often very successful. Direct broadcasting from satellites (*DBS*) eliminates problems of shadowing.

shadow mask, *n.* the original type of TV receiver colour tube. The shadow mask was made from nickel–steel, with a low expansivity, and was perforated with holes in groups of three, using a triangular arrangement. This, combined with the deposition of phosphor dots on the screen in the same pattern, ensured that electrons from three separate guns arrived on the correct PHOSPHOR dots. The guns were also arranged in a triangular structure.

The weakness of the system lay in the number of controls and adjustments that were needed in order to preserve good CONVERGENCE, since each control had to deal with both vertical and horizontal effects. Very often, convergence had to be reestablished if a receiver was moved. The later development of the APERTURE GRILLE greatly reduced convergence problems, because it allowed the three guns to be constructed in line, so making all corrections along one axis only.

Shannon's sampling theorem, *n*. a theorem stating that an analogue signal must be sampled at least twice as fast as the highest frequency component contained within the signal if ALIASING errors are to be avoided.

shaped-beam tube, *n*. a form of display cathode-ray tube for alphanumeric displays. The characters are formed by acting directly on the shape of the beam with electric or magnetic fields, rather than by the scanning of the beam.

SHF, *abbrev. for* superhigh frequency. This refers to the range 3 to 30GHz (wavelength 1 to 10cm) in the MICROWAVE range.

shifting, *n*. the action of moving binary digits in a REGISTER. In a shift action, the bits are moved from one flip-flop to the next in line. The bit at one end of the register will be lost, and a zero bit will be loaded in at the other end.

shift register, *n*. a set of FLIP-FLOPS connected in series. The flip-flops are connected with the output of one taken as the input to the next. When a clock pulse is applied to all of the flip-flops together, the bit (0 or 1) in each flip-flop will be transferred to the next in line. The connections can be made either for left-shift or for right-shift, or by way of gates so that both left- or right-shift can be obtained by using a shift-direction signal. The shift register is the basis of SERIAL MEMORY.

shock excitation, *n*. the production of oscillations by a pulse. This causes RINGING (1).

Shockley diode, *n*. à general name for a pnpn diode, such as a THYRISTOR or SCS.

short, see SHORT CIRCUIT.

short circuit, *n*. a low-RESISTANCE connection, wanted or (more usually) unwanted. Sometimes abbreviated to *short*. The effect of a short circuit is to equalize voltages at two points, and to allow current to flow. If the short circuit is a fault condition, it will usually cause problems such as loss of signal, loss of control, or damage to components. Deliberate short circuiting is used in signal switching, or for making high-voltage circuits safe to touch.

short-circuit impedance, *n.* a measurement on a NETWORK. The short-circuit IMPEDANCE at the input of a network is the impedance at the input when the output is short-circuited to signals. The short-circuit impedance at the output is the output impedance when the input is short-circuited to signals.

short wave, *n.* a radio signal in the frequency range of about 3 to 30MHz. This range contains many of the most-used amateur bands, as well as many of the international communications channels.

short-wave converter, *n.* an add-on circuit to allow SHORT-WAVE reception by a MEDIUM-WAVE receiver. The converter contains a local oscillator and mixer that converts short-wave signals into signals in the medium-wave band, so that the receiver is being used as the second part of a DOUBLE-SUPERHET RECEIVER.

shot noise, see SCHOTTKY NOISE.

shunt, 1. *n.* a COMPONENT connected in PARALLEL with a SIGNAL. A *meter shunt* is a low-value RESISTOR that is connected in parallel with the movement in order to allow measurement of currents greater than the FSD current of the movement. **2.** *vb.* to connect a COMPONENT in PARALLEL with another.

shunt-derived filter, *n.* a form of FILTER in which parallel (SHUNT) resonant circuits are used.

shunt feedback or **voltage feedback,** *n.* the FEEDBACK of a part of the VOLTAGE output to the input of an amplifier.

shunt network, *n.* a NETWORK that is connected in PARALLEL with a SIGNAL.

shunt stabilization, *n.* the STABILIZATION, usually of voltage, by a device connected in parallel with the load. The simple use of a ZENER DIODE in parallel with a voltage source is an example of shunt voltage stabilization. The stable voltage is the voltage across the diode, with a series resistor used as a load. Variations in the supply voltage cause current variations that appear as voltage changes across the resistor, not across the Zener diode. Changes in the load current cause changes in the current through the Zener diode, with negligible effect on the voltage

Fig. 85. **Shunt stabilization**. A simple form of shunt stabilizer, another form of the AMPLIFIED-ZENER circuit. The total current is divided between the transistor and the load (not shown) and the voltage is maintained constant by the action of the Zener diode. If the load current increases, the transistor current decreases, keeping the total current constant.

output. The stabilization breaks down if the current through the Zener diode falls below the stabilizing limit, or if the supply voltage is reduced to the level of the stabilized voltage. See Fig. 85.

sideband, *n.* a range of frequencies caused by the MODULATION of a carrier. Any form of modulation of a carrier will result in the appearance of sidebands. One set, the upper sideband, will be at higher than carrier frequency, with the other set, the lower sideband, at a (symmetrically) lower frequency. For AMPLITUDE MODULATION, the sideband frequencies are directly related to the modulating frequency. Each upper-sideband frequency is the sum of the carrier frequency and a modulating frequency, and each lower-sideband signal is the difference between the carrier frequency and a modulating frequency. The useful part of the signal is carried in the sidebands, but these together constitute only up to 50% of the total signal energy. For frequency modulation, the inner sidebands have the same frequencies as for AM, but there are also outer sidebands unless the MODULATION INDEX is very small.

side frequency, *n.* a single frequency in a SIDEBAND.

side lobe, *n.* a region of sensitivity or signal strength to the side of the required directional axis of an AERIAL. Most DIRECTIONAL AERIALS allow some side-lobe formation, but this is harmless unless it causes interference.

siemens or (formerly) **mho,** *n.* the unit of CONDUCTANCE that is equal to the inverse ohm. Symbol: S.

signal, *n.* a variation in VOLTAGE or CURRENT that is used for carrying information.

signal electrode, *n.* an ELECTRODE from which a signal output is taken. The term usually denotes the signal output electrodes of TV CAMERA TUBES, PHOTOMULTIPLIERS and TRANSDUCERS.
See BACKPLATE.

signal generator, *n.* a laboratory instrument which is a combination of controllable calibrated oscillator (see CALIBRATION) and ATTENUATOR. Signal generators are used to supply known-amplitude signals at known frequencies for test purposes.
See also PULSE GENERATOR.

signal level, *n.* the AMPLITUDE of a SIGNAL. This is often quoted relative to some standard, such as the 1V video signal. When the standard level is well known, the signal level is often quoted in (voltage) dB.

signal-to-noise ratio (S/N), *n.* the ratio of levels of desired SIGNAL to unwanted NOISE, in decibels. The usefulness of a received signal is determined by its S/N. An acceptable video signal needs an S/N in the region of 45dB, a hi-fi audio signal requires at least 60dB.

signal winding, *n.* the WINDING of a MAGNETIC AMPLIFIER to which the low-frequency AC signal is applied.

silent zone, *n.* the area around a TRANSMITTER that receives neither the ground wave nor a strong echo. See also SKIP DISTANCE.

silicon, *n.* a semiconducting ELEMENT, obtained from sand (silicon oxide).

silicon cell, *n.* a PHOTOCELL that uses silicon as its sensitive material.

silicon chip, *n.* a small thin rectangular piece of silicon, typically 2mm × 1mm × 0.1mm, that has been cut from a thin circular WAFER.

silicon-controlled rectifier, see THYRISTOR.

silicon-controlled switch (SCS), *n.* a four-layer (pnpn) DIODE in which connections are made to the inner P-LAYERS and N-LAYERS. A positive voltage is applied to the anode, the outer p-layer, and the cathode (outer n-layer) is at zero voltage. In this condition, a pulse to the first gate, the inner p-layer, will switch the device on. A positive pulse on the second gate, the inner n-layer, will switch current off. The SCS is used for low-power switching as compared to the THYRISTOR, which has a similar structure, and can be used only for comparatively low switching rates because of its comparatively long turn-on and turn-off times.

silicon diode, *n.* a DIODE that uses a rectifying silicon junction. The FORWARD DROP is rather high, of the order of 0.6V, but the resistance in the REVERSE DIRECTION is also very high. Silicon diodes are extensively used in manufacturing because of their cheapness.

silicone grease, *n.* a synthetic grease that is an excellent electrical INSULATOR, but is also a reasonably good heat CONDUCTOR. The grease is similar in chemical structure to a natural grease but with silicon substituted for carbon, hence the name.

silicon-on-sapphire (SOS), *n.* a construction technique for metal-oxide semiconductor INTEGRATED CIRCUITS, used particularly for military and other applications where high reliability is required. Synthetic sapphire is used as a SUBSTRATE, and silicon is deposited on it by EPITAXY. The resulting chips have a very high performance, but the construction is difficult and costly.

silicon rectifier, *n.* a SILICON DIODE of any type used as a RECTIFIER.

silver mica, *n.* the highest quality of mica used for mica capacitors.

simplex, *n.* a data channel that allows communication in one direction only.

Compare DUPLEX, HALF-DUPLEX.

simulator, *n.* a SYSTEM, usually computer-based, that imitates the behaviour of another system. The simulator may, for example, imitate the reaction of a NETWORK to a PULSE, the response of an aircraft to a downwind, the reaction of an office organization to the death of a manager. The importance of simulation is that any reasonably well understood system can be simulated, and the simulation used to predict behaviour of the main system. For a partly-understood system, the simulation may be used to gain understanding by comparing the predictions of the simulator with the actual outcome of an experiment.

sine/cosine potentiometer, *n.* a POTENTIOMETER, seldom encountered in modern use, in which the DIVISION RATIO is proportional to the sine or cosine of the angle of rotation of the shaft.

sine wave, *n.* a WAVEFORM whose shape is that of a graph of the sine of an angle plotted against the angle. A sine wave is the natural waveform of voltage generated by a coil of wire revolving in a uniform magnetic field.

singing, *n.* an OSCILLATION with an audible OUTPUT.

single-ended or **unbalanced,** *adj.* (of a circuit) having one terminal at earth at both input and output. The signal at the input or output consists of a voltage that will vary with respect to earth. In a BALANCED AMPLIFIER the sum of the signals at two inputs or outputs is always zero.

single-phase, *adj.* (of an AC system) having one supply conductor and a return.

single-pole switch, *n.* a switch that changes the connection of one line only.

single-shot, see MONOSTABLE.

single-sideband (SSB), *adj.* (of a transmitter or receiver) transmitting or receiving radio signals with one SIDEBAND only. In a conventional amplitude-modulated signal, all of the information in the modulating signal is held in each one of the SIDEBANDS. This means that there is redundancy of signal that can be reduced by transmitting only one sideband. Since one sideband represents only one quarter of the total transmitter power of a double sideband system, this implies that the transmitted power can be reduced with no loss in reception range. By eliminating the carrier as well, all of the power of the transmitter can be devoted to the information-bearing sideband. The drawback is that much more elaborate transmitters and receivers are needed.

single-throw switch, see DOUBLE-THROW SWITCH.

sink, 1. *vb.* to accept CURRENT from a TERMINAL. TRANSISTOR-TRANSISTOR LOGIC ICs require any driving device to be able to accept (sink) a current of up to 1.6mA to earth when a terminal is at logic 0. **2.** *n.* see HEAT SINK.

sinusoidal, *adj.* (of a WAVEFORM) having the shape of a SINE WAVE.

SIPO register, *n.* a serial-in, parallel-out REGISTER in which data is fed in serially, using one clock pulse per bit of data, and then read out on a set of parallel lines, using one line output for each FLIP-FLOP in the register.

See Fig. 86 on page 304. Compare SISO REGISTER, PIPO REGISTER, PISO REGISTER.

SISO register, *n.* a serial-in, serial-out REGISTER in which bits are clocked in, travel through the register and are clocked out of the other terminal.

See Fig. 87 on page 304. Compare SIPO REGISTER.

SI unit, *n.* any of the units adopted for international use (Système Internationale) in science and engineering, based on the metre, kilogram, second and ampere.

skeleton slot, *n.* a form of SLOT AERIAL in which the metal surrounding the slot has been reduced to a tube or wire frame.

skew, *n.* the time difference between signals, particularly PULSE signals.

skin effect, *n.* the conduction of high-frequency currents on the outside surface of a CONDUCTOR. Conductors for high-frequency currents can be made from thick wire or tube, and use silver plating to increase conductivity.

skip distance, *n.* the distance between a transmitter and the region in which the first reflection from the IONOSPHERE is received. There will be a SILENT ZONE in the area that lies between the skip distance and the greatest distance covered by the ground wave.

parallel outputs

serial input

clock

Fig. 86. **SIPO register**. The set and reset terminals have been omitted for clarity.

serial input

clock

serial output

Fig. 87. **SISO register**. The set and reset terminals have been omitted for clarity.

sky wave or **reflected wave,** *n.* the DIRECT WAVE that reaches a RECEIVER from a TRANSMITTER after reflection from the IONOSPHERE.

Compare GROUND WAVE.

slave circuit, *n.* a LOGIC CIRCUIT that is solely driven by the output of another, and which reproduces the output waveform. The slave portion of a MASTER–SLAVE FLIP–FLOP, for example, reproduces a voltage level from the master section, but is clocked at a different time.

slave processor or **coprocessor,** *n.* a MICROPROCESSOR in a computer or controller circuit that is totally controlled by a main microprocessor. The usual type of slave processor is used for memory access, screen control, or mathematical operations.

slew rate, *n.* the rate of change of SIGNAL voltage. This is a better guide to the frequency response of transistors and amplifiers (particularly OPERATIONAL AMPLIFIERS) to large signals than the use of high-frequency cutoff figures, which only relate to small signals. Slew rate is very important to feedback amplifiers because of the possibility of breakdown of feedback. If the slew rate is slower than the response of the feedback loop, for example, the amplifier will effectively be operating without feedback during the time of rapid voltage change at the input.

slope resistance, see INCREMENTAL RESISTANCE.

slot aerial, *n.* an AERIAL that consists of a rectangular slot in a metal sheet or in a metal mesh. The long dimension of the slot is along the plane of the magnetic field, so that the transmitted wave is POLARIZED (1) at 90 degrees to the polarization of a conventional DIPOLE AERIAL. The balanced feed is to or from the midpoints of the edge of the slot, and the CHARACTERISTIC IMPEDANCE is of the order of 500ohms.

See also SKELETON SLOT.

slotted waveguide, *n.* a WAVEGUIDE into which slots are cut in places to allow a PROBE (1) to be inserted.

slow-break switch, *n.* a SWITCH that uses no form of spring-assisted snap-over action. An example is the old-fashioned KNIFE SWITCH.

slow wave, *n.* an electromagnetic wave that has been slowed to about the speed of electrons in a beam. The slowing can be achieved by propagating the wave in a spiral path, as in a TRAVELLING-WAVE TUBE.

slugged relay, *n.* a form of RELAY in which a copper loop, the slug, has been placed over the magnetic circuit. This makes the action of the relay slower because of the effect of EDDY CURRENTS.

slug tuning, see PERMEABILITY TUNING.

small-signal gain, *n.* the GAIN figure of a system obtained from the ratio of output to input signal amplitudes for signals that are of small amplitude compared to the power supply voltage.

small-signal parameters, *n.* the PARAMETERS such as input resistance, transfer current ratio, etc., that are measured for small-signal (not DC) quantities. The term denotes particularly the parameters that are used to specify transistor action.

smoothing, *n*. **1.** the removal of unwanted AC content from DC. **2.** the filtering of any signal by a LOW-PASS FILTER.

SMPTE, *abbrev. for* Society of Motion Picture and Television Engineers (US).

snap-off diode, *n*. see CHARGE-STORAGE DIODE.

snow, *n*. a slang term for the effect of NOISE on a TV or radar picture signal.

socket, *n*. a female connector. Compare PLUG.

soft magnetic material, *n*. a material with very high PERMEABILITY but very low RETENTIVITY. Such a material will become very strongly magnetized when in a magnetic field (from a coil or another magnet), but retains practically no magnetism when the field is removed. See MOVING-IRON METER.

software, *n*. the programs for a MICROPROCESSOR-controlled system. Compare HARDWARE.

soft x-ray, *n*. an X-RAY beam that has been created using a comparatively low-energy electron beam. Soft x-rays have a lower frequency range than the more penetrating hard x-rays.

solar cell, *n*. a PHOTOVOLTAIC CELL that is used to obtain electrical power from light. Cells based on gallium arsenide have been used for satellites and spacecraft to provide power over long periods. The voltage output is low, a fraction of a volt per cell, and the efficiency is also poor, about 10%. For situations where no practical alternative exists, however, solar cells can provide useful power.

solar noise, *n*. the radio NOISE that is generated from the random movement of ions in the sun.

soldering, *n*. the joining of metals with a low-melting alloy of tin and zinc known as solder. Soldering is the most common method of making mechanical and electrical connections to electronic components. For hand work and repair work, an electrically heated soldering 'iron' is used, along with a solder alloy that is in the form of hollow wire, with a core of flux. The flux is a resin that spreads over the metal that is being soldered to prevent oxidation. Mass-produced printed circuit boards are soldered using a HOT-DIP system. For very high-reliability systems, assemblies are made by robot methods, using spot-welding rather than soldering. See also DIP-SOLDERING.

solenoid, *n*. **1.** a tubular coil of wire whose length is large compared to the diameter. **2.** an electromechanical actuator that consists of a coil with a moveable core. When current flows in the coil, the core is drawn into the coil, and this mechanical action is made use of.

solid conductor, *n*. a single-core wire, as opposed to stranded or hollow-cored wire.

solid-state circuit, *n*. any CIRCUIT that makes use of semiconductors as active components, with no mechanical moving parts or any vacuum devices other than a CATHODE-RAY TUBE.

solid-state camera, *n*. a TELEVISION CAMERA that dispenses with the conventional vacuum tubes (VIDICONS) for image pick-up. Of the several methods that have been tried, the most promising and practical has been the use of CHARGE-COUPLED DEVICES as photosensors. This allows charge that has accumulated in a row of CCD cells to be read out in the time of a line flyback pulse by a number of clock pulses. A few simple CCD cameras have appeared for use with computers, but their major role to date has been in TV systems for use in space, and as a result of this work, such cameras can now be obtained as part of a video recorder system.

solid-state memory, *n*. a MEMORY system that uses semiconductors as distinct from MAGNETIC CORE (2) devices. See also ROM, RAM, DYNAMIC RAM.

solid-state physics, *n*. the branch of physics that deals with the structure and behaviour of solids, particularly of SEMICONDUCTORS.

sonar, *n*. a form of acoustic RADAR. ULTRASONIC waves in water are used to locate objects in the water, using the reflection from a pulse output. The principles are used in echo sounding.

sound, *n*. any audible pressure waves in air. Sound waves can also be transmitted at higher speeds in liquids and in solids. The frequencies above the range of hearing are called ULTRASONIC, these below the range of hearing SUBSONIC signals.

sound carrier, *n.* the radio frequency CARRIER (1) for the sound of a TV picture. In the UK PAL system, the sound is frequency modulated on to a separate carrier whose frequency is 6MHz higher than the vision carrier. See also INTERCARRIER SOUND.

sound recording, see RECORDING OF SOUND.

sound reproduction, *n.* the recovery of audio signals from a recording and their conversion into sound. A sound reproduction system consists of a TRANSDUCER, amplifier and loudspeaker system.

A general description of a good hi-fi system shows what is required for each type of reproduction system separately. The transducer converts the recorded sound into audio signals. For the most common form of recording, the mechanical disc, the transducer consists of a PICK-UP head. This uses a stylus fitting into the groove on the disc, which vibrates, driven by the modulation of the groove. The disc has to be spun at a steady speed, generally $33\frac{1}{3}$ revolutions per minute, though 45 revolutions per minute is used for shorter recordings. For a stereo recording, this modulation will be picked up as vibration in two mutually perpendicular directions at 90 degrees to each other. Transducers connected to the stylus will then convert these vibrations into electrical signals. The transducers can use PIEZOELECTRIC CRYSTALS, or the MOVING-IRON PICK-UP, or MOVING-COIL PICK-UP principles. The small signals from the pick-up are voltage-amplified by a PREAMP, and any corrections, such as EQUALIZATION are performed.

If the source of signals is tape, then a tape transcriptor must be used to pull the tape at a constant (and correct) speed past the replay head. The fluctuations of magnetic field on the tape are converted into induced voltages in the head, and these signals are de-emphasized as required in the preamplifier. The signals from a cassette unit may require to be expanded (see COMPANDER) if they have been compressed during recording for noise-reduction purposes. For COMPACT DISCS, the speed of the disc is controlled by a motor in such a way as to present a constant linear speed to the pick-up unit. The start of the recording is in the inner track, and reading is carried out by a solid-state LASER and optical system. The reflection of light from a flat surface indicates that a 0 is present, its scattering by an etched pit indicates a logic 1. The digital bit signals are detected by a photocell, and these signals are amplified before being passed to the preamp unit. For radio signals, a TUNER is used. This will normally be an FM tuner, though several designs allow for medium wave reception also. The carrier from the aerial is tuned, converted to IF, amplified and demodulated. The audio signal is de-emphasized (see DE-EMPHASIS), and then passed to the preamp.

At the preamp, a switch allows the user to select any of the sound sources for reproduction. Simple systems make use of mechanical switches, but good-quality systems use the switch to operate separate MOSFET switches (see FIELD-EFFECT TRANSISTOR), so that switch pulse noise and switch contact noise are eliminated. The signal is then voltage-amplified, and potentiometer controls for gain, bass and treble are included. The signal then passes to the main amplifier in which several stages of voltage amplification are followed by a power amplifier stage. This provides an output with enough power to drive a loudspeaker, usually of the magnetic type. See also SOUNDTRACK, RECORDING OF SOUND.

soundtrack, *n.* the edge of a cinema film that is used to carry the sound MODULATION. The sound is modulated in the form of variable density bands in which the density is proportional to amplitude. Because the film passes through the projection gate in PULSES, being held for about $\frac{1}{24}$ second, and then rapidly jerked on, the sound recording and reproduction must be done at a different part of the film that is moving steadily. This part of the film is ahead of the picture, following the loop that allows the film to regain steady motion after its intermittent movement through the projection gate. Because of this, any splicing because of film breakage can cause sound synchronization to be lost. The SIGNAL-TO-NOISE RATIO for film sound is very poor unless methods such as the DOLBY SYSTEM are used. The reproduction of film sound makes use of a light source and a PHOTOCELL. The photocell must be capable of reasonably fast response, so that sensitivity has to be sacrificed, and a high-gain amplifier needs to be used for the output signals. Magnetic tape is also used for film soundtracks.

source, 1. *n.* (a) an emitter of CHARGE CARRIERS in a FIELD-EFFECT TRANSISTOR. (b) any device that produces signals. **2.** *vb.* to provide CURRENT to drive a LOAD, e.g. drivers for logic devices. See also SINK (1).

source follower, *n.* a FIELD-EFFECT TRANSISTOR common-drain amplifier circuit. This is the FET equivalent of an EMITTER FOLLOWER, with high input impedance and low output impedance.

source impedance, *n.* the complex ratio of voltage amplitude and phase to current amplitude and phase for any source of signal (see IMPEDANCE).

space charge, *n.* a cloud of ELECTRONS or other CHARGE CARRIERS, originally denoting the electrons around the hot CATHODE of a vacuum emitter. Space charges also exist in semiconductors around a junction. The existence of space charge causes a form of bias to exist even when no external voltage is applied because the charge acts as a POTENTIAL BARRIER to the movement of electrons.

space-charge density, *n.* a measure of the SPACE-CHARGE effect equal to the amount of charge per unit volume in a space-charge region.

space-charge limiting, *n.* the limiting of CURRENT because of the effect of a SPACE CHARGE. This type of limiting means that the electron current that can be drawn from the region around the cathode is not greatly affected by variations in the cathode temperature, provided that the cathode can maintain the space charge. Most transmitting valves operate under space-charge limited conditions rather than in the alternative temperature limiting conditions.

spark, *n.* an electrical discharge caused by the breakdown of INSULATION in air. Sparking in air can occur much more easily if the air is ionized (see IONIZATION) by, for example, radioactive particles.

spark counter, *n.* a detector for alpha particles. Alpha particles have very high ionizing (see IONIZATION) capability, but are stopped by thin layers of materials of ordinary density. A spark counter detects alpha particles in air by using a high voltage between an ANODE and a CATHODE. The presence of an alpha particle will ionize the air and cause a spark. If the anode is supplied through a large value load resistor, there will be a voltage pulse at the anode that can be amplified and used as the input to a counter.

spark gap, *n.* an arrangement of ELECTRODES to encourage a SPARK to pass under fault conditions. The arrangement is used to protect devices like CATHODE-RAY TUBES from voltage surges that would otherwise cause internal sparking. See SURGE DIVERTER.

spark-suppression circuit, *n.* a CIRCUIT intended to reduce SPARKS at switch or relay contacts. Typical circuits use capacitor-resistor networks that form a damped oscillating circuit, greatly reducing the rate of change of voltage as the contacts open. Spark suppression is particularly important if the contacts switch an inductive load, and suppression using diodes is then more common.

speaker, see LOUDSPEAKER.

spectrum, *n.* a range of FREQUENCIES or WAVELENGTHS. The electromagnetic spectrum consists of all electromagnetic waves, from the very low frequencies up to the gamma-ray range and beyond. The term is often used to denote a band of frequencies, e.g., *microwave spectrum*.

spectrum analyser, *n.* an instrument whose output is a graph that shows a plot of amplitude or phase against frequency for a complete FREQUENCY BAND.

speech bandwidth, *n.* the minimum BANDWIDTH that is needed for intelligible speech, about 300Hz to 2.7kHz.

speech coil, *n.* the active part of a LOUDSPEAKER. The speech coil is located by the SPIDER inside the gap of the magnetic circuit. A current flowing through the speech coil causes the coil, the carrier on which it is wound, and the cone attached to it, to move. This in turn moves the air around the loudspeaker so producing sound.

speech recognition, *n.* a method of controlling a computer by spoken commands. The voice sounds are picked up by a MICROPHONE, and processed into digital codes that are compared with stored codes that are standardized. If an input causes a code to be generated that is sufficiently similar to a stored code, then the action corresponding to the stored code will be executed.

See also RECORDING OF SOUND.

spider, *n.* a metal or plastic flat spring that locates a LOUDSPEAKER cone and SPEECH COIL in place. The term arises from the traditional shape of the spring.

spiral PDA, *n.* a form of POST-DEFLECTION ACCELERATION that uses a spiral of high-resistivity film.

spiral scanning, *n.* a form of CATHODE-RAY TUBE scanning. A spiral SCAN starts at the centre of the fact of the tube, and traces out a spiral path until it reaches the edges.

sporadic-E effect, *n.* an effect that causes unusual PROPAGATION conditions. At times, very highly ionized (see IONIZATION) layers form in the E LAYER, about 100km above the Earth's surface. This heavily-ionized layer reflects frequencies that normally pass through the IONOSPHERE, and therefore causes long-distance reception of signals, such as VHF TV signals whose range is normally 'line of sight'. This in turn causes severe INTERFERENCE between transmissions that are normally not within range of each other. Sporadic-E conditions are associated with intense sun-spot conditions, and are usually predictable.

See also SUNSPOT CYCLE.

spot, *n.* **1.** the area on the screen of a CATHODE-RAY TUBE that is lit by the electron beam. **2.** an imperfection on a screen that will not illuminate.

spot speed, *n.* the rate of scanning of a CATHODE-RAY TUBE in terms of SPOT (1) diameters per second.

spreading resistance, *n.* the internal RESISTANCE of collector or base connection due to the semiconductor material between the junction and the contact.

spurious response, *n.* an unwanted signal, particularly in a RADAR system.

sputtering, *n.* a coating method that makes use of a low-pressure gas discharge in which the material to be coated is the ANODE and the coating material is the CATHODE. Any material can be coated by sputtering, and almost any refractory coating material can be used, such as tungsten, platinum, diamond (carbon), silica, etc.

square–law detector, *n.* a form of amplitude DEMODULATOR. The output voltage of a square-law detector is proportional to the square of the input voltage. A small amount of carrier modulation can therefore produce a comparatively large output from the circuit, so that the detector is sensitive. Metal-oxide semiconductor devices are particularly good square-law detectors.

square–loop hysteresis, *n.* a characteristic shape of HYSTERESIS LOOP that is straight-sided.

square wave, *n.* a WAVEFORM with a square shape. The waveform has vertical sides, representing a rapid switch between low voltage and high voltage. The time spent at high voltage is equal to the time spent at low voltage, making the MARK-SPACE RATIO equal to unity. Waves with steep sides that do not have unity mark-space ratio should be described as *rectangular waves*, but are generally known as 'square waves' unless the mark-space ratio is very low, when the waves are called PULSES.

square–wave response, *n.* the OUTPUT of a CIRCUIT for a SQUARE-WAVE input. Poor high-frequency response (too low SLEW RATE) shows up as sloping sides in the output wave, and poor low-frequency response as a sagging top (see SAG). Any instability also shows itself as RINGING (1) after a change of voltage.

squegging, *adj.* (of an OSCILLATOR) biasing off at intervals. A squegging oscillator uses too much FEEDBACK, driving the circuit into NONLINEAR conditions and causing a capacitor in the circuit to charge, so biasing off the oscillator. The oscillation then resumes when the capacitor has discharged. The BLOCKING OSCILLATOR is a deliberately designed form of squegging oscillator.

squelch, *n.* a CIRCUIT technique for reducing interstation NOISE. The voltage on the AUTOMATIC GAIN CONTROL line is used to suppress the audio stages unless a signal is tuned that is strong enough to operate the line. This allows a radio to be tuned from one station to another without hearing the noise in between carriers. The squelch technique has obvious benefits in, for example, car radio reception.

SSB, see SINGLE SIDEBAND.

SSI, *abbrev. for* small-scale integration, i.e. about 100 active devices (such as transistors) per chip.

stabilization, *n.* a CIRCUIT technique for making a quantity resist changes in INPUTS or LOADS. VOLTAGE STABILIZERS are circuits whose output voltage remains stable despite changes in load current or supply voltage. *Current stabilizers* are circuits that supply a constant current despite changes in load resistance or supply voltage. Stabilization of the GAIN of an amplifier against changes in component values can be achieved by using NEGATIVE FEEDBACK. A circuit can also be said to be stabilized if phase correction is used to prevent unwanted oscillations or RINGING (1).

stable circuit, *n.* a circuit that will not break into oscillation under any normal working conditions. If the circuit is truly stable, it will not show RINGING (1) under SQUARE WAVE testing. Compare BISTABLE CIRCUIT.

stage, *n.* a clearly defined part of an AMPLIFIER, such as the circuitry around one transistor or IC.

stage efficiency, *n.* the ratio of power output from a stage to the power that has to be supplied to it (DC supply as well as signal power), used mainly of transmitter stages.

stage gain, *n.* the gain, usually VOLTAGE GAIN, of a STAGE. This is often expressed in decibels, using $20 \log (V_{out}/V_{in})$.

stagger tuning, *n.* a method of obtaining a large BANDWIDTH in a TUNED AMPLIFIER. Several tuned circuits in different stages of an amplifier are tuned to slightly different frequencies, so that the overall tuning is wideband.

staircase voltage, *n.* a voltage waveform that takes the form of a RAMP with a number of level sections so that the shape is that of a flight of stairs. See Fig. 88.

Fig. 88. **Staircase voltage**. The form of a typical staircase waveform.

See also DIGITAL VOLTMETER.

standardization, *n.* the setting up of a basis of comparison of units of measurement. Standardization of an instrument, such as a voltmeter or oscilloscope, means that its readings are compared with those of a standard, usually a SECONDARY STANDARD. The instrument is then corrected or calibrated. The term is also used to denote the establishment of written standards for the manufacturing, testing and specification of components and devices.

standing wave or **stationary wave,** *n.* a wave fixed in space, so that the amplitude of wave oscillation at any given point along the wave's axis is fixed for as long as the wave pattern persists.

A NODE of the standing-wave pattern is a point of minimum amplitude, and an ANTINODE is a point of maximum amplitude. The pattern has the same wavelength as the wave that generates it, so that wavelength can be measured from the pattern (see LECHER LINES).

Compare TRAVELLING WAVE.

standing-wave ratio (SWR), *n.* a measurement of the efficiency of line transmission that applies also to WAVEGUIDES and AERIALS. The SWR is the ratio of the maximum amplitude at any point on the line to the minimum amplitude. The smaller the SWR (the minimum possible value is unity), the better the MATCHING of the line.

See also SWR METER.

star-delta transformation, *n.* a theorem for finding the equivalent component values for star and delta arrangements of connections for THREE-PHASE SUPPLY AC. The principle

Fig. 89. **Star-delta transformation**. See main entry.

states that the 'star' network (see Fig. 89a) is equivalent to the 'delta' network (see Fig. 89b), with component values given by the following equations:

$$y_1 = Y_1 Y_3 / S$$
$$y_2 = Y_2 Y_3 / S \qquad \text{where } S \text{ (the sum)} = Y_1 + Y_2 + Y_3$$
$$y_3 = Y_1 Y_2 / S$$

start and stop bits, *n*. logic pulses of defined height and duration that indicate the onset and end of a stream of digital data.

starter, *n*. **1.** an additional electrode in a GAS–FILLED TUBE that starts IONIZATION. **2.** the DEVICE that generates a VOLTAGE impulse to start the discharge in a fluorescent tube.

starting current, *n*. the current flowing during starting conditions. The term usually denotes the heater current of a MAGNETRON, which can be reduced when oscillation starts.

state, *n*. the condition of output or signal level of a device, or level of any measurable quantity relating to the device. For many electronic devices, the state of the device will denote the voltage level at the output. Digital devices will allow two states only, 0 and 1.

static, *n*. a form of radio or television INTERFERENCE. Static is produced by electrostatic discharges, and is worst in thundery conditions.

static characteristic, *n*. a graph-plot of one quantity against another with all other variables held at constant values, such as a plot of transistor output current against input voltage, with collector voltage held constant. In a *dynamic characteristic*, the effect of varying collector voltage would have to be considered, as this would then represent the changes in a working transistor.

static memory, *n.* any form of memory that will store information without the need to rewrite the data at intervals (see REFRESH). Static memory may be VOLATILE, like STATIC RAM, or nonvolatile, like MAGNETIC CORE (2) storage. Neither type needs any signals to maintain storage as would be needed by a DYNAMIC RAM memory.

static RAM, *n.* a form of semiconductor MEMORY based on FLIP-FLOPS. Each flip-flop stores one bit of data, but only one output of each flip-flop is used. The same value of current will pass through each flip-flop whether a 1 or a 0 is being stored, so the power consumption and the number of devices is greater for this type of memory than for a DYNAMIC RAM memory.

stationary wave, see STANDING WAVE.

stator, *n.* the stationary part, usually a magnet, of a motor or generator.

   Compare ROTOR.

steady state, *n.* the state of any system after any transient oscillations or other initial disturbances due to switching on have died away.

steerable aerial, *n.* an aerial whose main LOBE can be rotated. This can be done either by moving the whole aerial structure (like a radar dish) or by altering the phases of signals to separate components of the aerial array.

steering diode, *n.* a DIODE that is used as part of a FLIP-FLOP circuit to permit TOGGLING. For a conventional flip-flop, two steering diodes are needed. The diodes are biased by the collector voltages of the transistor, so that a voltage input pulse of the correct amplitude can pass through only one diode. This will be the diode that is connected to the input of the shut-off transistor, so that the pulse switches over the state of the flip-flop. After the changeover, the bias on the diodes will have changed also, so that the state will reverse on the next pulse again. See Fig. 90 on page 318.

step-down transformer, *n.* a TRANSFORMER connected so that

Fig. 90. **Steering diodes**. The steering diodes used in a bistable transistor circuit.

its signal output is of lower voltage than its input. This implies that the SECONDARY WINDING has fewer turns than the PRIMARY WINDING.

Compare STEP–UP TRANSFORMER.

step-function, *n*. a sharp change of voltage from one level to another, equivalent to half of a SQUARE WAVE.

stepping relay, *n*. a type of RELAY once used in telephone exchanges. The relay has a contact arm that can touch several other contacts in sequence as the arm rotates.

step-recovery diode, see CHARGE–STORAGE DIODE.

step-up transformer, *n*. a TRANSFORMER whose signal output is greater than its input. The SECONDARY WINDING contains a greater number of turns than the PRIMARY WINDING. Compare STEP–DOWN TRANSFORMER.

stereo amplifier, *n*. an audio AMPLIFIER that has two channels. The channels must be separate, allowing virtually no CROSSTALK. They must, however, use ganged volume, treble and bass control (see GANGED CIRCUITS).

stereophonic or **stereo,** *adj*. (of a sound–reproducing system) using more than one independent channel to produce the effect of sound that appears to come from an extended source, rather than from a small LOUDSPEAKER.

Compare MONOPHONIC.

stereo receiver, *n.* a radio receiver or TUNER that can make use of stereo transmissions. The FM signal is demodulated to recover the L + R signal, where L and R mean the left- and right-channel signals. At the same time, the sideband of the SUBCARRIER of the L − R signal is amplified, the carrier regenerated, and the L − R signal recovered by DEMODULATION. The L + R and L − R signals are then combined so as to separate the L and R signals.

stereoscopic, *adj.* (of an imaging system) producing an optical image that appears to have three dimensions, as in a LASER hologram.

stereo tape recorder, *n.* a tape recorder that uses separate amplifying systems to record and replay stereo signals on two separate tracks of tape. A stereo record/replay head is needed, with two separate magnetic circuits, gaps and coils.

stop band, see REJECTION BAND.

stopper, *n.* a RESISTOR used to suppress OSCILLATIONS. The stopper is connected close to a terminal of an active device. Its action is to add damping (see DAMPED) in an unintentionally oscillating circuit.

See also BASE STOPPER.

stopping potential, *n.* the reverse voltage that is needed to prevent an electron from landing on a surface. The stopping potential required on an ANODE measures the energy of the electrons liberated by light from a PHOTOCATHODE.

storage oscilloscope, *n.* an oscilloscope that can retain a trace of a transient input, such as a short pulse. This was originally done using a direct-view STORAGE TUBE, but is now performed by using digital storage.

storage time, *n.* the time for which data can be stored before requiring to be refreshed.

See REFRESH, DYNAMIC MEMORY.

storage tube or **charge-storage tube,** *n.* a form of CATHODE-RAY TUBE that uses charge storage to retain its trace. Most types of TV CAMERA TUBES are storage tubes in this sense, but the term is usually reserved to denote direct-view display storage tubes. These tubes, developed in the 1950s, used metal mesh coated with an insulator, and 'written' with positive charges by an electron beam, using SECONDARY EMISSION to charge the insulator. The pattern of charge then affected the passage of an overall FLOOD GUN beam through the apertures in the mesh. This type of tube, the *direct-view storage tube (DVST)* is still useful for some radar and oscilloscope applications, but has been superseded by the use of digital storage of waveforms for most purposes.

strain gauge, *n.* a method of measuring mechanical strain by electrical methods. The most useful methods are the RESISTANCE STRAIN GAUGE and the semiconductor strain gauge. See ELASTORESISTANCE.

strapping, *n.* a technique for stabilizing MAGNETRON operating frequency. Strapping means the connecting of alternate cavities so that they share signals in the correct phase.

stray capacitance, *n.* the CAPACITANCE that exists between parts of a circuit but which is not deliberately designed into the circuit. This consists of the capacitance of connectors, wires, leads, and components themselves, both to earth and to other components. Stray capacitance is unwanted, but cannot be forgotten. It causes unwanted resonances, sometimes oscillations, and is responsible for the loss of gain at high frequencies in wide-band amplifiers.

striking potential, *n.* the POTENTIAL DIFFERENCE between two electrodes that is needed to start a gas discharge. See also STARTER (1).

strip core, *n.* a magnetic core for an inductor that is made by winding a ribbon of SOFT MAGNETIC MATERIAL. Using a ribbon rather than a LAMINATED CORE allows the use of a material that is highly ANISOTROPIC magnetically.

strip line, *n.* a form of TRANSMISSION LINE using one broad conductor, an insulating strip, and one narrow conductor.

strobe, *n.* **1.** a gating pulse for a signal. See STROBED DISPLAY. **2.** See MOIRE PATTERN.

strobed display, *n.* a display, usually of the SEVEN-SEGMENT type, that is displayed section by section. The display is operated by ENABLING (strobe) pulses that connect the anode voltage and so illuminate each section of the display in turn. The rate of pulsing is such that all of the units appear to be operating together. Strobing allows all the connections to the segments to be taken to seven inputs irrespective of the number of digits in the display. When a strobe pulse is applied, the data for the correct unit is applied to the inputs. For example, when the 'tens' unit is strobed, the data that is applied is for the tens figure. This data will also affect the bars of all the other units, but only the tens unit is visible because of the strobing.

strobe pulse, *n.* a PULSE that is used to select one of a number of units, or in a MULTIPLEXER.

stub, *n.* a short length of TRANSMISSION LINE used for MATCHING sections. The stub may be either short-circuited or open-circuited at its far end. It is connected to the main line at a point where matching is needed, such as where the line joins to a device. The stub is then adjusted by cutting or by using a tuning capacitor connected to the end so as to achieve the minimum STANDING-WAVE RATIO.

subcarrier, *n.* a second CARRIER (1) modulated onto a main carrier. See COLOUR TELEVISION, PAL, STEREO RECEIVER.

subharmonic, *n.* a frequency that is an integer fraction ($\frac{1}{2}$, $\frac{1}{4}$, etc.) of a FUNDAMENTAL FREQUENCY.

Compare HARMONIC.

subsonic or **infrasonic,** *adj.* (of frequencies) being below the range of audible sound frequencies, less than 20Hz.

substandard, *n.* an instrument that is a SECONDARY STANDARD.

substrate, *n.* the material of a chip on which and of which an INTEGRATED CIRCUIT is constructed, applied mainly to the main part of the semiconductor chip on which the IC components and connections are made.

sunspot cycle, *n.* the periodic changes of conditions in the outer layers of the sun. These cause considerable changes in the IONIZATION of layers in the IONOSPHERE, thus affecting radio reception.

superconductivity, *n.* a complete loss of electrical RESISTANCE. This occurs in many metals at very low temperatures close to absolute zero. See also JOSEPHSON EFFECT.

superheterodyne (superhet) receiver, *n*. the most important type of RADIO RECEIVER circuit for virtually all usable
frequencies. A superhet receiver is based on the principle of
changing the frequency of received signals to a lower
frequency, the INTERMEDIATE FREQUENCY, at which most of the
amplification is carried out. This ensures that any unintended
FEEDBACK, such as is inevitable in the early tuned stages of a
receiver, will not be at a frequency which causes oscillation. In
addition, the main amplification can be carried out at a fixed
frequency, allowing greater gain and bandwidth than would
be possible if a variable frequency had to be amplified.

The intermediate frequency is obtained by mixing the
incoming frequency with the signal from a LOCAL OSCILLATOR.
The oscillator-tuned circuit is adjustable, and the tuning of the
oscillator is ganged (see GANGED CIRCUITS) to the tuning of the
mixer input stage, and to any tuned premixer stage. In this
way, the frequency of the oscillator is kept in step with that of
the input signal so as always to produce the correct intermediate frequency.

By convention, the oscillator frequency is higher than that
of the incoming signal. See Fig. 91.

Fig. 91. **Superheterodyne receiver**. A block diagram for the
superheterodyne receiver principle.

Supermalloy, *n*. *Trademark*. a magnetic nickel–iron alloy.
Supermalloy contains 5% molybdenum and has very high
permeability and low saturation field.

Supermendur, *n*. *Trademark*. a magnetic cobalt–iron alloy.

Supermendur contains vanadium and has very high saturation field strength.

superposition theorem, *n.* a useful electrical theorem for LINEAR NETWORKS of PASSIVE COMPONENTS. In a linear network that contains several sources of voltage or current, the effect of each voltage or current at a selected point can be found separately, and these effects added to find the effect of all the voltages or currents at that point. Suppose, for example, a network contains two signal voltages. To find the voltage across one resistor in the network, imagine one signal source replaced by its internal resistance. Calculate the voltage across the resistor that is due to the remaining signal. Now reverse the situation, replacing the first signal, but removing the second and substituting its internal resistance. Calculate the voltage across the resistor due to the second signal. Now add these voltages. The result is the voltage that would be caused by the two signal sources. The use of the superposition theorem is often simpler and quicker than methods based on KIRCHOFF'S LAWS.

super-regeneration, *n.* a method of operating a RECEIVER circuit for exceptionally high SENSITIVITY. The circuit is regenerative, meaning that positive feedback is used. The amount of positive feedback is so high that the circuit oscillates, but the circuit is arranged as a SQUEGGING oscillator, with the squegging at an ultrasonic frequency and suppressed by the incoming signal. Super-regenerative receivers can achieve astonishingly high gain, allowing the use of two-transistor receivers, for example, but with poor selectivity. In addition, the radiation that they set up by their oscillation interferes with other receivers around them, so super-regeneration is a technique that is used only in receivers for emergency use that must be of minimal size and power consumption. See REGENERATIVE RECEIVER.

suppressed-carrier transmission, *n.* a system of TRANSMISSION and reception of AMPLITUDE MODULATION. In the suppressed-carrier system, the carrier frequency is suppressed or filtered to very low amplitude at the transmitter. Since half of the power of a conventional AM transmitter is used to transmit the carrier, but all of the information lies in the SIDEBANDS, the suppression of the carrier greatly improves the efficiency of transmission. This can be increased still further if only one sideband is transmitted. The missing carrier must be regenerated at the receiver for purposes of DEMODULATION. This can be done either by CRYSTAL CONTROL of both transmitter and receiver, or by transmitting a small carrier signal that can be filtered, amplified and used to synchronize a local oscillator in the receiver.

suppressed-zero indicator, *n.* an indicator in which the scale does not start at zero. A simple example is the voltmeter in a car that has a range of about 10V to 14V only.

suppressor, *n.* a DEVICE that reduces the radiation of INTERFERENCE. The term usually denotes series resistors fitted in automotive spark-ignition systems. These damp out the VHF oscillations in the system. Other suppressors make use of C-R networks, diodes, inductors and other components to slow down sudden voltage changes and damp out oscillations.

surface acoustic wave (SAW), *n.* an ULTRASONIC wave along the surface of a QUARTZ CRYSTAL or other material. Surface acoustic waves are generated by crystal TRANSDUCERS, and can be of very high frequencies. The wave can be very precisely filtered by mechanical treatment of the surface along which it travels. Surface wave filters (SAW filters) are therefore extensively used wherever a purely electronic filter could not provide sufficiently sharp band edges and/or amount of attenuation.

surface-barrier device, *n.* a transistor that makes use of SCHOTTKY DIODE junctions in place of the normal p-n type of junction.

surface leakage, *n.* a leakage current along the surface of a material rather than through it.

surface passivation, *n.* the treatment of a semiconductor or other surface so that it cannot be affected by its environment.

surface resistivity, *n.* the RESISTANCE per unit area of a surface. The resistance is measured between two opposite sides of a square.

surface wave, *n.* a CARRIER (1) that follows the ground contours between transmitter and receiver.

surge, *n.* a large and abrupt change of VOLTAGE. Surges are produced by lightning striking power cables, cable faults, reflections on a transmission line, or switching transients.

surge arrester, *n.* a DEVICE that opens a CIRCUIT when a SURGE occurs.

surge diverter, *n.* a CIRCUIT that limits the effect of a SURGE by limiting the surge voltage. A SPARK GAP is a simple form of surge diverter.

surge impedance, *n.* the IMPEDANCE of a TRANSMISSION LINE to a sudden step of voltage. The value is determined by the values of inductance and capacitance per metre of line.

sweep, *n.* a combination of a RAMP and a FLYBACK.

sweep voltage, *n.* the linear rate of change of VOLTAGE from a TIMEBASE circuit that is used to deflect an ELECTRON BEAM. For magnetically deflected cathode ray tubes, *sweep current* is a more useful quantity.

swing, *n.* a range of values of VOLTAGE or CURRENT that is used by a DEVICE. The output swing of an amplifier stage might, for example, be between 1V and 9V when a 10V supply was used.

swinging choke, *n.* an INDUCTOR whose inductance is deliberately made NONLINEAR. The inductance value of a swinging choke decreases as the current increases, so that the filtering effect of the choke is less effective for high currents.

switch, *n.* a method of making, breaking, or changing electrical connections. Mechanical switches use moving contacts to make connections, but switching can also be carried out by semiconductor devices, e.g. SILICON–CONTROLLED SWITCHES, THYRISTORS, TRANSISTORS, FIELD–EFFECT TRANSISTORS, DIODES.

SWR, see STANDING WAVE RADIO.

SWR meter, *n.* a form of radio-frequency measuring bridge that can measure the amplitude of forward and reverse waves on a line. By doing so, it indicates the value of voltage STANDING WAVE RATIO.

sync, see SYNCHRONIZING PULSE.

synchronizing pulse, *n.* a PULSE that is used to start an action so that the action will be in time with the pulse. Sometimes shortened to *sync*. The source of a sync pulse is called a *clock generator*. Synchronizing pulses are essential in MICRO-PROCESSOR equipment, and are used extensively in TELEVISION circuitry.

See also RASTER.

synchronous, *adj*. (of a SIGNAL) being forced into step with another signal. When different circuits are fed with the same sync pulse, they will be acting in a synchronous way. The action of a television SYNCHRONIZING PULSE is to make the TIMEBASE of a TV receiver operate in a synchronous way with respect to the transmitted signals. Synchronous action is also important in a computer system, in which virtually every waveform is synchronized to a main CLOCK PULSE. Compare ASYNCHRONOUS; see also SYNCHRONOUS COUNTER.

synchronous counter, *n*. a set of FLIP-FLOPS arranged so as to act as a counter of PULSES that are fed to each flip-flop in the counter. Unlike the ASYNCHRONOUS COUNTER in which each flip-flop is toggled (see TOGGLING) by the output of the previous flip-flop, the synchronous counter applies the input pulses to the clock terminals of each flip-flop, so that clocking occurs at the same time for each unit. The counter uses J-K FLIP-FLOPS, and the counting logic is determined by the way in which the J and K inputs are interconnected using GATES.

synchronous demodulation, see SYNCHRONOUS DETECTION.

synchronous detection or **synchronous demodulation** or (formerly) **homodyne detection,** *n*. a form of DEMODU-LATION in which a modulated signal is mixed with a sine wave that is at carrier frequency. The modern synchronous detector is phase sensitive (see PHASE DISCRIMINATOR), so its output is affected by any difference between the phase of the incoming signal and the phase of the locally-generated carrier.

synchronous gating, *n*. a method of opening and closing signal paths in response to a SYNCHRONIZING PULSE.

synchronous logic, *n*. the use in a LOGIC CIRCUIT of FLIP-FLOPS that are clocked (see CLOCK). The clock signal is independent of the inputs to the flip-flops, and the advantage of the system is that it avoids RACE HAZARDS by ensuring that all logic stages operate at precisely controlled times.

synchronous motor, *n.* a form of AC motor in which the rotating speed is determined entirely by the supply mains frequency. In general, the synchronous motor will either run at its synchronous speed or not at all. Some types, such as those used in mains electric clocks, are not self-starting.

sync separator, *n.* a circuit in a TELEVISION RECEIVER used to separate the two SYNCHRONIZING PULSES from the VIDEO SIGNAL and from each other. The sync separator firstly separates the synchronizing signals from the video waveform, using a biased amplifier stage. The two sync signals are then separated from each other. A differentiator circuit is used to give a sharp spike for each sync pulse, so providing a horizontal (line) synchronizing pulse (see RASTER). The differentiator will also give an output for each of the field sync pulses, but this is unimportant. An integrating circuit provides a negligible output for each line sync pulse, but the more closely-spaced field sync pulses cause a rise in voltage that can be used to synchronize the vertical (field) timebase generator. See Fig. 92.

See also RASTER.

Fig. 92. **Sync separator**. The general form of a sync-separator STAGE before ICs took over the actions.

synthesis, *n.* the construction of a WAVEFORM or a desired response from standardized components (see STANDARDI-ZATION). An example is *filter synthesis*, the technique of designing filters of desired characteristics from standard values of inductors, capacitors and resistors.

synthesizer, *n.* a DEVICE that uses electronic CIRCUITS for generating SOUNDS. Synthesizers are based on the generation of SQUARE WAVES in the audio range. These waves are rich in HARMONICS. FILTERS are used to modify the shape of the waves, and modulators, limiters, clippers and other devices are used to shape the sound wave and form an envelope of waves. This permits a synthesizer to imitate the sounds of instruments and, more important, to create new types of notes and effects. Many synthesizers can be interconnected to computers using the MIDI (musical–instrument digital interface) system to permit a degree of control that is difficult to achieve manually.

system, *n.* a set of interacting parts that make up a working entity. The term can denote a circuit, device, a construction such as a radio receiver or a radar station, or a large assembly such as a steelworks. Anything can be treated as a system if it has definable inputs, outputs and control actions.

T

tachogenerator, *n.* a miniature electrical GENERATOR for rotational speed measurement. The tacho is designed to give a linear voltage output at all speeds of rotation of the shaft. This allows rotating components to be included in a FEEDBACK loop, with the tacho providing the feedback signal proportional to speed.

tachometer, *n.* any form of angular speed sensor. Electronic tachometers can use revolving magnets with static pick-up coils, light beams that are interrupted by a revolving object such as a slotted disk, TACHOGENERATORS, etc.

tap changer or **ratio adjuster,** *n.* a device for changing a TRANSFORMER ratio. The term is usually reserved to denote a switching type of changer that can be used while the transformer is energized. An alternative to tap changing is to use a fixed ratio transformer in conjunction with a variable transformer such as a VARIAC.

tape, see MAGNETIC TAPE, PAPER TAPE.

tape hiss, *n.* the NOISE that is heard when a magnetic tape is replayed. The noise is concentrated in the higher audio frequencies, so that it sounds like a hiss rather than a rumble or boom. The hiss can be minimized by using a wide section of tape for recording, and moving the tape rapidly past the head. Where these solutions are not available, noise–reduction systems that rely on companding (see COMPANDER) must be used. See also DOLBY SYSTEM, DBX, RECORDING OF SOUND.

tape recording, see RECORDING OF SOUND.

tapped–coil oscillator, see HARTLEY OSCILLATOR.

tapping, *n.* a connection to a component that is not to either end terminal. RESISTORS and INDUCTORS are the most common tapped components.

target, *n.* an ELECTRODE at which an ELECTRON BEAM is aimed. The electrode is used in TV CAMERA TUBES and other charge STORAGE TUBES. The target of an X-RAY TUBE is also called *anticathode.*

target voltage, *n.* **1.** the voltage between the CATHODE of an electron gun and the TARGET of a TV camera tube. This voltage is normally low, in the order of 10 to 30V. **2.** the voltage between the filament and the target of an x-ray tube. In this case, the voltage will be very high, of the order of 100kV.

tearing, *n.* the breakup of a TV image because of faulty synchronization of timebase waveform (see RASTER). The most common form is line tearing, in which the picture seems to be torn horizontally. In colour receivers, faulty colour synchronization can cause colour tearing (see HANOVER BARS).

Teflon, see PTFE.

telecommunications, *n.* the transmission and reception of signals in electrical form by wire or by electromagnetic wave.

telegraphy, *n.* communication by signal codes along wires or by radio. For message telegraphy, MORSE CODE is still in use, but the increasing use of computers has led to the acceptance of BINARY CODE systems.

telemetry, *n.* the remote measurement of physical quantities by TRANSDUCERS and some form of transmitter, e.g., radio. See also RADIOSONDE, RADIO PILL.

telephony, *n.* any method of transmitting audio–frequency signals, either by wire or by radio.

teleprinter, *n.* an electrically–operated typewriter that is controlled by digital signals. The term is now restricted to denote the obsolete type of electromechanical device that has mainly been superseded by DOT-MATRIX and daisywheel printers.

teletext, *n.* a television information service providing data consisting of digits, letters and some standardized graphics symbols. These are coded, using the digital ASCII code system, and transmitted along with the TV signal. The transmission of teletext takes place during the field–flyback period, and the signals are decoded, stored, assembled and displayed by a suitable receiver or adaptor. The signals can also be received by an adaptor connected to a suitable computer, such as the Acorn–BBC microcomputer. In the UK, both the BBC and ITA use identical systems, called CEEFAX and ORACLE respectively.

television (TV), *n.* a method of transmitting sound and animated vision signals. The TELEVISION CAMERA uses light-sensitive CAMERA TUBES, on the face of which the image is projected by lenses. The tubes are scanned, so that data on brightness (and colour) is extracted serially to form the VIDEO SIGNAL. To this is added BLANKING and SYNCHRONIZING PULSES, and the modulated colour SUBCARRIER signals, forming a COMPOSITE video signal. Sound signals from microphones are separately amplified. The two sets of signals are modulated onto separate UHF carriers, with the SOUND CARRIER 6MHz (in the UK) above the vision carrier frequency, and frequency modulated. See also TELEVISION RECEIVER, COLOUR TELEVISION.

television camera, *n.* a camera whose input is an optical image and whose output is a VIDEO waveform. The camera consists of an optical system, CAMERA TUBES, and PREAMPLIFIER stages. For a colour camera, at least three pick–up tubes will be used, and the optical system is very elaborate. It must consist of a main lens, often of the zoom variety, in which the image path is split into as many sections as there are camera tubes, so that each tube has an image focused on its face. By using dichroic prisms or mirrors, these images will be in the primary colours of blue, red and green – some designs use a black/white image also.

The pick-up tubes are almost always VIDICONS and their output consists of video signals. The electron beams of the vidicons are deflected by TIMEBASE signals, all of which are synchronized to a master generator in a camera control unit, often separate from the camera. BLANKING pulses are used to suppress the output from the vidicons during the FLYBACK time of the timebases. The separate video signals are each amplified in a preamplifier, and any frequency corrections and corrections for other distortions such as aperture distortion are made at this point.

The convention is that the video waveforms are amplified to a peak-to-peak amplitude of 1V. The video signals are then transmitted from a low output impedance current amplifier through a cable to the camera control unit. In this unit, further correction is carried out, sync signals are added, and the colour signals are processed. This consists of forming a LUMINANCE signal (black/white) from the colour signals if no separate luminance signal has been generated. The colour signals, in pairs, are then mixed to form the U and V signals of the PAL system, and these signals are modulated onto SUBCARRIERS, using in-phase and quadrature phase modulators. The COLOUR BURST of subcarrier frequency is added to the BACK PORCH of the line sync pulse, and the modulated subcarrier signals are added to the video signal, with the carrier itself suppressed.

television receiver, *n.* a device containing circuitry for receiving TV signals and producing an image. The receiver follows the pattern of a SUPERHETERODYNE RECEIVER system, and a broadband IF signal is obtained, containing both video and sound signals. The vision demodulator produces the main LUMINANCE signal, and allows the colour signals (modulated onto a SUBCARRIER) and the INTERCARRIER SOUND signals to be separated off. The sound signal is separately amplified, demodulated and passed to the audio stages. The COLOUR BURST is used to synchronize a local colour oscillator, and the output of this is used in two synchronous detectors (see SYNCHRONOUS DETECTION) to obtain the two colour difference signals. These signals are then mixed with the luminance signal in the correct proportions to recover the separate red, green and blue signals for the guns of the colour cathode-ray tube.

Picture synchronization is achieved by separating off the mixed sync pulses from the luminance signal in a sync separator that also separates the sync pulses from each other. These pulses are used to synchronize the TIMEBASE circuits that generate the linear sweep (ramp) currents for the deflection coils. The line-sweep current must be switched off rapidly to achieve a fast flyback, and the voltage that is produced by this rapid change of current in the line output transformer is stepped up in a WINDING, rectified by a VOLTAGE MULTIPLIER, and used to provide the accelerating voltage (EHT) for the picture tube.

telex, *n.* a system in TELEGRAPHY for digitally-coded signals. Telex users can type or receive messages on a TELEPRINTER or other terminals, and adaptors can be used to allow computers to be linked to the network.

temperature coefficient, *n.* a measure of the effect of changing temperature on a physical quantity. The coefficient is defined as the fractional change of quantity per unit temperature change. The temperature coefficient may be positive (increasing quantity for increasing temperature) or negative (decreasing quantity for increasing temperature). The most important temperature coefficients in electronics are of resistivity (or resistance) and of capacitance. Most ohmic conductors have a positive temperature coefficient of resistivity or resistance, semiconductors generally have a negative coefficient. Either PTC or NTC capacitors can be obtained, and oscillator circuits often use a mixture of capacitor types in order to balance out the effect of temperature changes on the tuned circuit.

TEM wave, *n.* a transverse electromagnetic wave, i.e. a wave in which the electric and the magnetic fields are perpendicular to each other and also to the direction of PROPAGATION. This is the type of wave that is propagated through space and along

TRANSMISSION LINES. It cannot be propagated along a WAVEGUIDE.

terminal, *n*. **1.** a place to which leads can be attached into or out from a CIRCUIT. **2.** the remote keyboard and display unit of a computer system.

terminal impedance, *n*. the IMPEDANCE at the end of a TRANSMISSION LINE.

termination, *n*. a MATCHING load for a TRANSMISSION LINE that prevents reflections.

tertiary winding, *n*. an additional WINDING on a TRANSFORMER. The tertiary winding may be used to supply a FEEDBACK signal, to provide a voltage level that differs from that on the SECONDARY WINDING, or to ensure insulation. For example, a well–insulated tertiary winding is used on a transformer for an oscilloscope to supply the heater voltage for the CATHODE–RAY TUBE, because the cathode may be operating at a large negative voltage. A tertiary winding that is electrically connected to another winding is often called an *overwind*. See also PRIMARY WINDING.

test pattern, *n*. a definition and shading pattern used to check a television system. The chart contains fine close-spaced lines and shaded blocks that should be distinguishable from each other, even by domestic TELEVISION RECEIVERS.

tetrode, see THERMIONIC VALVE.

TE wave, *n*. a transverse electric wave in a WAVEGUIDE in which the electric field is POLARIZED (1) at right angles to the direction of propagation, but with a magnetic field component whose polarization varies with distance travelled along the waveguide.

THD, *abbrev. for* total harmonic distortion, the sum of the ROOT–MEAN–SQUARE amplitudes of all HARMONICS that are generated by an amplifier whose input is a pure sine wave. The THD is usually expressed as a percentage, and quoted for full rated power, or shown as a graph plotted against power. For ordinary purposes, a THD of up to 10% is tolerated. Hi-fi sound systems deal with THD amounts in the region of 0.1% or less.

thermal breakdown, *n*. the complete loss of correct action of a component due to overheating. The overheating may in turn be caused by RUNAWAY.

thermal conductivity, *n*. a quantity that measures the ability of a material to conduct heat through its bulk. The thermal conductivity coefficient for a material is defined as the quantity of heat transmitted, due to a unit temperature gradient, in unit time under steady conditions in a direction normal to a surface of unit area. The coefficient is independent of sample size and shape. See also THERMAL RESISTANCE.

thermal imaging, *n*. the process of producing an image of an object from its heat radiation. Thermal–imaging cameras use TV techniques with infrared–sensitive CAMERA TUBES. The system is used for military purposes and in crime prevention and detection. It is also used in medicine, because cancerous cells are often at a slightly higher temperature than healthy tissue, and show up differently on the thermal display.

thermal instrument, *n*. any type of measuring instrument that makes use of heating. See HOT–WIRE.

thermal noise or **Johnson noise,** *n*. the electrical NOISE signal caused by the thermal agitation of current CARRIERS (1). In any conductor, the current carriers vibrate as well as moving along a current path. The vibration constitutes a noise signal, and its amplitude is proportional to the square root of (absolute) temperature. If very low noise is required an amplifier may have to be operated at a very low temperature.

thermal resistance, *n*. a measure of the RESISTANCE of a material to heat flow. The practical units used in electronics are of degrees Celsius per watt, and the measurement expresses the change of temperature caused by the dissipation of each watt of power. The thermal resistance of a collector junction to the case of a transistor is a very important PARAMETER for a power transistor, because it determines the maximum power level at which the transistor can safely be used.

thermal runaway, *n*. the loss of control over a device at high temperature. See RUNAWAY.

thermionic, *adj*. of or relating to any DEVICE that uses ELECTRONS emitted from a hot surface.

thermionic cathode, *n*. a hot electron–emitting surface. This may be a tungsten or tungsten/thorium wire that is heated to temperatures of around 2,500K by passing direct current through it. A cathode of this type is called directly-heated, i.e. a FILAMENT.

Indirectly heated cathodes are used in CATHODE-RAY TUBES, CAMERA TUBES, and some small VACUUM VALVES. These use cathodes that are hollow nickel tubes coated with a mixture of oxides of barium, strontium and calcium. This material emits electrons copiously at comparatively low temperatures, around 1,000K. The cathode is heated by an insulated molybdenum spiral filament inside the nickel tube. The disadvantage of using such materials is that the cathode material is easily damaged, particularly by sparking or by the electrostatic removal of the coating in large fields, and it tends to liberate gas when used for high currents. For these reasons, transmitting valves use tungsten or thoriated tungsten filaments.

thermionic valve (UK) or **vacuum tube** (US), *n*. an evacuated tube that contains a thermionic cathode and other electrodes. The most common form of valve is the triode transmitter valve, which is the thermionic equivalent of a BIPOLAR TRANSISTOR. This uses a directly-heated FILAMENT that is surrounded by a framework carrying a metal spiral, the control grid. In a *triode*, this in turn is surrounded by a metal cylinder, the ANODE (plate in the US). For high-power valves, the anode is the exterior casing of the valve and will be finned on the outside, or attached to a water jacket for cooling. Small valves contain the anode and other electrodes inside a glass tube, the ENVELOPE. The valve that uses one grid is a triode, adding another grid between the first grid (control grid) and the anode makes the valve a *tetrode*. The cathode is heated to provide electrons, and the anode is connected to a high voltage, typically 1KV upwards. The flow of electrons is controlled by the control grid voltage, and a sufficiently negative voltage on this electrode will cut off the electron stream. For transmitting purposes, the grid voltage is often swung between negative and positive voltage values relative to the cathode, and current will flow to the grid only during the positive parts of the cycle.

thermistor, *n.* a nonohmic resistor (see OHMIC). Thermistors are made from semiconducting materials, and most types have very large NEGATIVE TEMPERATURE COEFFICIENTS. They are used for temperature measurement, temperature warning devices, and for temperature compensation. Thermistors are also used in the FEEDBACK circuits of R-C oscillators to stabilize the amplitude of oscillation by increasing the amount of NEGATIVE FEEDBACK when the amplitude of oscillation becomes too great.

thermoammeter, *n.* a current METER that uses the heating effect of CURRENT. The thermoammeter uses either the HOT-WIRE METER principle, or a THERMOCOUPLE heated by current through a strip of resistive material. Thermoammeters are imprecise, but are often the only way of measuring a radio-frequency current. They can also be calibrated in terms of true RMS values.

thermocouple, *n.* a JUNCTION (1) between two different metals. Two thermocouples connected in series will generate a voltage if the junctions are at different temperatures. The voltages are of millivolt level, but comparatively large currents can be passed. Thermocouples are used extensively for measuring temperature because the sensor (junction) can be remote from the meter at which the reading is taken. See also THERMOELECTRIC EFFECT.

thermoelectric effect, *n.* a term applied to a set of discoveries by Thomas Seebeck (1770–1831), Jean Peltier (1785–1845) and Lord Kelvin (1824–1907). The *Seebeck effect* is the action of the THERMOCOUPLE. The *Peltier effect* is the opposite – the heating of one junction and the cooling of the other when current is forced to flow through two junctions. Using metal/semiconductor junctions, large temperature changes can be obtained, so that refrigeration by Peltier junction is possible. The *Kelvin effect* is a voltage in a single conductor caused by temperature differences that affect the electron ENERGY BANDS.

thermography, *n.* a form of THERMAL IMAGING that produces a permanent image on paper or on film.

thermojunction, *n.* a single junction of a THERMOCOUPLE. The favourite pairs of materials for junctions include copper and constantan, iron and constantan, platinum and rhodium.

thermopile, *n.* a set of THERMOCOUPLES wired in series or in series-parallel to form a source of ELECTROMOTIVE FORCE comparable to that of a chemical battery.

thermostat, *n.* a temperature-operated SWITCH. The usual thermostat principle uses a BIMETALLIC STRIP carrying a switch contact. This device, however, suffers from considerable HYSTERESIS which limits its usefulness as a method of maintaining a constant temperature. The simple thermostat is now being superseded by the use of THERMISTORS, often as part of a MICROPROCESSOR system.

Thevenin's theorem, *n.* a method of analysing linear resistance networks. Thevenin's theorem states that any two-terminal LINEAR NETWORK that contains sources of voltage (DC or signal) and resistances can be represented by an equivalent single voltage source and series RESISTANCE. The use of Thevenin's theorem therefore allows an EQUIVALENT CIRCUIT to be drawn up for any linear network. See also NORTON'S THEOREM.

thick-film circuit, *n.* a type of miniature PRINTED CIRCUIT BOARD, but with PASSIVE COMPONENTS formed in the connections. The circuit is formed by photolithographic techniques, and uses metal films for connections and for resistors, with capacitors formed from metal and oxide layers. INTEGRATED CIRCUITS can be bonded to a thick-film circuit by compression welding to bonding pads. Compare THIN-FILM CIRCUIT.

thin-film circuit, *n.* a form of circuit that uses sputtered (see SPUTTERING) or vacuum-coated films rather than thick films. Compare THICK-FILM CIRCUIT.

thoriated tungsten, *n.* a thorium-tungsten alloy material, used for directly-heated CATHODES in transmitting valves. The presence of thorium allows electron EMISSION at considerably lower temperatures than tungsten alone. When a thoriated tungsten cathode starts to lose emission, it can often be regenerated by running the FILAMENT for a short time at a higher temperature than normal, so allowing more thorium to diffuse to the surface.

three-phase supply, *n.* a supply of AC along three separate lines, with 120 degrees between the voltage phases of any two lines.

three-state logic, *n.* a LOGIC CIRCUIT arrangement for INTEGRATED CIRCUITS. In a three-state logic terminal, the voltage may be at logic 0, logic 1, or FLOATING. In the floating state, the voltage may be changed by external voltages without any damage to the internal circuits of the chip. The floating state is the third state of the title. See also TRI-STATE DEVICE.

threshold, *n.* a point at which a cause just produces an effect. The threshold frequency for the PHOTOELECTRIC EFFECT is the light frequency for which EMISSION can just be detected. The threshold voltage for a conducting device is the voltage at which the device just starts to pass current. The threshold signal for a receiver with SQUELCH is the signal that overcomes the squelch, thus enabling the audio section of the receiver.

thyratron, *n.* a GAS-FILLED TUBE that acts as a form of RELAY. Thyratrons have been largely replaced by their semiconductor equivalent, the THYRISTOR.

thyristor or (formerly) **silicon-controlled rectifier (SCR),** *n.* a SEMICONDUCTOR pnpn device. The thyristor has three electrodes, ANODE, CATHODE and GATE (1). A voltage that can be of either polarity is applied between the anode and the cathode. Current will flow between the anode and the cathode only when the anode is positive with respect to the cathode, and when the gate has been triggered. The TRIGGER PULSE is applied to the gate at the time when the anode is positive. The effect of the trigger pulse is to make the device conduct heavily. Conduction then continues until the anode voltage drops to almost the cathode voltage level, or until the current falls to a very low value. Thyristors have almost completely replaced THYRATRONS for most purposes.

tight coupling, *n.* a form of tuned COUPLING in which the COUPLING COEFFICIENT is large so that a large fraction of the input signal is transferred to the output. A tight coupling is efficient in terms of signal transfer and can provide optimum signal transfer conditions if the coupling is critical (see CRITICAL COUPLING). If the coupling passes the critical point, then OVERCOUPLING will result, causing the bandwidth to increase considerably, and the shape of the transfer characteristic (the graph of output plotted against input) to develop a trough between two peaks. Compare LOOSE COUPLING.

timebase, *n.* a CIRCUIT that produces a WAVEFORM for ELECTRON BEAM deflection. The most common type is the linear RAMP (or SWEEP) circuit that produces a SAWTOOTH WAVEFORM. Timebase generators uses a combination of a SQUARE-WAVE generator and an INTEGRATOR to produce the linear ramp (or sweep), and some form of switching circuit to produce a rapid FLYBACK. By separating the square-wave generator portion from the integrator, it is possible to control the frequency and the slope of the timebase sweep separately. The square-wave generator may be a MONOSTABLE, in which case the timebase is a triggered one, producing a sweep voltage only when a TRIGGER PULSE arrives.

time constant, *n.* a measure of the time required to change the VOLTAGE across a CAPACITOR or INDUCTOR. For a capacitor-resistor circuit, the time constant is given (in seconds) by $C \times R$, where C is in farads and R in ohms. For an inductor-resistor circuit, the time constant is L/R, with L in henries and R in ohms. The time that is obtained from these calculations is the time needed for the voltage across the capacitor or the current through an inductor to decrease to $\frac{1}{e}$ or 36.8% of the starting value. Time constant values are particularly useful in estimating the effect of a CR or LR network on a square wave.

time delay or **time lag,** *n.* the time between a signal being applied to the INPUT (1) and appearing at the OUTPUT of a signal.

time-delay switch, *n.* a SWITCH that operates after a specified time delay. In equipment that makes use of indirectly-heated CATHODES, a time-delay switch is often used to ensure that no high voltage is applied until the cathode has warmed up.

time discriminator, *n.* a demodulator for pulse-time modulated signals. The time discriminator generates a signal whose amplitude is proportional to the time between pulses. A simple form of time discriminator is a TIMEBASE that is triggered by one pulse and terminated by the next.

time-division multiplexer, *n.* a SYSTEM by which a cable or radio channel may be shared by several signals. Each signal is sampled and the sample amplitudes are transmitted in sequence. At the receiver, the same rate of sampling has to be used to reconstitute the signals correctly. SYNCHRONIZING PULSES can be transmitted at intervals to keep the transmitter and the receiver in step.

time lag, see TIME DELAY.

time-sharing, *n.* the sharing of the use of a computer among several users. By interleaving the signals to and from the main computer, each user can be served with almost unnoticeable time delays. The system becomes unworkable if each user simultaneously needs the full speed of the computer.

time switch, *n.* a form of CLOCK, either electromechanical or digital quartz, that will switch circuits on or off.

time to trip, *n.* the circuit-breaking time for a relay. This is the time between activating the coil (or deactivating it) and breaking the circuit that is operated by the relay.

T-junction, see HYBRID JUNCTION.

TM wave, *n.* a transverse magnetic wave in a WAVEGUIDE in which the magnetic field is POLARIZED (1) at right angles to the direction of propagation, but with an electric field component whose polarization varies with distance travelled along the waveguide.

toggling, *n.* the switching of STATE, as of a FLIP-FLOP, in which each PULSE at the INPUT (1) causes the OUTPUT to change state. A toggling circuit is a divide-by-two COUNTER, because two complete pulses at the input produce one complete pulse at the output. A series of connected toggling circuits may be used to provide divide-by 4, 8, 16 and so on counters.

tolerance, *n.* the amount of variation about a nominal value. Most passive components in electronic circuits are specified with quite wide tolerances, up to 20%. The tolerance of value for electrolytic capacitors can be as high as 50% of nominal value, and semiconductors also have very large tolerance values.

The problem is dealt with in analogue circuits by using NEGATIVE FEEDBACK circuits in which only a few components in the feedback loop need be of close tolerance. In digital circuits, tolerances have very little effect on the action of a correctly designed circuit.

tone arm, *n*. the arm that holds and guides the PICK-UP of a gramophone. The design of a tone arm is complicated by conflicting requirements, among them the need to hold the pick-up head rigidly, yet allow free movement to follow the record track, with no vibrational resonance that will cause peaks in the response.

tone control, *n*. a control over the FREQUENCY response of an audio AMPLIFIER. Simple radio receivers sometimes incorporate a treble cut control, but good quality sound reproduction demands a more comprehensive system of tone controls. These should include the actions of boosting or cutting BASS response, with a choice of the CROSSOVER FREQUENCY, and a similar variable boost or cut for TREBLE with a choice of crossover.

toroidal inductor, *n*. an INDUCTOR wound around a ring-shaped core. The toroidal shape of MAGNETIC CORE (1) is particularly efficient because it is easy to ensure that all of its flux passes through the coils that are wound round it. Now that machines for winding toroidal coils are widely available, toroidal transformers are displacing the older LAMINATED CORE type.

total emission, *n*. the total electron current from a CATHODE to all forms of GRID or ANODE.

totem-pole circuit, *n*. a SINGLE-ENDED push-pull circuit. This is a popular type of transistor output stage for digital devices and audio amplifiers. In its simplest form, it consists of two COMPLEMENTARY TRANSISTORS connected in series. The same signal is taken to both bases, with a steady bias voltage superimposed. Each transistor then deals with one half of the output signal. Since each transistor is being used in CLASS B, the stage is very efficient, and with NEGATIVE FEEDBACK and some care about biasing, can produce good-quality output. See Fig. 93 on page 342.

touch control, *n*. a form of SWITCH that is operated by touching. The switch contains contact areas, and touching with the finger makes a high resistance connection that triggers a transistor circuit and operates a THYRISTOR. The touch portion

signal input
and bias
voltages

load

Fig. 93. **Totem-pole circuit.** The general form of a totem-pole circuit using complementary transistors. The output can sometimes be direct-coupled if balanced positive and negative supplies are used.

of the circuit must be completely isolated from the thyristor circuit. Some touch switches ensure safe use by making use of the capacitance between an insulated contact and the body of the user.

trace, *n.* the shape drawn by the SPOT (1) of light on the face of a cathode-ray tube.

track, *n.* a conducting line on a PRINTED–CIRCUIT BOARD, or a line of stored information on a TAPE or a DISC.

tracking, *n.* **1.** the maintenance of a fixed relationship between quantities. **2.** in a SUPERHETERODYNE RECEIVER, the maintenance of correct tuning in the RF and oscillator circuits, so that the difference between their frequencies is constant (see also GANGED CIRCUITS). **3.** the locking of a RADAR beam onto a target which will continue to follow that target to the extremes of its range until reset. **4.** in a GRAMOPHONE transcriptor, the arrangement of the TONE ARM so that the stylus is always correctly located in the groove of the disc. **5.** the formation of conducting tracks that will cause sparking on an insulator.

trailing edge, *n.* the rear, falling-voltage, edge of a PULSE.

transconductance, see MUTUAL CONDUCTANCE.

transcriptor, *n.* a device comprising a gramophone turntable, TONE-ARM and PICK-UP cartridge.

transducer, *n.* a CONVERTER of energy from one form to another. For electronics purposes, the transducers of interest are those that have either an electrical input (actuators) or output (sensors).

transductor, see SATURABLE REACTOR.

transfer characteristic, *n.* a graph plot of output against input for a device or circuit. The CHARACTERISTIC may be of current (output current/input current), voltage, or a hybrid such as output voltage/input current.

transfer current, *n.* the current to the STARTER (1) of a gas-filled device.

transfer parameter, *n.* a PARAMETER that is calculated from the slope of a TRANSFER CHARACTERISTIC.

transformer, *n.* a general term for a pair of mutual inductors (see INDUCTANCE). For high-frequency signals, a transformer can take the form of two coils placed close to each other. For lower frequencies, MAGNETIC CORES (1) must be used to concentrate the FLUX and ensure that all the flux from one winding cuts the turns of the other winding. The winding to which a signal is applied is the PRIMARY WINDING, the winding from which a signal is taken is the SECONDARY WINDING. For an IDEAL TRANSFORMER, the ratio of secondary voltage to primary voltage is the same as the ratio of secondary turns to primary turns.

transient, *n.* a brief pulse of voltage or current.

transistor, *n.* a three-electrode SEMICONDUCTOR device. The main types of transistor are the BIPOLAR TRANSISTOR and the FIELD-EFFECT TRANSISTOR (FET). In either type of device, a main current between two of the electrodes is controlled either by a much smaller current at the third electrode (in the bipolar transistor) or by a small voltage at the third electrode (FET). Both types make use of semiconductor material of both DOPING types, p-type and n-type, but they differ in the way in which the main current is conducted and controlled. In the bipolar transistor, the main current between emitter and collector terminals flows through two JUNCTIONS (1) and is controlled by passing current into or out from the region between the junctions. In the field-effect transistor, the main current flow between source and drain terminals is along a path of one material type, which can be p-type or n-type. The modern methods of fabrication of transistors are EPITAXY and ION IMPLANTATION, and although DISCRETE devices are still manufactured in huge numbers, most transistors are now formed as parts of INTEGRATED CIRCUITS.

transistor parameters, *n.* the measurements that allow the action of a transistor to be represented in an EQUIVALENT CIRCUIT. Many sets of PARAMETERS were devised during the development stages of transistor technology, and many of these are no longer used. The almost universal adoption of silicon as a transistor material has meant that many of the old transistor parameters have values that can be ignored. A useful equivalent circuit of a silicon bipolar transistor is one in which the transistor is considered as a current generator producing 40mA per input volt for each milliamp of bias current. This leads to a figure of voltage gain of $40 \times$ (bias current in mA.) for transistors operated with small signals in the audio frequency region. More detailed analysis is needed if the transistors are being used in radio frequency or wideband circuits, and for switching circuit design, the large-signal equivalent circuit must be used.

For further details see Ref. 1.

transistor-transistor logic (TTL), *n.* a system of constructing gate and other logic circuits in INTEGRATED CIRCUIT form with BIPOLAR TRANSISTOR techniques. The gates use integrated transistors whose bases are connected through a resistor to the supply positive voltage terminal. The input logic signals are to the EMITTERS(1) of these transistors. A logic 1 input, therefore, requires no current to or from the source. A logic 0, however, requires the source voltage to drop to zero, and to accept current from the integrated circuit input (the driving circuit

Fig. 94. **Transistor-transistor logic**. The basis of TTL circuits. The input is to a transistor with multiple emitters, and the output is from a form of totem-pole circuit.

must be able to SINK(1) current). TTL circuits are fairly fast-acting, but require a considerable amount of supply current. The later Schottky devices make use of SCHOTTKY DIODES in circuits that permit input to the base of a transistor. These devices require much lower driving currents, and are very fast in operation. See Fig. 94.

transition, *n*. a sudden change from one STATE to another, usually of electron energy level inside an atom.

transit time, *n*. the time that an ELECTRON or HOLE takes to travel from one ELECTRODE to another in an ACTIVE COMPONENT. The transit time for a device limits its ability to operate with high-frequency signals.

transmission, *n*. the sending of SIGNALS from one place to another. Compare RECEPTION.

transmission line or **line,** *n*. a CABLE or arrangement of cables for transmitting SIGNALS. The important features of a transmission line are that it should not radiate nor reflect signals. If the signal at the input of the line is to reach the end of the line substantially unaffected, then the line must be matched (see MATCHING) to the impedances of the load and the source so that the STANDING-WAVE RATIO is as low as possible. The use of a balanced or a shielded line reduces radiation, and correct matching reduces reflection to a minimum. The loss of power on the line can be minimized by good construction and suitable materials.

transmission loss, *n.* the ratio of power out to power in for a TRANSMISSION LINE or other system. The loss figure is often converted into decibels.

transmission primary, *n.* a primary colour for COLOUR TELEVISION use. The transmission primaries are red, blue and green. These are not the primary colours of paint, because the primary light signals add to white, the paint primaries add to black.

transmit/receive (TR) switch, *n.* a gas-discharge device used in a RADAR system. The gas ionizes (see IONIZATION) during the transmission period, placing a short circuit across the receiver waveguide. This prevents the receiver from being paralysed by the transmitted signal. Following transmission, the gas deionizes, and the receiver waveguide opens again. Compare ANTI-TRANSMIT/RECEIVE SWITCH.

transmitted-carrier transmission, *n.* a conventional amplitude-modulation system with full carrier amplitude present. See SUPPRESSED-CARRIER TRANSMISSION, VESTIGIAL SIDEBAND.

transmitter, *n.* a device that sends out a carrier signal at radio frequency modulated by audio, video or other waveforms. Compare RECEIVER.

transponder, *n.* a DEVICE that receives a coded signal, the interrogating signal, from a distant TRANSMITTER, and responds with another coded signal for recognition purposes. The transponder is the basis of the IFF system, a form of SECONDARY RADAR.

transposed line, *n.* a LINE (1) or cable in which the positions of the conductors are interchanged at intervals to reduce any possibility of losses caused by any asymmetry of capacitance or inductance.

transputer, *n.* a complete computer, including the MICROPROCESSOR and its MEMORY, fabricated on a single CHIP.

transverse wave, *n.* any wave in which OSCILLATION occurs at right angles to the direction of PROPAGATION. All electromagnetic waves are transverse, but acoustic waves are often longitudinal, oscillating along the direction of propagation.

trap, *n.* a form of FILTER that reduces the amplitude of one particular frequency, usually by means of a resonant tuned circuit. A trap is used in a colour TV receiver, for example, to eliminate the 4.43MHz colour subcarrier signal from the luminance signal before the luminance signal is applied to the cathode-ray tube.

trapezium distortion, *n.* a form of distortion of a TV image in which the normal rectangular shape is distorted into the shape of a trapezium.

travelling wave, *n.* an electromagnetic wave (see ELECTRO-MAGNETIC RADIATION) travelling in space or along a TRANSMIS-SION LINE with no reflections. At any point along the direction of travel, the wave amplitude will vary with time at the wave frequency. Compare STANDING WAVE.

travelling-wave tube (TWT), a type of AMPLIFIER for MICROWAVES. The waves are forced to travel in a spiral path along a line inside a vacuum tube. A beam of electrons is made to travel down the axis of the tube at the same speed, with the result that the ELECTRON BEAM is modulated by the waves. The electron beam, which is now bunched (see BUNCHER) by the interaction, passes its power back to the wave at a later part of the spiral, so that the output power is much greater than the input power. In a variation of the principle, the direction of the electron beam is opposite to the direction of the wave, constituting a BACKWARD-WAVE TUBE. The travelling-wave tube is an important means of low-noise amplification at microwave frequencies, but it has been eclipsed to some extent in this role by the MASER.

treble, *n.* the AUDIO FREQUENCIES in the range 2kHz upward.

treble response, *n.* a feature of an AMPLIFIER or SYSTEM that is measured by the amplitude of treble frequencies relative to lower frequencies. The standard frequency for response is often that of a 1kHz wave, and the relative values of amplitude are usually expressed in decibels.

triac, *n.* a form of two-way THYRISTOR. The triac uses an electrode (the gate) to trigger conduction between two other electrodes, usually labelled M1 and M2 since the terms anode and cathode are not appropriate. The conduction ceases when the current through the device falls to below the HOLDING CURRENT value or when the voltage between M1 and M2 drops to below the holding value.

trickle charge, *n.* a small amount of CURRENT supplied to a SECONDARY CELL in order to charge the cell slowly or maintain it in a fully charged state.

trigger level, *n.* a critical level of VOLTAGE that must be exceeded by a TRIGGER PULSE in order to start an action.

trigger pulse, *n.* a brief PULSE that will start an action. A trigger pulse will normally have a very sharp rise, but may not have a fixed duration, though its amplitude may be critical.

trimmer capacitor, *n.* a small-value preset VARIABLE CAPACITOR or RESISTOR used for the fine adjustment of a CIRCUIT. A trimmer is adjusted only during manufacture or calibration of a circuit. One example of a trimmer in use is in the oscillator TRACKING of a SUPERHETERODYNE receiver. A trimmer capacitor is connected in parallel with the main tuning capacitor, and another form of trimmer (known as a padder) is sometimes connected in series. By adjusting these capacitors, the tracking of the oscillator frequency can be made almost perfect at the two extremes of the frequency range.

Trinitron, *n. Trademark.* the Sony aperture grille colour TV tube.

triode, see THERMIONIC VALVE.

trip, *n.* a RELAY connected so as to open-circuit a supply in the event of a fault. See also OVERCURRENT TRIP.

triple-detection receiver, see DOUBLE SUPERHET.

tripler, *n.* a form of AC VOLTAGE MULTIPLIER circuit whose output voltage is three times the input voltage.

Tri-state device or **Tri-state output,** *n. Trademark.* a digital device that combines the speed of PUSH-PULL outputs with the interconnection ability of OPEN-COLLECTOR DEVICES by providing a control input that effectively disconnects an output when it is not required. See also THREE–STATE LOGIC.

TR switch, see TRANSMIT–RECEIVE SWITCH.

true RMS, *n.* the measurement of the true ROOT–MEAN–SQUARE value of an ALTERNATING CURRENT quantity. Many AC meters operate by rectifying the AC and measuring the resulting unidirectional current. The meter resistors can be adjusted so that for a sine-wave input, the readings will correspond to the values of RMS current or voltage. This is not a true RMS reading, however, because using the meter on any waveform other than a sinusoid (with a different FORM FACTOR) will give incorrect results. Only meters that operate on a square-law principle, such as a MOVING–IRON METER or a HOT–WIRE METER will give true RMS values for any waveform.

trunk, *n.* a main set of CABLES connecting from one unit to another.

truth table, *n.* a table that shows all of the possible inputs and outputs for a LOGIC CIRCUIT.

T-section, *n.* one half-section of a filter, the other being the pi-section. See Fig. 95.

Fig. 95. **T-section**. The T- and Pi sections of a filter, and the ladder network that results from joining the sections. The elements of the network have been shown as impedances.

TTL, see TRANSISTOR–TRANSISTOR LOGIC.

T-type flip-flop, *n.* a FLIP–FLOP circuit of the toggled (see

TOGGLING) type. The T-type flip-flop has one input, the toggle input. Each pulse at this input will cause the output to reverse the output state between logic 0 and logic 1.

tube, see CATHODE RAY TUBE, THERMIONIC VALVE.

tuned aerial, *n*. an aerial, such as a DIPOLE AERIAL, that is tuned in the sense of being cut to some multiple of the wavelength. This allows the formation of a STANDING WAVE on the aerial.

tuned amplifier, *n*. an AMPLIFIER in which load RESISTORS are replaced by RESONANT CIRCUITS so that amplification is a maximum at the frequency of resonance of the tuned circuit in each stage. See also STAGGER TUNING.

tuned circuit, see RESONANT CIRCUIT.

tuned filter, *n*. a FILTER that is designed to accept or reject a very narrow frequency band. See also TRAP.

tuned-load oscillator, *n*. a form of OSCILLATOR in which both INPUT (1) and OUTPUT of an AMPLIFIER are tuned to the same FREQUENCY. The FEEDBACK through STRAY CAPACITANCE ensures that the circuit will oscillate at this frequency.

tuner, *n*. the portion of a RADIO RECEIVER that consists of the RF, IF, and DEMODULATOR stages. A separate tuner is often a part of a hi-fi system because, in general, the incorporation of a tuner and an amplifier in the same casing can lead to NOISE problems.

tuning indicator, *n*. a DEVICE used to indicate the accuracy of manual tuning. At one time, a form of vacuum device known as the *magic eye* was used for this purpose, but in the few examples where tuning indicators are still used they consist now of meters, solid-state displays, or modern forms of VACUUM–FLUORESCENT DISPLAY.

tunnel diode, *n*. a heavily-doped P-N JUNCTION diode that contains a negative-resistance region in its current-voltage CHARACTERISTIC. Because of this negative-resistance region, the tunnel diode will oscillate when biased into the appropriate region, and by connecting a suitable RESONANT CIRCUIT, usually a resonant cavity, the oscillations can be tuned to any desired frequency. The tunnel diode is normally used as a very low power microwave or radar oscillator.

turn–off time, *n*. the time for current to stop flowing in a THYRISTOR once the turn–off conditions have been reached.

turns ratio, *n.* the ratio of secondary to primary turns in a TRANSFORMER.

turret tuner, *n.* a tuning system once used for TV receivers and FM tuners. This consisted of a cylinder that carried the tuning inductors inside with a set of connecting contacts outside. By rotating this cylinder inside a casing, the connections to each coil could be made, so tuning from one TV channel to another.

tweeter, *n.* a LOUDSPEAKER intended to reproduce high-frequency notes. Compare WOOFER.

twin cable or **twin line,** *n.* a CABLE made from two insulated close-spaced conductors. This cable has low radiation loss when used as a TRANSMISSION LINE. Compare COAXIAL CABLE.

twin line, see TWIN CABLE.

twin-T network or **parallel-T network,** *n.* **1.** a form of FILTER network using resistors and capacitors that is frequency selective. The device is used as a FILTER or as the frequency-selecting part of an OSCILLATOR circuit.

twisted pair, *n.* a cable consisting of a pair of conductors twisted around each other and carrying a (usually digital) signal and its complement. This results in increased noise immunity, and such cables are used when serial digital data has to be transmitted by cable over distances greater than a few metres.

twisted-ring counter, *n.* a COUNTER circuit that uses J-K FLIP-FLOPS in a ring that is closed with one J-to-K and K-to-J connection.

two-phase, *adj.* (of an AC supply) using one live and one neutral line, as in the normal domestic AC supply.

TWT, see TRAVELLING–WAVE TUBE.

U

UHF, *abbrev. for* ultrahigh frequency, the range of about 300MHz to 3GHz, 1m to 10cm wavelength. This range is widely used for television broadcasting.

ULA, see UNCOMMITTED LOGIC ARRAY.

ultrahigh definition, *n.* a development of television intended to enhance picture quality. In place of the existing line standards of 525 (USA and Japan) or 625 (Europe) lines per picture, ultrahigh–definition systems plan to use 1,000 or more lines per picture, abandoning existing standards of bandwidth and frequency. The problems involved in so doing are political rather than technical or artistic.

ultrasonic, *adj.* (of an acoustic wave) having a frequency above the audible range. The ultrasonic range is usually taken as being 20kHz and above, but most ultrasonic devices use frequencies in the range 100kHz to 5MHz. The waves are generated by PIEZOELECTRIC CRYSTALS or, for the lower frequencies, magnetostrictive transducers (see MAGNETO-STRICTION).

ultrasonic delay line, *n.* a DELAY device for signals that makes use of ultrasonic waves. Because ultrasonic waves travel through solids or liquids at speeds that are much lower than the speed of radio waves in space or along conductors, a short length of ultrasonic wave path can cause a delay of several microseconds. The signals are converted to ultrasonic form by a TRANSDUCER, travel through a solid or liquid, and are then converted back into electromagnetic waves by a second transducer. The early ultrasonic delay lines used mercury as the wave medium, and were known as *mumble-tubs*. Later varieties have used glass and other solid materials. The main require-ment for delay lines originally was in integration of signals for radar purposes, but a huge new market opened up when the PAL colour TV system was adopted. The PAL delay lines use glass, with a V-shaped signal path that allows the delay time to be adjusted by grinding the reflecting surface at the apex of the V.

ultrasonic light valve, *n.* a method of modulating a light beam, using ULTRASONIC waves to affect the polarizing properties of a crystal through which the light passes.

ultraviolet, *n.* the range of electromagnetic wave frequencies that lies between the violet end of the visible spectrum, and the start of the x-ray region. Ultraviolet radiation is of higher energy than light, and can have destructive effects on the eye and the skin. One important use is in erasing PROMS.

unbalanced, see SINGLE–ENDED.

unclocked, *adj*. (of a gate circuit or flip-flop) not controlled by a CLOCK pulse. See also ASYNCHRONOUS.

uncommitted logic array (ULA), *n*. an INTEGRATED CIRCUIT that consists of a large number of gates whose interconnections are not made at the time of initial manufacture. The interconnection pattern can be determined by the customer, using a large chart, and then applied to the ICs by one final process. This permits the flexibility of custom-designed ICs at almost the price of mass-produced chips.

undercoupling, see LOOSE COUPLING.

undercurrent release, *n*. a CONTACT BREAKER that operates when the current in a circuit is lower than a specified level. See also TRIP, OVERCURRENT TRIP.

underdamped, *adj*. (of a RESONANT CIRCUIT) oscillating for a few cycles after a sudden voltage change. Compare DAMPED, OVERDAMPED.

underscan, *n*. a SCAN of a TV CAMERA TUBE or receiver tube with less than normal amplitude. This is usually avoided because of the danger of creating a visible boundary at the edge of the scan.

undershoot, *n*. a transient decrease of voltage at the trailing edge of a PULSE. Compare OVERSHOOT.

undervoltage release, *n*. a CONTACT BREAKER that operates when the voltage in a circuit is below a set level. See also TRIP, UNDERCURRENT RELEASE.

undistorted wave, *n*. a WAVE whose WAVEFORM has not been changed in an electronic circuit.

unidirectional, *adj*. (of a CURRENT, usually rectified alternating current) travelling in one direction.

uniform line, *n*. a TRANSMISSION LINE whose constants of CAPACITANCE, INDUCTANCE and CHARACTERISTIC IMPEDANCE are the same throughout its length.

uniform waveguide, *n*. a WAVEGUIDE whose CHARACTERISTICS are the same throughout all of its length.

unijunction or **double-base diode,** *n*. a form of pulse-generating semiconductor device. The unijunction consists of a

Fig. 96. **Unijunction**. A simple unijunction oscillator and the waveforms at the electrodes.

bar of lightly-doped N-TYPE silicon with an OHMIC CONTACT at each end. Between these ohmic contacts, a junction is formed to a heavily-doped p-region, the emitter. The action is that the resistance between the two ohmic contacts is very high until carriers are injected from the junction. The unijunction is therefore nonconducting until the voltage at the emitter reaches a definite fraction of the voltage between the ohmic connections. This fraction is called the INTRINSIC STAND-OFF RATIO. When the emitter voltage reaches the value that causes conductivity, comparatively large current can flow both between emitter and the earthed base contact and between the two base contacts. The main application is in pulse generators and sawtooth oscillators. See Fig. 96.

unilateral network, *n.* a NETWORK that conducts in one direction only. This normally applies to signals, so that a transistor is a unilateral network in the sense that the direction of signal is from input to output, not the reverse. This is true only if the collector-base capacitance is low and collector-base resistance is high. At very high frequencies, a transistor may allow signal transfer through the collector-base capacitance, and the correction of this unwanted feedback is called *unilateralization*. See also NEUTRALIZATION.

unipolar, *adj.* (of a SEMICONDUCTOR device) having the main current carried by MAJORITY CARRIERS in one polarity of material, without passing through a JUNCTION. The FIELD-EFFECT TRANSISTOR is one example of a unipolar device.

unit, *n.* a physical quantity of strictly defined and reproducible size. The fundamental units are the kilogram, metre, second and ampere. The lumen is used for light measurement.

unit-step, *n.* a sudden change of VOLTAGE between specified limits, such as logic 0 level to logic 1 level.

universal motor, *n.* an electric motor that operates on either AC or DC. A universal motor uses an electromagnet field coil rather than a permanent magnet, and a commutator to feed the rotor coils. Compare AC MOTOR.

universal shunt, *n.* a meter SHUNT that is tapped so that the ratio of series to shunt resistance in the current path can be varied. This allows a MOVING-COIL METER connected to the shunt to be used for a whole set of current ranges.

unloaded Q, *n.* the value of Q FACTOR for a RESONANT CIRCUIT that is not supplying any form of load.

untuned aerial, *n.* an AERIAL whose dimensions are unrelated to the wavelength of the signal, as, for example, a long-wave transmitting or receiving aerial.

untuned circuit, see APERIODIC CIRCUIT.

up-down counter, *n.* a logic COUNTER based on FLIP-FLOPS that are interconnected by GATES (2). The gates are controlled by a single line so that one voltage level on the line produces up-counting (incrementing), the opposite level produces down-counting (decrementing).

upper sideband, *n.* the SIDEBAND of a modulated carrier whose frequencies are higher than the carrier frequency.

V

vacuum capacitor, *n.* a CAPACITOR that uses a vacuum as its insulating dielectric. Vacuum capacitors are widely used in transmitting circuits because they can be made variable (by varying their geometry) and because they do not suffer from nonlinear effects.

vacuum evaporation, *n.* a method of depositing thin films, mainly of metals. The material that is to be deposited is attached to a tungsten filament that can be electrically heated. The surface to be coated is arranged at about 10–15cm distance, and the arrangement is enclosed and evacuated. When the filament is heated, the material on it evaporates and condenses as a thin film on the cool surface. See also METALLIZING, SPUTTERING.

vacuum fluorescent display, *n.* any type of display for ALPHANUMERIC characters that uses a CATHODE emitting electrons that strike shaped anodes coated with a phosphorescent material. Vacuum fluorescent displays have been widely used for pocket calculators and for metering indicators. They allow reasonably high brightness to be achieved at low power levels, and are often more satisfactory in this respect than LEDs. Their disadvantages are relative fragility and the need for a supply voltage that is higher than the normal +5V used in digital equipment.

vacuum switch, *n.* a SWITCH whose CONTACTS are in a vacuum so as to avoid contact oxidation through sparking.

vacuum tube, see THERMIONIC VALVE.

valley point, *n.* the minimum-current point in a TUNNEL DIODE characteristic. See Fig. 97.

valve, see THERMIONIC VALVE.

vapour cooling, *n.* a method of cooling transmitter valves. The ANODE is surrounded by a jacket through which vapour (usually water vapour) is circulated. The vapour can be circulated much faster than water, and acts as a much more efficient method of transferring heat.

varactor, *n.* a SEMICONDUCTOR diode with voltage-variable CAPACITANCE. The diode is operated with REVERSE BIAS, and the effect of the bias on the DEPLETION LAYER at the junction makes this layer act like a variable thickness of dielectric. The capacitance is therefore least with large reverse bias, and greatest with small reverse bias.

varactor tuning, *n.* a form of tuning that makes use of an

Fig. 97. **Valley point**. The valley point of a tunnel diode. The region of negative resistance is between the peak and the valley.

INDUCTOR and a VARACTOR. The varactor is normally connected in series with another capacitor to ensure DC isolation from the tuned circuit. Varactor tuning is widely used at VHF and UHF, where only small variations of capacitance are needed, and where AUTOMATIC FREQUENCY CONTROL circuits are essential.

variable capacitor, *n*. a CAPACITOR whose value is mechanically variable. The usual variation method is to have a set of (fixed) STATOR plates and a set of (rotating) ROTOR plates whose meshing can be altered by rotating the shaft to which the rotor plates are connected. The rotor plates are normally earthed to avoid problems of BODY CAPACITANCE. TRIMMER CAPACITORS can use compression, in which a threaded bolt tightens or loosens plates that clamp a solid dielectric. The *beehive trimmer* uses concentric rings for rotor and stator and varies the interaction by screwing the rotor plates into or out of the stator plates. Variable capacitors may be ganged (see GANGED CIRCUITS).

variable inductor, *n*. an INDUCTOR whose value can be mechanically varied. The method of variation is normally to alter the position of a high-permeability core relative to the inductor windings.

357

variable reluctance, *n.* the principle used for the MOVING-IRON PICK-UP. The movement of an armature that is part of a magnetic circuit alters the reluctance, the magnetic-flux equivalent of resistance.

variable resistor, *n.* a RESISTOR whose RESISTANCE value can be mechanically changed. The construction is as for a POTENTIO-METER, but only one end and the moving tap of the potentio-meter are used.

Variac, *n. Trademark.* a variable AUTOTRANSFORMER.

variometer, *n.* an INDUCTOR whose value of SELF–INDUCTANCE is variable, seldom used now.

varistor, *n.* a nonohmic resistor (see OHMIC). Varistors are made from semiconductor material, have an exponential current-voltage characteristic, and are used as over-voltage limiters, because the current through the varistor will greatly increase for a very small increase in the voltage across it. The METROSIL was an early form of varistor.

V band, *n.* the MICROWAVE band of wavelength range 53.6 to 63.2mm, frequency range 46 to 56GHz.

VDU, see VISUAL DISPLAY UNIT.

velocity microphone, *n.* a MICROPHONE that is operated by the velocity of air moving past it rather than by pressure. The essential feature of a velocity microphone is that the sound waves can strike all sides of the vibrating element. See also RIBBON MICROPHONE.

velocity modulation, *n.* the interaction between an ELECTRON BEAM and an electromagnetic wave. The velocity of electrons in the beam is modulated by the wave, causing the beam of electrons to become bunched.

See KLYSTRON, TRAVELLING–WAVE TUBE, CARCINOTRON, BACK-WARD–WAVE OSCILLATOR.

Veroboard, *n. Trademark.* a BREADBOARD system. The original Veroboard is a PRINTED CIRCUIT BOARD that consists of parallel strips of copper on an insulating sheet. The strips are drilled at regular intervals (originally 0.15″, later 0.1″) so that compon-ents can be inserted and soldered to the board. Strips can be cut across where necessary for isolation. Veroboard allows experimental circuits to be made and tested in a form that is closer to the final production shape than is usually possible with breadboard systems.

vertical blanking, *n.* the suppression of video signal in the time of the field or frame flyback. See RASTER, VERTICAL TIMEBASE.

vertical hold, *n.* a TELEVISION RECEIVER control for the synchronization of the VERTICAL TIMEBASE.

vertical timebase, *n.* the TIMEBASE circuit in a TELEVISION RECEIVER that generates the field (vertical scan) waveform. The WAVEFORM consists of a current sweep with a duration of about 20 milliseconds, followed by a rapid flyback.

vestigial sideband, *n.* a method of TV signal transmission. The use of single-sideband SUPPRESSED–CARRIER TRANSMISSION methods, though advantageous from the point of view of efficiency, is impossible for TV signals because of the severe distortion that would be caused to the video signals. A compromise is to attenuate the modulated signal in such a way that the carrier amplitude is only half of its original amplitude, and the lower sideband contains only the lower frequencies of the video signal. This makes the lower sideband vestigial, and allows more efficient use of the transmitter power. See Fig. 98 on page 360.

VHF, *abbrev. for* very high frequency, the range of approximately 30MHz to 300MHz, 10m to 1m wavelength.

vibrator, *n.* see CHOPPER.

video, *adj.* relating to or employed in the transmission of picture information, i.e., TV camera signals or any other signals (computer-generated graphics, for example) that can produce an image. The VIDEO SIGNAL is of wide bandwidth, typically 5.5MHz, and may be a COMPOSITE SIGNAL with SYNCHRONIZING PULSES included.

video amplifier, *n.* a form of BROADBAND amplifier for video signals, typically in the range of DC to 5MHz. For TV purposes, the video amplifier need cater only for unidirectional signals, so that TV video amplifiers can use AC coupling, with DC restoration at the output. For oscilloscopes and other instruments, video amplifiers may have to be direct-coupled,

Fig. 98. **Vestigial sideband**. The upper sideband is allowed to extend for its full 6MHz extent, but the lower sideband is filtered so as to extend only to 2MHz below the vision carrier frequency. This represents a good compromise between bandwidth conservation and distortion problems.

capable of amplifying pulses of either polarity, and with an upper frequency limit of 30MHz or more.

video cassette recorder, *n.* a system that uses a cassette containing MAGNETIC TAPE for TV signal recording. The two competing commercial systems for domestic use are Sony's Betamax and JVC's VHS, though the recent 8mm standard may supplant both. Half-inch wide tape is used, and the tape speed is in the region of 1.8cm/second for Beta, 2.34cm/second for VHS. The recorder can take signals directly from an aerial, and has normal receiver circuits that will produce the LUMINANCE (black/white), chroma (colour) and sound signals. The luminance signal is frequency-modulated onto a carrier of around 6MHz. The colour signals are frequency-shifted to a lower frequency range, and then added to the FM luminance signals. The use of FM allows the luminance signals to be recorded at a constant amplitude, so avoiding the problems of the limited amplitude range of tape. The record/replay heads rotate, and the tape direction is skewed so that the recording tracks are across the tape at a shallow angle, allowing a high rate of tape scanning for a slow rate of tape movement.

The BANDWIDTH of the system is limited, so that the resolution of the replayed picture is lower than that of a transmitted picture, typically about half of the resolution in terms of lines. The audio signal is separately recorded on one track that lies parallel to the length of the tape (SEE RECORDING OF VIDEO). A synchronizing control track is recorded in the same way on the other edge of the tape. On replay, the two sets of video signals have to be reconstituted and modulated onto another UHF carrier, and the sound signal is also modulated so that the complete UHF video output can be used by any domestic receiver. Most recorders feature a composite video output so that a monitor can be used for a better-quality display. The more recent 8mm standard offers better quality of video, greatly improved sound quality, and compatibility with miniature video cameras.

See also DYNAMIC TRACKING.

video frequency, 1. *n.* a frequency in the video range of about DC to 5MHz. **2.** *adj.* (of a circuit) being designed to cope with video signals.

video mapping, *n.* a computer technique applied to a RADAR display. A map or photographic image of an area is superimposed over a radar trace so that the geographical position of targets can be seen.

video recording, SEE RECORDING OF VIDEO.

video signal, *n.* a SIGNAL that can be used to provide a picture. The term usually denotes a COMPOSITE SIGNAL that contains the video waveform along with colour signals and all of the synchronizing signals.

video tape, *n.* a form of MAGNETIC TAPE for recording VIDEO SIGNALS. The tape is wider than audio tape, typically half-inch for video cassettes, and 50mm (just under 2 inch) for professional machines for broadcast use. The coating material is usually ferric oxide with cobalt oxide.

vidicon, *n.* the almost universally used TELEVISION CAMERA tube. A vidicon makes use of a photoconductive semiconductor, such as antimony trisulphide or lead oxide. The optical image from the camera lens is projected onto the flat face-plate of the vidicon, typically one inch in diameter,

target
connector

mesh

electron beam

cathode
OV

glass
faceplate

target

+10V
to
+40V

anode
250V

G2
300V

G1
−15V

Fig. 99. **Vidicon**. See main entry.

though half-inch wide vidicons are used in miniature cameras. Inside the faceplate, a transparent conducting layer on the glass forms the output terminal, with a connection at the edge of the faceplate. The conducting layer is coated with the photoconducting material, the TARGET, which in turn can be scanned by a low-velocity ELECTRON BEAM. An optical image causes a corresponding pattern of low and high conductivity paths in the photoconductor, and these allow the inner surface to charge from the steady voltage at the target. The scanning electron beam discharges these parts of the inner surface, causing a signal voltage to appear by capacitive coupling on the conducting side. This signal voltage is the video signal out of the vidicon. See Fig. 99.

virtual cathode, *n.* an area of SPACE CHARGE that behaves as a supply of electrons.

virtual earth, *n.* **1.** a point in a CIRCUIT at which there is no SIGNAL at any time, though the point is not directly connected to EARTH. Also called *Wagner earth*. **2.** the INPUT (1) to an amplifier in which large amounts of negative feedback are used.

visual display unit (VDU), *n.* a CATHODE–RAY TUBE display or large screen LCD display for a computer.

VLF, *abbrev. for* very low frequency, the range of approximately 3kHz to 30kHz, 100km to 10km wavelength. These frequencies are not particularly useful for surface radio use, but allow some degree of underwater communication.

VLSI, *abbrev. for* very-large-scale integration, i.e. more than a hundred-thousand active devices per chip. The search is on for a suitable phrase to express even larger scales of integration. See also LSI, MSI.

voice coil, *n.* the active part of a LOUDSPEAKER. The voice coil is wound on a tubular former, supported in the field of a magnet by a SPIDER and by the cone of the loudspeaker. An alternating current through the voice coil causes to and fro movement that displaces air, forming a sound wave.

volatile, *adj.* (of the MEMORY of a SEMICONDUCTOR) not retaining stored information when the power supply is switched off. Compare NONVOLATILE. See also ROM, MAGNETIC MEMORY.

volt, *n.* the unit of ELECTRIC POTENTIAL and POTENTIAL DIFFER-ENCE. The volt is defined as the joule per coulomb, the amount of work done per unit charge in moving a charge from one place to another.

voltage, see ELECTRIC POTENTIAL.

voltage amplifier, *n.* an AMPLIFIER that has VOLTAGE GAIN. The output signal from a voltage amplifier will be a copy of the input signal, but with greater voltage amplitude.

voltage doubler, *n.* a RECTIFIER circuit that provides double the peak voltage of the AC input. This is twice as much as would be obtained from a conventional half- or full-wave rectifier. See also VOLTAGE MULTIPLIER.

voltage drop, *n.* the VOLTAGE between the ends of a CONDUC-TOR or a COMPONENT. The voltage drop is due to the RESISTANCE or IMPEDANCE of the conductor or component when a current flows.

voltage feedback, *n.* the FEEDBACK of a SIGNAL that is a selected fraction of the OUTPUT voltage signal to the input of a circuit.

voltage gain, *n.* the ratio of OUTPUT signal voltage to INPUT(1) signal voltage for an AMPLIFIER. The voltages must be measured in the same way, both peak-to-peak, or both RMS, and may be converted into decibels. Voltage GAIN takes no account of the phase between output and input.

voltage level, *n.* the signal VOLTAGE at some point in a CIRCUIT, compared to a standard level. For VIDEO SIGNALS, for example, the standard level is one volt peak-to-peak, ignoring synchronizing pulses.

voltage multiplier, *n.* a RECTIFIER circuit whose DC output may be several times the peak voltage of the AC input. The technique uses a chain of DIODES and CAPACITORS, with each rectifier having as its input the DC level of the previous rectifier, plus the original AC signal attenuated only slightly by the capacitor chain.

voltage reference diode, *n.* a diode using AVALANCHE BREAKDOWN. The diode is usually called a ZENER DIODE and catalogued as such. The voltage reference diode is operated with REVERSE BIAS, and the voltage across the diode is almost independent of the current. By using the diode with a current that is already partly stabilized, a very precisely constant voltage value can be generated. The reference diode is used in VOLTAGE STABILIZERS.

voltage regulator, see VOLTAGE STABILIZER.

voltage stabilizer or **voltage regulator,** *n.* a circuit whose output is a voltage that is steady. The output voltage should not, within limits, be affected by differing load currents or by changes in the AC supply voltage. Most voltage stabilizers make use of NEGATIVE FEEDBACK amplifiers with direct coupling. A fraction of the output voltage is compared with the voltage of a VOLTAGE REFERENCE DIODE, and any difference is used to correct the output. The simplest designs make use of an EMITTER FOLLOWER with the reference diode in the base circuit. Voltage stabilizers can be of series or shunt design, but are overwhelmingly of the series type.

voltage standing-wave ratio (VSWR), *n.* the STANDING-WAVE RATIO measured from signal voltage amplitude levels.

volt-ampere, *n.* the product of VOLTS and AMPERES for a SIGNAL. Even if both quantities are measured as RMS quantities, the product is not necessarily equal to dissipated power because of PHASE DIFFERENCES. To obtain power, the volt-ampere figure must be multiplied by the POWER FACTOR, which is the cosine of the phase angle.

voltmeter, *n.* a METER for measuring VOLTAGE. The predominant type is the MOVING-COIL METER, with a set of DC ranges. A limited range of AC measurements are made possible by using a RECTIFIER, but these readings are of lower precision and are affected by the frequency and waveform of the AC, see TRUE RMS. DIGITAL voltmeters are increasingly replacing the moving-coil type for DC measurements, and OSCILLOSCOPES are more satisfactory for work with signals. Voltmeters with MOSFET inputs (see FIELD-EFFECT TRANSISTORS) can be used for making measurements that require an exceptionally high input resistance. These meters have replaced the old valve voltmeters and the even older electrostatic voltmeters.

volume, *n.* **1.** the AMPLITUDE of sound as heard by the ear. For a sound of constant amplitude level, the effect on the ear is not constant but varies with the frequency because of the NONLINEAR response of the ear. **2.** the amplitude of an AUDIO SIGNAL.

volume compressor, *n.* a CIRCUIT that reduces the range of amplitudes in an AUDIO SIGNAL. This is done typically by a nonlinear amplifier, whose gain is inversely proportional to the signal amplitude. Volume compression is extensively used in sound recording, because no recording system or broadcasting system can cope with the full amplitude range (dynamic range) of orchestral music. See also WHITE COMPRESSION, VOLUME EXPANDER, COMPANDER, DOLBY SYSTEM, DBX.

volume control, *n.* the POTENTIOMETER control on sound reproduction equipment for adjusting the intensity of sound by altering the amplitude of audio signals.

volume expander, *n.* a CIRCUIT that increases the AMPLITUDE range of SIGNALS. The volume expander is a NONLINEAR amplifier that has higher gain for larger amplitude signals. Volume expanders are usually designed in conjunction with VOLUME COMPRESSORS, to form COMPANDERS, so that a signal that has been compressed and then expanded will be restored to normal amplitude range. Companding is extensively used in tape recording and optical film recording systems. See DOLBY SYSTEM, DBX.

volume limiter, *n.* a CIRCUIT that prevents the AMPLITUDE of a SIGNAL from exceeding a preset limit. This is commonly used for TELEPHONY, so that overmodulation of the carrier (which causes severe sideband distortion) is impossible. Crude limiters simply clip the waveform, but modern types use a NONLINEAR amplifier that affects only the amplitude range near the limit.

von Neumann architecture, *n.* the conventional scheme of computer design, in which each instruction is carried out in sequence. The alternative is some form of parallel architecture, and current research is devoted to the problems of parallel architecture (in which several instructions can be carried out simultaneously) and the computing languages that will be required to make efficient use of it. Named after John von Neumann (1903–57), US mathematician.

VSWR, see STANDING WAVE RATIO.

VU–meter, *n.* volume–unit METER, a form of recording-level meter for a tape recorder. The meter measures the average signal level, and should give an indication that is proportional to the power level of the signal, so allowing for the differences between smooth and spiky waveforms.

W

wafer, *n.* a circular thin slice from a large crystal of SEMICONDUCTOR material. Wafers of 3″ and 4″ diameters are processed by PHOTOLITHOGRAPHY so that several hundred CHIPS can be formed in one set of operations. After the wafer processing, the individual chips are automatically tested by a machine that marks the rejects, and the chips are separated by ruling the wafer with a diamond cutter. The good chips are then selected and passed for mounting on to headers.

Wagner earth, see VIRTUAL EARTH(1).

walkie-talkie, *n.* a miniature portable sound transmitter-receiver. The TV equivalent has been termed a *creepie-peepie*.

warble, *n.* a small variation in FREQUENCY, usually at an AUDIO rate. This can be due to speed variations in a motor of a film projector, gramophone disc player or tape recorder.

warm–up, *n.* the time after switch-on during which the

behaviour of a CIRCUIT changes. Warm–up time for a circuit that contains a CATHODE-RAY TUBE includes the time that is needed to heat the cathode until its electron emission is steady.

watt, *n.* the unit of POWER. Electrically, the power value in watts is obtained by multiplying the DC voltage value in volts by the DC current value in amperes. For AC or signal quantities, ROOT-MEAN-SQUARE values must be used, and any differences in phase expressed by a POWER FACTOR correction.

wattless component, *n.* the product of signal VOLTAGE and CURRENT when the PHASE DIFFERENCE is 90 degrees. This quantity does not represent dissipated power since only the product of the in-phase component's voltage and current in phase gives the true figure of power dissipated.

wattmeter, *n.* an instrument that measures electrical power.

wave, *n.* an alternating quantity whose effect can spread through a material, or through space. For electronics purposes, the most important waves are electromagnetic waves, which are the familiar radio waves used as CARRIERS. See also ULTRASONIC.

wave analyser, *n.* an instrument, based on a CATHODE-RAY OSCILLOSCOPE display, that analyses a wave into its components. A typical output from a wave analyser would be a set of vertical bars in which the height of each bar indicated the amplitude of a sine wave, and the bar position indicated frequency. In this way, the wave analyser shows the amplitudes of the fundamental and each HARMONIC for a complex waveform. The CRO type of display is now being replaced by computer displays. See also FOURIER ANALYSIS.

waveform or **waveshape,** *n.* a graph–plot of wave AMPLITUDE against time for the time of one CYCLE. The common waveforms are sine, square, pulse and triangle.

wavefront, *n.* the line of advance of a WAVE through a material. The wavefront of a wave from a point source, for example, is in the shape of a sphere. The wavefront consists of all the points at which the wave has travelled through the material for the same time.

waveguide, *n.* a hollow CONDUCTOR for MICROWAVES. Because of radiation and surface resistance, microwaves cannot be efficiently conducted along conventional open lines. A waveguide, consisting normally of a rectangular section metal tube, is much more efficient. The metal may be silver-plated to increase surface conductivity, and the wave is held inside the guide by reflections from the wall. The dimensions of the waveguide have to be chosen appropriately for the wavelengths that are to be propagated, and the ratio of width to depth for the cross section will determine the pattern (see MODE) of electric and magnetic fields inside the waveguide.

wave heating, *n*. the heating of materials by means of MICROWAVE bombardment. This has been used for fast-drying of damp materials, setting adhesives, and cooking food. See also MICROWAVE COOKER.

wavelength, *n*. the distance between one wave peak and the next in a wave. The wavelength is a particularly easy feature of a wave to measure (see LECHER LINES), and its size determines many of the features of the wave, such as the ease of PROPAGATION. The value of wavelength multiplied by FREQUENCY gives speed of propagation in the medium in which wavelength is measured.

wavemeter, *n*. a form of frequency METER. A RESONANT CIRCUIT is adjusted so as to resonate with an incoming wave, and the resonant current is displayed on a meter. The frequency can then be read from a dial. The wavemeter can be calibrated in terms of wavelength, assuming that the waves are in the air.

waveshape, see WAVEFORM.

wave train, *n*. a set of WAVES, usually implying a limited number.

wave trap, *n*. a form of wave FILTER that rejects a particular frequency.

W band, *n*. the range of 3mm to 5.36mm wavelength, 56 to 100GHz of microwave frequency.

Wheatstone bridge, *n*. the original and classical form of BRIDGE circuit used for resistance comparison.

whistle, *n*. an INTERFERENCE effect caused by another CARRIER. The beating of two carriers close to each other in frequency causes a whistle to be heard at the receiver. The *whistle frequency* is the difference between the carrier frequencies.

white compression, *n.* a form of volume compression (see VOLUME COMPRESSOR) on a VIDEO SIGNAL. This compresses the amplitudes that correspond to the white (brightest) areas of the picture.

white noise, *n.* an electrical or other form of NOISE that has a broad spectrum of FREQUENCIES and a uniform AMPLITUDE over the whole of the frequency range.

white peak, *n.* an AMPLITUDE peak in a VIDEO SIGNAL that corresponds to a bright white part of the picture.

wideband, see BROADBAND.

Wien bridge, *n.* a form of BRIDGE circuit used mainly as a filter or as a tuning circuit for a low-frequency oscillator. The circuit was originally used as a measuring bridge for frequency, hence its name. See Fig. 100.

Fig. 100. **Wien bridge.** The components R_1, R_2, C_1, C_2 are the Wien bridge components.

Winchester drive, *n.* a low-cost form of HARD DISK used for small computer systems.

winding, *n.* a length of coiled CONDUCTOR that is used to produce a MAGNETIC FIELD or have a VOLTAGE induced in it by a magnetic field. See also PRIMARY WINDING, SECONDARY WINDING.

window, *n.* **1.** a material that is transparent to radiation. **2.** the range of FREQUENCIES that can pass through the IONOSPHERE from outer space, the 'radio window'. **3.** the thin mica cover of a GEIGER–MÜLLER TUBE that allows ionizing particles and radiation to pass into the tube. **4.** the faceplate of a TV camera tube. **5.** a vacuum-sealed connection between a MICROWAVE GENERATOR and a WAVEGUIDE.

wire, *n.* **1.** a metal CONDUCTOR in wire form. **2.** any connecting conductor that is not a strip in a PRINTED-CIRCUIT BOARD.

wire broadcasting, *n.* the distribution of SIGNALS at radio frequencies by wire rather than through space.

wired-OR, *n.* a method of connecting OUTPUTS from IC gates. Some types of gate with open–collector outputs (see OPEN-COLLECTOR DEVICE) can have their outputs connected to a common load. This allows the output voltage to be pulled down to logic 0 if any one of the gates conducts, giving an OR logic action. Gates of conventional PUSH-PULL TTL stages may be destroyed if they are connected together in this way.

wireless, *n.* an old term for RADIO, shortened from wireless (meaning without CABLES) telegraphy.

wire wrapping, *n.* a prototype construction method in which a special kind of wire is wrapped tightly round a solder-coated pin. When using this technique no heat is applied to the pins, connections being made solely by the tight contact achieved by the wrapped wire.

wire-wound resistor, *n.* a form of RESISTOR constructed by winding fine-gauge insulated wire around an insulating former. The power dissipation of such a resistor can be large, but it is difficult to make the resistor noninductive.

wiring diagram, *n.* a diagram that shows the physical connection of wires in a circuit. Compare CIRCUIT DIAGRAM.

wobbulator, *n.* an OSCILLATOR that uses FREQUENCY MODULATION to check BANDWIDTHS. By using the wobbulator as an INPUT(1) to a CIRCUIT, and displaying the AMPLITUDE of the OUTPUT on an oscilloscope whose TIMEBASE is provided by the wobbulator, a plot of amplitude against FREQUENCY can be obtained on which band limits can be marked. The wobbulator is particularly useful for checking the IF and video response of TV receivers.

woofer, *n.* a LOUDSPEAKER that is particularly suitable for reproducing BASS notes. A woofer uses a large cone that is very freely suspended. At high frequencies, such a cone would resonate, with standing waves forming on it, so that the woofer is isolated from high frequencies by means of the CROSSOVER NETWORK. See also TWEETER, LOUDSPEAKER.

work function, *n.* the amount of energy that is needed to liberate one ELECTRON from a material, usually quoted in terms of ELECTRONVOLTS.

wound core, *n.* a TRANSFORMER core that consists of one ribbon of magnetic material wound into a core shape.

wow, *n.* a slow frequency modulation of sound from a disc or tape source. Wow is caused by uneven disc or tape speed. Compare FLUTTER.

write, *vb.* to store data into a MEMORY. Compare READ.

X Y Z

x-axis, *n.* the horizontal axis of a graph or of a CATHODE-RAY TUBE display.

x band, *n.* the MICROWAVE band range of 27.5mm to 57.7mm, 5.2GHz to 10.9GHz.

xerography, *n.* a method of paper-copying that relies on ELECTROSTATIC charging and PHOTOCONDUCTIVITY. The principle is also used in laser printers for computers.

XOR gate, see EXCLUSIVE OR.

x-plates, *n.* the horizontal DEFLECTION PLATES of an INSTRUMENT TUBE. The timebase waveforms are normally applied to these plates.

x-ray, *n.* the range of electomagnetic radiation with WAVELENGTHS much shorter than those of visible light. X-rays penetrate most materials, and cannot be focused, reflected or refracted by conventional methods.

x-ray tube, *n.* a vacuum tube in which X-RAYS are generated. The tube generates a very high energy ELECTRON BEAM that is focused onto a metal anode, the TARGET. The bombardment of this target produces x-rays. The wavelength of the x-rays can be reduced by using higher voltages between cathode and target.

x-y plotter, *n.* an instrument that produces a two–dimensional plot on paper. The plot is similar to that produced by an OSCILLOSCOPE, but the x-y plotter is more useful if the rate of production of the pattern is slow.

yagi aerial, *n.* a form of DIRECTIONAL AERIAL consisting of a DIPOLE AERIAL, fitted with a REFLECTOR and several DIRECTORS. The direction of the yagi is the heading from reflector to director. The GAIN as compared to a simple dipole is large, and the directional properties of the aerial are very useful in overcoming interference problems.

y–axis, *n.* the vertical axis of **1.** graph paper, **2.** the TRACE on a CATHODE–RAY TUBE.

yttrium–iron–garnet (YIG), *n.* a magnetic crystal of the FERRITE type that is used in microwave circuits, and also for magnetic BUBBLE MEMORY applications.

yoke, *n.* a set of DEFLECTION COILS for a TV CATHODE–RAY TUBE.

y–parameters, *n.* a set of PARAMETERS formerly used for measuring TRANSISTOR characteristics.

y–plates, *n.* the vertical DEFLECTION PLATES for an INSTRUMENT TUBE.

Zener breakdown, *n.* the reverse BREAKDOWN of a DIODE in which the p- and n- regions are heavily doped. Zener breakdown is more gradual than AVALANCHE BREAKDOWN, but the name of Zener is used to denote any diode in which reverse breakdown is used.

Zener diode, *n.* any VOLTAGE STABILIZER diode that operates with reverse bias. The breakdown voltage of these diodes is almost independent of the amount of reverse current, so they can be used as voltage reference sources. See Fig. 101. See also VOLTAGE REFERENCE DIODE.

zero, *n.* the minimum point on the complex S–plane of a POLE–ZERO DIAGRAM.

zero error, *n.* a METER fault in which the needle of the meter does not return to zero. Instruments that use digital displays

Fig. 101. **Zener diode**. A typical Zener diode CHARACTERISTIC. The forward characteristic is normal, but the reverse characteristic exhibits an abrupt breakdown, so that the reverse voltage is almost constant over a wide current range after breakdown.

may also exhibit zero errors so that the reading is not zero with the meter disconnected or short-circuited.

zero frequency (zf), *n*. the frequency at which alternating current is absent, and direct current is steady.

zero level, *n*. the level of comparison for SIGNALS. This need not necessarily be zero voltage, but the voltage of the signal baseline.

zero-level trigger, *n*. a TRIGGER PULSE that is generated when an AC wave passes through the zero voltage level. Zero voltage triggers are used when a THYRISTOR is being switched in such a way as to generate little or no interference.

zero potential, see EARTH POTENTIAL.

zf, see ZERO FREQUENCY.

z-modulation, *n*. the MODULATION of the ELECTRON BEAM of a CATHODE-RAY TUBE, so modulating screen brightness. The term particularly denotes the modulation of an INSTRUMENT TUBE, since TV cathode-ray tubes are normally modulated in this way.

z-parameters, *n*. a set of PARAMETERS formerly used for measurements of TRANSISTOR characteristics.

APPENDIX A: Resistor Colour Code

1st   2nd   3rd   tolerance (if used)

Band Coding

First Band – first figure of resistance value (first *significant* figure)

Second Band – second figure of resistance value (second *significant* figure)

Third Band – number of zeros following second figure (multiplier)

Tolerance Band – percentage tolerance of value (5% or 10%). No tolerance band is used if the resistor has 20% tolerance.

Code Colours (also used for capacitor values)

Figure	Colour
0	black
1	brown
2	red
3	orange
4	yellow
5	green
6	blue
7	violet
8	grey
9	white
0.01	silver
0.1	gold

} used as multipliers (3rd band) only

Tolerance	
10%	silver
5%	gold

APPENDIX B: Resistance Value Coding

Resistance values on components and in component lists are often coded according to BS 1852. In this scheme no decimal points are used, and a value in ohms is indicated by R, kilohms by K (not k), and megohms by M. The letter R, K or M is used in place of the decimal point, with a zero in the leading position if the value is less than 1 ohm. For example:

1K5 = 1.5k or 1500 ohms; 2M2 = 2.2MΩ; 0R5 = 0.5 ohms.

APPENDIX C: Symbols

The use of symbols in electronics can be very confusing, and many manufacturers do not follow a coherent scheme. Most of the problems are caused by the use of letters such as R, C and L to denote components (resistors, capacitors, inductors) in circuit diagrams, and also to denote values of resistance, capacitance and inductance in equations. Another source of confusion is the use of a letter to denote both a quantity (such as voltage) and the unit used for measurement (volt). This is particularly noticeable on graphs, where, typically, a graph axis might be labelled as V/V, using the italic letter to mean the name of the quantity (voltage) and the roman to mean the unit (volts).

In this volume, the use of symbols is summarized in the following tables. The tables have been divided to show the use of symbols in circuit diagrams (roman letters), in equations (italics for scalars and bold for vectors or complex quantities), as abbreviations for units (roman letters), and graphical representation (see Appendix D). The symbols used in equations have been subdivided into separate tables for English and Greek symbols.

Circuit diagrams

The symbols used in this way employ roman letters, which may be followed by a number or letter identifier in a smaller type. This is indicated in each entry.

A, B, C	inputs to a digital circuit
C	carry output from an adder
C, C_1, C_b	capacitor
D, D_1, D_d	diode
E, E_1, E_c	EMF or voltage
I, I_1, I_b	current
L, L_1, L_e	self-inductor, coil

Q	main output from digital circuit
Q̄	inverted output from digital circuit
Q, Q_1, Q_a	transistor
R, R_1, R_b	resistor
Sw_1, Sw_a	switch
T, T_1, T_b	transistor
Tr, Tr_1	transformer or transistor
V, V_1, V_c	voltage level
ZD, ZD_1	zener diode

Symbols in equations
Roman letters

Italic type denotes a scalar quantity, **bold type** a vector or complex number. Principal meanings are given first.

Note the important distinction: dB = decibel (unit); **dB** = change of magnetic flux density.

In complex number notation, both **i** and **j** are used to mean the square root of -1. In general, mathematicians use **i**, and engineers use **j**.

B	magnetic flux density
B	susceptance (inverse of reactance)
C	capacitance
c	velocity of light
D	electrostatic displacement
E	EMF; voltage
E	electrostatic field strength
F	mechanical force
f	frequency
Fm	magnetomotive force
G	conductance (inverse of resistance)
H	magnetic field strength
I	current
J	current density
k	coefficient of coupling
L	self-inductance
M	mutual inductance
P	dielectric polarization
Q	electric charge; quality factor of tuned circuit
R	resistance; magnetic circuit reluctance
T	period of an oscillation
V	potential difference (voltage)
X	reactance
Y	admittance (complex quantity)
Z	impedance (complex quantity)

Greek letters

ϵ	absolute permittivity

ϵ_o	permittivity of free space
ϵ_r	relative permittivity
θ	phase angle
κ	conductivity
λ	wavelength
μ	absolute permeability
μ_o	permeability of free space
μ_r	relative permeability
ν	frequency
ρ	resistivity; charge density
σ	conductivity; leakage coefficient
ϕ	magnetic flux; phase difference
χ	electrostatic susceptibility
ψ	electrostatic flux
ω	angular frequency

Symbols for units

Note: the unit symbols that use upper-case (capital) letters are those which carry the name of the discoverer or researcher associated with the unit. The unit name itself uses a lower-case letter.

Symbol	Unit name	Quantity
A	ampere	current
C	coulomb	electrostatic charge
cd	candela	luminous intensity
dB	decibel	sound
F	farad	electrostatic charge
H	henry	inductance (self or mutual)
Hz	hertz	frequency
J	joule	energy
K	kelvin	temperature (absolute)
kg	kilogram	mass
m	metre	length
mol	mole	amount of substance in terms of number of particles
N	force	newton
Pa	pascal	pressure
S	siemens	conductivity (inverse ohm)
s	second	time
T	tesla	flux density
V	volt	potential; potential difference (voltage)
W	watt	power
Wb	weber	magnetic flux
Ω	ohm	resistance

APPENDIX D: Graphical symbols

AC	$\sim$	neon bulb	
AND gate		NOT gate (inverter)	
capacitor		operational amplifier	
cathode		OR gate	
connector terminals		positive pulse	
crystal		resistor	
DC	=	sawtooth wave	
diode		sine wave	
earth		square wave	
electrolytic capacitor		switch	or
flip-flop		transformer	
heater		transistor (NPN)	
inductor		triangle wave	
lamp		tunnel diode	
meter		XOR gate	
meter or motor		Zener diode	or
negative pulse			